THE RISE OF THE TECHNOCRATS

DATE DUE

STUDIES IN SOCIAL HISTORY

edited by

HAROLD PERKIN

Senior Lecturer in Social History, University of Lancaster

◇◇◇

THE RISE OF THE TECHNOCRATS

A Social History

by

W. H. G. Armytage

Professor of Education
University of Sheffield

LONDON: Routledge and Kegan Paul
TORONTO: University of Toronto Press

First published 1965
in Great Britain by
Routledge and Kegan Paul Limited
and in Canada by
University of Toronto Press

Printed in Great Britain by
W. & J. Mackay & Co. Ltd., Chatham

Contents

Preface

WHILST trying to convince his fellow-citizens to reject the wooden horse left by the Greeks, Laocoön was crushed to death by two serpents emerging from the sea. Similarly latent, but aggressive, social forces emerge from below the 'social horizon' to confound historians. Just such a one was identified by E. M. Forster as 'the implacable offensive of science'.[1]

This implacable offensive has not arisen from its environment in a simple unilinear fashion as that stern determinist, Karl Marx, himself acknowledged.[2] Its momentum, though owing much to what Max Scheler called 'real factors'—race, geo-politics, political power structures or the production machine—has increased by accretion.[3] The aggregation of those sustaining the momentum—demonstrators of truths based on observable facts, or exploiters of trustworthy methods for discovering 'new truths'—has taken place as the offensive intensifies.[4]

The following pages offer an interpretation of the attitude of such groups to social policy over the last 400 years. 'The histori-cal setting appears, indeed,' said Carl Becker, 'to be an instruc-tive procedure of the modern mind. We do it without thinking, because we can scarcely think at all without doing it.'[5] But in doing so, he warned us that 'We can identify a particular thing only by pointing to the various things it successively was before it became that particular thing that it will presently cease to be'.[6]

These attempts to identify various knowledge-producing groups began as a clumsy response to the generous invitation of the University College of North Wales at Bangor to deliver the Ballard-Matthews lectures in 1963. They sketch the rise of the technical intelligentsia, whose outlook and activities are so absorbing that, for those whose interest may be whetted, further reading is offered in the notes. For the index that follows I have to thank Anne Gray, Margaret Revitt and Kay Johnson for much help at short notice.

PART I

Seed–Beds of Science

1

Garden Economies

(1)

FOUR hundred years ago, a green curtain divided the world. On one side were the Portuguese and Spanish; on the other the Dutch and English. A glimpse of what lay behind the Portuguese curtain was provided in 1563 by a little book, the third in the European language to be printed in Asia, *Coloquios dos simples, e drogas he cousas medicinais da India* (1563). Its author, Garcia de Orta (1501–68) was a militant Marrano, who went in terror of the Inquisition for most of his life. He leased Bombay for the Portuguese and established a botanic garden at Goa. His book also recorded the plants available in the Indies, and for it the poet Camoëns, then resident at Goa, wrote a poetic preface. The book excited great interest. It was précised four years later by Charles de l'Écluse in his *Aromatum Historia* (1567) and by Cristobal Acosta in his *Tractado de las Drogas y medicinas de las Indias Orientales*. It was also translated into English by James Garret. But of all nations, perhaps the Dutch were most excited by it, and sent a spy to work for the Archbishop of Goa to glean more of its contents.[1] This spy's copy of Orta's book is still preserved today.

The Dutch took plants seriously. When the citizens of Leyden were offered exemption from taxation for ten years or having a university, they chose a university and annexed to it a botanic

3

garden, the Hortus Botanicus Academicus Lugduni-Batavorium. This, from the time of its Padua-trained[2] first director, Gerait de Bondt (1536–99), became one of the sinews of its overseas empire. To protect plants from the Dutch settlement at the Cape of Good Hope, like geraniums and mesembryanthemums, a greenhouse was established in 1599. Bondt's successor, Charles de l'Ecluse (1526–1609) was a man of international reputation, whose activities were probably of more direct consequence to the history of gardening than those of any of his contemporaries. He was responsible for the introduction and first successful cultivation of the bulbous plants for which the Dutch horticultural industry has been renowned.

Just after he died, the Dutch introduced tea to Europe, cornering the market for three-quarters of a century. Not till the English King Charles II married a Portuguese queen did the English take up the habit, and not till 1689 did their East India Company begin to import it from China. Tea-drinking initiated a minor technological revolution. Utensils for brewing and drinking it were devised not from pewter but porcelain. And porcelain demanded coal, engines, chemistry and design, which in England, was quite a story.[3]

The Dutch foraged yet farther, when Prince Maurice of Nassau reached Brazil in 1631, accompanied by a party of forty-six scientists who founded the town now known as San Antonio, established a zoological and botanical garden, and the first astronomical and meteorological station in the New World.[4] In 1696 Engelbert Kaempfler (1651–1761), the chief surgeon to their fleet, visited Japan in the same year as the University of Yedo was established.

There they crept through another curtain, lowered by the Shogun to prevent his barons acquiring knowledge of the West. But Dutch botanists influenced a group of Japanese known as Rangaku-sha, or the Dutch scholars. So Western science began to seep into Asia.

Meanwhile in Holland, Leyden, with its botanic garden, became a seed-bed of science for the world. F. Sylvius (1614–72), fumbling towards a chemical view of the body, was trying, in his way, to differentiate between organic and inorganic chemistry. Three of its famous pupils were Jan Swammerdam (1637–80), a microscopist whose minute studies of the anatomy of mayflies, bees and frogs led him on to identify the red corpuscles in the blood; Regnier de Graaf (1641–73) who worked out the action of the pancreas; and Thomas Willis (1641–75) who identified *diabetes mellitus*. Its international character under Herman Boerhaave (1668–1738)[5] can be seen by the composition of one of his classes in 1737. It numbered ninety-seven; twenty-three were English, five Scottish, three Irish, ten Germans, three Swedes, two Russians, a Dane, a Frenchman and a Greek. Indeed the very name 'Leyden' was such that when Musschenbroek (1692–1761) and his pupil Cunaeus, in working on the nervous system, discovered a device for storing electricity, it was known as the 'Leyden jar', even though it had previously been discovered by Kleist of Pomerania.[6]

One of these 'Leyden jars', taken by a Scotsman Dr. Spence to Boston in 1746, was used by Benjamin Franklin to experiment on electricity. His *Experiments and observations* on the subject being printed in London, were received in Europe with excitement.[7]

Throughout Europe, Leyden's influence spread: to Göttingen, through Albrecht von Haller (1708–77);[8] to Vienna through Gerhard van Swieten (1700–72)[9] to Edinburgh, through Alexander Munro I (1697–1767); to Moscow through L. Blumentrost and Nicholas Bidloo, where botanical gardens were laid out in 1713[10] and to America through Phineas Bond (M. D. Leyden, 1742).[11]

(2)

In 1565 another intelligence report came to Europe from the West. Some inkling of its importance can best be obtained from the title of the English translation: *Joyfull Newes out of the New Found World*.[12] The joyful news was that the ague, dysentry, the pox and rheumatism could now be treated by Peruvian bark, ipecacuanha, guiacum and gontard. In addition, it told of three new products: tobacco for smoking, sassafras root as a stimulant and 'a gumme called Tacamachachaca' or rubber.

Like Holland, Britain had a plant-based economy. Its wood was being used so rapidly that charcoal burning and smelting were forbidden near shipbuilding areas. Alkalis were increasingly needed for soap and glass, and prospecting for them was going on to supplement the tedious and costly method of burning seaweed. Increasing prosperity was widening the spectrum of dyes from the traditional reds (from madder), yellows (broom), green (bracken), brown (lichens) and blue (woad). Thanks to the acquisition of flax from Asia in the Middle Ages, cordage, canvas, sacking, bowstrings, fishing lines, thread and linen were now available for various economic activities. Now to the belladonna, whose atropine so enlarged Italian ladies' eyes that it got its name, the henbane whose narcotic and analgesic properties made it such a boon to those suffering from toothache, and the comfrey whose then unknown allatoin made it such a specific in bone-setting cases, and the scores of native remedies, came the news of these new sovereign remedies from the Spanish possessions in America.

The premium put by the King of Spain on what lay on his side of the curtain had been aptly recognized forty-three years earlier by the grant of a coat of arms to the first circumnavigator of the globe. It depicted two Malay kings, each holding a spice branch, supporting a glove with the motto *primus circumdedisti me*, whilst the shield bore the Castle of Castile, with two cinnamon sticks in saltire between three nutmegs and twelve cloves.[13]

The leakage continued. Jean de Léry, a Calvinist minister to the Huguenot Colony in Brazil published his *Voyage en Amérique, avec la description des animaux et plantes de ce pays* from the Huguenot centre of Rouen in 1578, whilst ten years later Thomas Harriot, the tutor and familiar of Sir Walter Raleigh published *A brefe and true report of the new found land of Virginia: of the commodities there founde and to be raised, as well marchantable, as others for victualling, building and other necessary uses for those that are and shall be the planters there; and of the nature and manners of the naturall inhabitants.* (1588.)

The study and propagation of these new vegetable products needed gardens. A year before Harriot's book was published, John Gerard agreed to superintend a garden for the College of Physicians at Nightrider Street, London, and to keep it full of simples. He kept another at Holborn where the potato made its first recorded appearance.[14] That shrewd Elizabethan statesman, Lord Burghley, also employed him to look after his own gardens in the Strand and at Theobalds, thereby earning the dedication in Gerard's *Herball*: 'What greater delight is there than to behold the earth apparalled with plants as with a robe of embroidered worke set with Orient pearls and garnished with great diversifie of rare and costly jewels? Though the delight is great, the use is greater and joined to necessitie.'

'Use and necessitie', as Burghley and Gerard realized, were the root of the matter. Gerard tried to grow dates and ginger, and perhaps it was because he had failed to grow other countries' plants that he synthesized other botanists' knowledge in his book. His *Herball* was most influential. One of its seventeenth-century revisers, Thomas Johnson, was the first to exhibit a banana, whilst an eighteenth-century schoolboy, Joseph Banks, took it up to Eton with him.

The transformation of the herb to the botanic garden proper was the work of John Tradescant, best known of the Guild of Gardeners—chartered in 1606. As well as managing his own garden at South Lambeth, he managed the garden of the Earl of Salisbury at Hatfield, acquiring plants and trees from the Low Countries, France and America. His enthusiasm for America, which led him to subscribe to the Virginia Company, was shared by his son and namesake who visited it on three collecting trips in 1637, 1642 and 1654. Tradescant's own major visits took in Russia, the Mediterranean, and the Island of Rhé. Indeed, his connections with the leader of the expedition to the Island of Rhé led to him being appointed 'garnetter'—a kind of embryo food controller.[15]

Tradescant's introduction of many new vegetable products like the plane tree and the Virginia creeper led to his appointment as keeper of the Oxford Botanical Garden, a post which he never took up. At the Oxford garden John Locke studied, collecting about 1,600 plants in the district alone.[16] Later, he was to collect ideas in Holland for his philosophical writings. Another garden was founded at Edinburgh in 1670 by two physicians just south of Holyrood House, known as the Royal Botanic Garden under James Sutherland, who also took charge of another botanic garden founded by the town council in the grounds of what is now the Waverley Railway Station.[17]

Another rallying centre for those interested in the vegetable kingdom was provided by Lord Zouche's garden at Hackney, under the Dutchman, Mathias de l'Obel. L'Obel virtually sponsored the Herball of John Gerard, that itself owed so much to another Dutchman: Rembert Dodoens. L'Obel was appointed by King James I to the newly created post, that of *Botanicus Regius* in 1607, and when he died in 1616 the title and his manuscripts devolved on Parkinson.

Though a physick garden had existed at Westminster in 1655,[18] it was not until 1673 that the Society of Apothecaries rented a garden at Chelsea from Lord Cheyne. The society found it difficult to keep going and twenty years later were thinking of abandoning it, and but for the enthusiasm of two apothecaries, Samuel Doody and James Petiver, might have had to do so. One proposal brought before the society in 1713 was that a tax should be levied on all apothecaries to sustain it. The land was conveyed to them by Hans Sloane in 1722.

(3)

Gardens elicited many experiments in technology too. Solomon de Caus, the 'Prince's Engineer' designed a 'force machine to make cascades and fountains at Hatfield. The Dutch drainage engineers like Vermuyden, Westerdyk and Kievet put so many thousands of acres into production in seventeenth-century England that Charles II asked Pepys how it came 'to pass that England has at all times served itself with strangers for engineers'.

The influence of the Low Countries on Britain at this time has been compared by one modern historian to that of the Normans in the Middle Ages: maps, clocks, binoculars, language even, all indicate this.[19]

With the advent of a Dutch king, William III, to the English throne, the passion for gardening intensified. According to Daniel Defoe,

> With (this) particular judgment of the King, all the gentlemen in England began to fall in; and in a few years fine gardens, and fine houses began to grow up in every corner; the King began with the gardens at Hampton Court and Kensington, and the gentlemen follow'd every where, with such a gust that the alteration is indeed wonderful thro' the kingdom.[20]

Apart from conspicuous display, the study of botany was especially congenial to some Anglican clergy. Their fine glebes provided tropes for sermons and examples to parishioners, as well as food for body and mind. John Lawrence's *Clergyman's Recreation* (1714) reached nine editions in twelve years. But more important was John Ray's great book—*The Wisdom of God manifested in the Works of Creation* (1691), which had an enormous influence—it reached a tenth edition by 1735. Bishop Butler used it in his *Analogy* in 1736. John Wesley drew on it for his *Survey of the Wisdom of God in the Creation*. Gilbert White made it famous in the *Natural History of Selborne* (1789). Its influence can be seen in Paley's *Natural Theology*. As Ray's most recent biographer, Canon C. E. Raven, remarks, 'more than any other single book it initiated the true adventure of modern science and is the ancestor of the Origin of Species as of L'Evolution créatrice'.[21]

As the Rev. Richard Bradley, Professor of Botany at Cambridge put it:

> Gardening and Husbandry are Sciences well becoming the greatest philosophers, they have the pleasure of taming or civilising the little Wildnesses of Nature, and by that means of ordering her works in such a Manner, as to make them become profitable and useful to our Interests;

he continued:

> We are free from noisy and impertinent Clamours, which daily present themselves in the hurry'd Part of the World; and if these Studies have the Same Effect upon the Minds of others, that they have upon me, they do not a little to set forth the Wisdom and Power of the Great *Creator*.[22]

Some clergymen-botanists opened up new vistas. In his quiet garden at Teddington, the Rev. Stephen Hales gave in *Vegetable Staticks* (1727) the first full scientific account of the flow of sap and the function of the leaves in plant respiration and nutrition. His discovery was hymned by a contemporary poet.

> By *Thee* the various vegetative Tribes
> Wrapt in a filmy Net, and clad with leaves,
> Draw the live Aether, and imbibe the Dew
> By *Thee* dispos'd into congenial Soils
> Stands each attractive Plant, and sucks, and swells
> The juicy Tide, a twining Mass of Tubes.
> At *Thy* command, the vernal Sun awakes

The torpid Sap, detruded to the Root
by Wintry Winds, now influent Dance,
And lively Fermentation, mounting, spreads
All this innumerous colour'd Scene of things.[23]

(4)

Stephen Hales was translated into French by G. L. Leclerc
du Buffon, Intendant of the famous Jardin du Roi in Paris from
1739 to 1788. He suggested that epochs of nature were seven,
in the last of which the power of man assisted the works of
nature.[24]

Those powers were well illustrated by the Jardin du Roi
which, by Buffon's time had acquired so many plants that it
spread down to the Seine and Buffon had to vacate his own
apartments to make room for further collections. Buffon's work
as a naturalist actually began under the influence of Dr. Hick-
man, but was sustained by translating Stephen Hales. It reached
to a brilliant conclusion, in a multi-volume synthesis of the discoveries of botanists, astronomers and mathematicians, illuminating the early history of the earth and contributing to
the idea of the modification of the species.[25] A hundred years
later, according to Bernard Shaw, 'every literate child knew
Buffon's Natural History as well as he knew Aesop's fables'.[26]

Begun as a project of the Paris School of Medicine in 1579
the Jardin became the instrument whereby the French exploited
the vegetable system of their empire. The change came when an
anatomical theatre was built on part of the site and Guy de la
Brosse proposed that another garden should be laid out and
placed under the Royal Physician. His idea was approved in
1626 but it was not until 1635 that the property was formally
occupied, when de la Brosse, working under the nominal superintendency of Charles Bouvard (1527–1658), the Royal Physician, began to stock it with a full complement of 2,000 plants.[27]

Rooms were opened for the teaching of not only botany, but
of chemistry and astronomy as well and it was renamed the
Jardin du Roi. When de la Brosse died in 1641 his nephew,
Guy-Crescent Fagon (1638–1718) carried on: augmenting the
plants by his travels in the Auvergne, the Alps and the Pyrenees.
He secured the appointment of J. P. de Tournefort (1656–1708),
who travelled even farther—to England, Holland and later to the

Levant and Africa—and published *Les Éléménts de botanique* (1694).

The Jardin du Roi was emulated in England by Tournefort's English friend Sir Hans Sloane.[28] Having made a fortune out of Peruvian bark (quinine) and been a pupil at Paris and Montpellier, Sloane knew what a botanic garden could do. So he purchased the freehold of the Chelsea garden—leased by the Society of Apothecaries in 1712—and conveyed the garden to them ten years later.[29] To ensure that the garden would not only be an organic factory for established drugs but should cultivate new ones he insisted that fifty specimens of its plants well dried and preserved should be presented to the Royal Society each year, up to the number of 2,000, and that the specimens should be different each year.

Tournefort's writings were translated by an apothecary, John Martyn (1699–1768) who organized a botanical society at the Rainbow Coffee House. Martyn's *Historia Plantarium Rariorum* came out between the years 1728 and 1737, during which time he became Professor of Botany at Cambridge. Another great French botanic gardener was Pierre Magnol (1638–1715), Director of the Jardin des Plantes at Montpellier, whose name comes down to us in the magnolia.

The botanical dynasty of the Jussieu family which followed Tournefort in 1708, laid the foundations for Buffon's work. The first, Antoine (1686–1758), built hot-houses, an amphitheatre and laboratories. The second, his brother Bernard (1699–1777), edited Tournefort's book, refined Linnaeus's sexual classification of plants, introduced the famous Cedar of Lebanon into the Jardin, and explored the potentialities of the coffee bean. A third, another brother Joseph (1704–77), introduced heliotrope and added to his medical abilities those of an engineer. A nephew, Antoine-Laurent de Jussieu (1748–1836), also a professor at the Jardin, carried the evolutionary idea perceptively forward in his *Genera Plantarum* in 1789 and became in 1808 a member of the Council of the Napoleonic University. Antoine-Laurent's son Andre (1797–1853) carried this remarkable intellectual dynasty up to the nineteenth century. Well might the secretary of the Royal Society of London tell Sir Joseph Banks in 1783 'that the collections of the Jardin du Roi are admirably arranged, and disgrace our Museum'.[30]

(5)

The synthesis of all this collecting and classifying came from Sweden, where Leyden-trained Olaf Rudbeck (1638–1706) (who believed that Sweden was the original site of the Garden of Eden and that the lost Atlantis of Plato was in an extension of the Scania peninsula) laid out a botanic garden at Upsala and designed canals.[31] In this garden Olaf Celsius (1670–1756) tried to track down all the plants mentioned in the Bible, and engaged Carl von Linné (Linnaeus) to help him.

Linnaeus was put in charge of Rudbeck's Botanical Gardens in 1730. After a successful expedition to Finland he visited Gronovius and Boerhaave in Holland, the Apothecaries' Garden at Chelsea and the Jardin du Roi in Paris, returning to Sweden to publish his *Genera Plantarum*: the starting point of modern botany. He followed this with his *Classes Plantarum*. Becoming Professor of Medicine in 1741, he exchanged it for the chair of botany in the following year and took up residence in the botanical garden. Nine years after he died a new botanical garden was built. His classification of plants in a complete hierarchy included specimens from outside Europe, for he was not only a consistent explorer, but a correspondent of other explorers for nearly fifty years.[32]

Nobody valued Linnaeus's work more than the British.[33] One of his pupils, Peter Kalm (1715–79) surveyed North America between 1748 and 1751. Another, D. C. Solander (1736–82) came to England in 1760 to instruct English botanists, helped to catalogue the natural history sections of the British Museum, and sailed with Captain Cook on the *Endeavour* in 1768. Linnaeus's work was translated into English by Erasmus Darwin and the Lichfield Botanical Society (Darwin subsequently bursting, as was his wont, into rhyme with a long poem), and his collections were purchased by Sir J. E. Smith (1759–1828) for £1,088. Smith even formed a society in his name. Apothecaries devoted themselves to popularizing his work. One of them, Richard Pulteney (1730–1801) was a radical non-conformist with a substantial practice in Hampshire, Dorset and Wiltshire.[34]

(6)

A new aesthetic sprang from the circulation of information about these gardens. Eyes and palates were sharpened by a

dynasty of illustrators. Claude Aubriet (1665–1742) after whom
the aubrieta (so often called the aubretia) is called,[35] drew for
the Jardin du Roi. Dr. Mead arranged for Elizabeth Blackwell
to live in Swan Walk, Chelsea, to draw illustrations of plants.
Here she was 'frequently visited by persons of quality, and many
scientific people who admired her performances and patronised
her undertakings'.[36] She worked hard to provide money to re-
lease her husband from prison and when the two volumes of her
herbal were published in 1739 he was freed. Towards the end
of the century it was regarded as a most moral occupation. 'At
all times of life the study of nature abates the taste for frivolous
amusements, prevents the torments of the passions and provides
the mind with a nourishment which is salutary by filling it with
an object most worthy of its contemplation', said Dr. Martyn in
his *Letters on the Elements of Botany addressed to the Ladies*
(1785). It was a gentleman's pursuit too. In 1787 Benjamin
Waterhouse of Harvard, where a botanic garden was then being
planted, remarked that 'gentlemen of leisure are taking to
botany and transplant wild plants to their gardens', but, he confessed, 'they are confused by the Linnaean system'.[37]

Everywhere wealthy men and universities established
gardens.[38] George Clifford, a Dutch East India Company
director, had his own botanic garden between Leyden and
Haarlem at Hartecamp. On the advice of Boerhaave, he engaged
Linnaeus in 1729 to look after it and the herbarium and to draw
up a Hortus Hartecampensis. Similarly Faujas de St. Fond
(1741–1819), had estates in the South of France where he
successfully cultivated Chinese hemp.[39] In England, more perhaps than anywhere, private botanic gardens flourished. Peter
Collinson, the correspondent of Benjamin Franklin, helped Lord
Holland to lay out a garden at Holland House, whilst Dr.
Richardson kept his own at Brierly.

Internationally famous, the creators of these English gentlemen's gardens were in European demand. James Meader,
gardener to the Duke of Northumberland at Sion House went to
Russia as gardener to Catherine the Great at Peterhof near St.
Petersburg. William Speechley, gardener to the Duke of Port-
land at Welbeck went to Holland to pick up tips on growing
grapes and pineapples. Their books and those of others show
such skill that Anthony Powell (gardener to George II),

Thomas Mawe (gardener to the Duke of Leeds) and Thomas Ellis (gardener to the Bishop of Lincoln), can claim to be professionals.

These gardener-botanists (the line between them was thinly drawn) were, as Jean Hecht reminds us 'skilled technicians' whose work was of 'major consequence' to their employers, aesthetically and practically. 'Much of this consequence', he continues, 'derived from the *furor hortensis* that swept through the century making the grounds of the country seat a new medium of competitive display.'[40]

Another of the roots of this *furor hortensis* was the ever-growing population, with its ever-lengthening inventory of the staples of life. Sugar, spice and vegetables, aromatic oils for chemists, fibre-bearing materials for the Navy, all, at some time or another, relied on the gardens for acclimatization.

Well might a professional spirit stir amongst British gardeners. In 1724 a 'Society of Gardeners' began to meet at Newall's Coffee House in Chelsea to defend their interests and to name some newly introduced plants. Men like Philip Miller kept the society together and after six years they decided to publish an illustrated survey of new introductions.[41]

(7)

The rapidity of these new introductions in the seventeenth century evoked comment. From Thomas Johnson, who marvelled at 'how many strange herbs, plants and annual fruits were daily brought into form . . . all part of the world' to shrewd John Aubrey, who calculated that over 7000 exotics had been introduced between 1660 and 1691, surprise was common.

Getting, growing and consuming these plants whether as foods, drugs, fuels or fibres elicited the professional skills of the plantocracy—or as they were known in England from 1588 onwards—the gentry, who moved, or caused others to move, confidently through the world, mapping, charting, uprooting and replanting. The activities of these collectivities of collectors acquired a sharp social significance between the years 1722 to 1725.

In the former year the English sent a packet of cotton seeds to Georgia; in the latter, La Condamine, exploring the Amazon, grasped the value of rubber. One was to lead, via Eli Whitney,

to the devising of the cotton gin and the system of mass production
by the principle of interchangeable parts; the others to man's
most ambitious emulation of the plant itself. Yet neither could
have led anywhere without the conviction that, provided its
actions were adequately studied, nature could be mastered.

Such conviction was cradled in conventicles of a new kind
whose origins and structure we must now explore.

2

◇◇

The Beat of the Imagination

◇◇

(1)

AWARE of the botanic garden as a seed-bed of science, young Francis Bacon wished to improve it. He suggested the idea of collecting a library in a house with 'a specious and wonderful garden and a goodly huge cabinet, and a still-house furnished with mills, instruments, furnaces and vessels'. Being the nephew of Lord Burghley (patron of John Gerard, the gardener), Bacon saw how states might prosper by cultivating, not only plants, but science in general. For the rest of his life he worked upon the design of an institution to be 'the Lanthorne of this Kingdom'. It was to be devoted to 'the knowledge of causes and secret notions of things; and the enlarging of the bounds of Human Empire, to the effecting of all things possible'. Nature's slow processes in the botanic garden were to be accelerated. Germination was to be speeded up, new foods found, new fibres compounded and new substances made. Macaulay later summed it up in his celebrated essay on Bacon when he asked, 'What was the end which Bacon proposed to himself? It was, to use his own emphatic expression, "fruit".'

Bacon called himself a 'bell ringer which is the first up to call others to church'. The ecclesiastical metaphor is significant for he was to be the catechist for later generations. His most telling injunction was that:

16

Nature cannot be conquered by obeying her. Accordingly these twin goals, human science and human power, come to an end in action. To be ignorant of causes is to be frustrate in action.[1]

It is possible to detect a veiled allusion to his uncle's gardener when he was dilating on the importance of endowing human life with 'new inventions and powers'. For Bacon remarked: 'only occasionally it happened that some artisan of unusual wit and covetous of honour applied himself to a new invention, which he mostly does at the expense of his fortune'.[2] But the garden could not fertilize the 'womb of nature' in which:

> lay many secrets of excellent use, having no affinity or parallelism with anything that is now known, but lying entirely out of the beat of the imagination which have not yet been found.[3]

That beat of the imagination Bacon proposed to enlarge by supplementing the gardens with 'laboritories and engines, vaults and furnaces and terraces for insulation'.

He designed the first blueprint of an institution devoted solely to scientific research. Its end was 'to effect all things possible'. With tremendous theological courage, Bacon called it the 'College of Six Day's Works', implying that Man had to make himself. It would have beggared any subscription. Towers half a mile high on hills were to be used as observatories; refrigerators and 'chambers of health' were to cure various diseases. Instruments of interrogation included 'some degrees of flying in the air, ships and boats for going under water, and brooking of seas', 'divers curious clocks and some perpetual motions'. The functional hierarchy of the staff was based on travelling fellows who were to reside abroad for twelve years obtaining information 'especially of the sciences, arts, manufactures and inventions of all the world; and withal to bring unto us books, instruments and patterns in every kind'. Such findings were to be collated, interpreted and assessed by 'Mystery Men' and 'Pioneers'. Practical applications were to be sought by 'Dowry Men', further experiments to be initiated by Lamps, and the final generalization to be effected by 'Interpreters of Nature'. All worked in groups of three, another theological aside.

Bacon was the first to appreciate that study of the 'philosophy of nature' was a full-time task which had 'scarcely ever possessed, especially in these later times, a disengaged and whole man (unless it were some monk studying in his cell or some gentleman in his country house)'. In addition (and this is more important), he suggested that it should be done in particular sciences, so that they might prosper. But even Bacon, considering on 26 July 1608 the possibility of obtaining an existing college (Westminster, Eton, Winchester, Trinity, St. John's—Cambridge or Magdalen College—Oxford) for such purposes, shrewdly included amongst possible backers for his scheme, Poe and Hammond (the Court physicians), the Earl of Northumberland, Chaloner Murray (the treasurer to Prince Henry), Bishop Andrews ('single, rich, sickly and professor to some experiments'), Sir Walter Raleigh and the Archbishop of Canterbury.[4]

(2)

The integration of botanic garden, observatory and laboratory, so powerfully advocated by Bacon, was followed in miniscule by Claude Fabri de Peiresc. At his homes at Aix and Belgentier, Peiresc built observatories, observed the nebulae in Orion, had dissections performed, collected fossils and imported plants. He even established half a dozen stations to observe the eclipse of 28 August 1635. He is credited with the discovery of chyle ducts in man.[5]

Peiresc took another step forward by corresponding with English disciples of Bacon like Cornelius Drebbell, Maker of Instruments to James I, whose 'grandes merveilles des inventions', included a cochineal dye, thermostatic ovens and an automatic clavicord.[6] He also corresponded with the brothers Pierre and Jacques Dupuy who had formed an 'academy' or 'cabinet' in Paris. When the brothers became librarians at the Bibliothèque du Roi in 1647 they were able to entertain many foreign visitors. Their 'academy' or 'cabinet' thus acquired a quasi-institutional status as opposed to the transitory-ephemeral character of most of the groups which met in Paris at that time.

Another physician, Theophraste Renaudot (1586–1653), organized a group which began to meet in 1622. From his house at the Great Cock in the centre of the Ile de la Cité he began to publish in 1631 a weekly gazette, known as the *Feuilles du Bureau d'Adresse*. A collected edition of the papers read at a 'conference', published in 1636, was also much sought after.[7]

Becoming bolder, Renaudot began to advocate free health clinics, to experiment with 'modern' medicines and to organize a school. This aroused the hostility of the Paris Faculty, which forbad him to practise medicine and to forgather with his group. But his *Gazette* continued to be issued. He died in 1653.[8]

Another of Peiresc's friends was the Minorite friar Marin Mersenne (1588–1648), who began in 1635 to organize 'colloquia' or conferences of those specifically interested in the natural sciences. To these came not only Descartes (who had been holding similar meetings since 1626 at his own and a relative's house), but Gassendi, Desargues, Roberval and the Pascals. From a cell in the Minorite Convent near the Place Royale, Mersenne conducted a steady correspondence on all kinds of scientific topics with Descartes, Fermat, Galileo, Torricelli and Theodore Haak. His 'colloquia' lasted for thirteen years.[9]

These 'colloquia' began to acquire institutional status when Descartes was offered a country house at Mesnil-Saint-Denis (near Port-Royal), by H. L. Habert de Montmor. Montmor was a wealthy member of the Académie Française, a body founded in 1635 to 'centralize' and 'standardize' French artistic opinion. This offer was subsequently extended to Gassendi who came to Paris in 1641 from Peiresc's Provençal observatory. Thus from 1654, Montmor's house became an embryo academy of science.[10]

(3)

The very name academy had botanical associations, for it had come from the garden of the mythical Academus where Plato had taught his young men. It had been revised in Italy where numerous academies took shape in the sixteenth century like the *Lunatici*, the *Extravaganti*, the *Fulmiales* (the smokers) and *della Crusca* (of the chaff). But one, formed in 1561, was particularly significant. It was called *Accademia dei Segreti*, so called because each member was obliged to have made a significant discovery in physical science. Its founder, Giambattista della Porta, had published a manifesto on *Natural Magic* which, when translated into French, Italian and German brought down on him the charge of witchcraft. So did the name and the activities of the *Segreti* and it was dissolved.

19

Undiscouraged, della Porta secured the patronage of a cardinal to travel around the Italian peninsula, investigating various matters. He made a parabolic mirror in Venice in 1580 and wrote a strange and exciting book, *De Humana Physiognomonia* (1586) showing the analogies between humans and animals. Meanwhile he brought his book on *Natural Magic* up to date with a confutation of witches, a treatise on magnetism and an account of the *camera obscura*. He disputed with Campanella, the noted Jesuit Utopist, wrote a rural encyclopaedia, and in 1593 explored the application of mathematical techniques to biological phenomena.

His ready pen won him disciples. In his home town of Naples his disciples used to meet in the house of Marco Aurelio Severino (1580–1656), a skilful surgeon and anatomist, who in the diphtheria epidemics of Naples used refrigerants to dull pain. Della Porta's own interests spread over many fields. He wrote a pioneer book on the force of steam, on fortifications, on distillation and on telescopes. As if this were not enough he wrote three tragedies (only one of which survives), twenty-nine comedies (of which fourteen survive) and one tragi-comedy.

Inspired by the *Segreti*, Prince Federigo Cesi of Rome convened a group in 1603 which took as its emblem the sharp-eyed lynx, hence their name: *Accademia dei Lincei*. Minutes were kept in cipher. It consisted of thirty-two members who conducted experiments on their own account. Cesi came down to Naples to establish a branch organization under della Porta as president. One of the original four, Francesco Stelluti made in 1625 the first systematic observations with the microscope on honeybees.

Within six years the Lincei had 'branches' in Germany, Rome and Florence.[11] Joined by Galileo in 1611, whom they encouraged to publish *Letters on the Solar Spots* (1613), the Lincei lasted until 1630. They ceased to exist and Galileo was sentenced by the Inquisition to recite the seven Penitential Psalms every week for three years and his books were placed on the Index.

One of Galileo's disciples, Torricelli, experimenting on the barometer in Florence, awakened the interest of the Grand Duke of Tuscany, Leopold II, who assembled other experimenters and built a laboratory in 1651. Six years later a group was formally organized as the *Accademia del Cimento* or the Academy of Experiment which devoted itself to developing Galileo's ideas.[12] Its nine members worked with apparatus supplied by the Medicis. One of them, Nicolaus Steno (1638–86) was the Danish doctor of the Duke whose work was translated into English by Henry Oldenburg. Another, Francesco Redi, did much to explode the so-called therapeutic effects of medicaments derived from vipers.

Redi's pupils at the Ospedale di Santa Maria Nuova in Florence included Giuseppe Zambeccari (1655–1728), who experimented on the excision of organs in dogs and (indirectly), the industrious Dutch naturalist Jan Swammerdam (1637–80) who devised a machine for underwater breathing. Their efforts, published as *Saggi di Naturali Esperienze* (1666), captured European attention, and were translated into English.

The Accademia del Cimento came to an end when Steno deserted his Lutheran faith and became a Catholic in 1667 (he even tried to convert Spinoza), and Prince Leopold was elevated to the Cardinalate. Another member of the academy, Antonio Oliva, was arrested by the Inquisition at Rome and subsequently committed suicide by jumping from the window of his prison.

A fourth group, this time of nine, was organized in Bologna by the surgeon Cavalieri. Known as the Coro Anatomico, its members kept in touch with the Neopolitan group, and devoted themselves to dissection. Bologna-born Marcello Malpighi so outraged the medical practitioners of the town that he had to leave for the University of Pisa and culminated in physical assault by two masked men in 1689. This time he sought safety in Rome where he became the papal physician.

(4)

Just as Peiresc had been stimulated by Giambattista della Porta, so were the Montmorians by Prince Leopold's Academia del Cimento. Through correspondents they proposed to learn 'what is in preparation, or already published or discovered in the Arts and Sciences'. Here they were helped by the astronomer Christian Huygens[13] who discovered the satellite of Saturn.[14] Other scientists read papers to them: the mathematician Giles Roberval (1602–75), Rohault, an early experimenter with electricity (who from 1658 began to organize meetings of his own), the surgeon Pecquet and two engineers, Melchisedec Thevenot and Pierre Petit. Petit (1594–1677), was later put in charge of the fortifications of the channel ports, and used to visit Blaise Pascal on his tours of duty.

But Montmor could not keep them together. He was too bereaved and poor to provide the laboratories, forges and observatories that they really needed. Moreover the mathematician Roberval was convinced the Huygens had plagiarized his ideas on Saturn. So they turned to the State. The French minister Colbert was approached (and so was the king), with the persuasive argument (voiced by the astronomer Adrien Azout, a member of yet another group, the Compagnie des Sciences et des Arts) that celestial observations were necessary for the reputation of France.

Yet Huygens had the most ambitious scheme of all; nothing less than an observatory, advisory council, centre of research, board of navigation, agricultural bureau and a medical research council, all in one.[15] His imaginative proposal won the day and with Azout as his adjutant, the Academy of Sciences was built round him. Four more were added on 1 July 1655: the mathematicians Roberval and Frenicle, the astronomer Jean Picard and the engineer Jacques Buot. As a meeting place the group were given the use of the Royal Library and the services of the Royal Librarian. They planned an academy with a mechanical and chemical bias, but Colbert, after further advice from Perrault, added three medical men: M. C. Chambre (1594–1669); S. C. du Clos and Louis Gayant.

Colbert himself favoured four separate academies (for belles-lettres, history, philosophy or mathematics), meeting on separate days and together once a month, but the Académie Française objected. So Colbert decided to concentrate on the sciences, especially astronomy. So the group met on 16 January 1666, to observe a lunar eclipse and a fortnight later a solar eclipse. Under the French astronomer Jean-Baptiste du Hamel 1624–1706 the group began to obtain pensions, funds and grants for apparatus from the king who openly took the society under his protection on 22 December 1666. They were to specialize in five fields: astronomy, mathematics, botany, anatomy and chemistry, no strangers were allowed at the meetings and no results were to be published.

The academy still further enriched the Jardin du Roi, for it mounted expeditions for astronomical purposes. Thus Jean Richer went to Cayenne in 1672 to compare simultaneous observations with Cassini in Paris; thereby discovering the shortened swing of the pendulum near the equator. This was to be the prototype of the many other expeditions, culminating in La Condamine's visit to the Quito region of Peru.

(5)

It was not so much an academy as an asylum that other kings had afforded to scientists. Indeed asylum was an apt name for the chemists and Paracelsians assembled round the Holy Roman Emperor, Rudolf II.[16] The 'unholy' nature of such imperial preoccupations went back to the days of his illustrious twelfth-century forbear, Frederick II who turned the imperial Court into an experimental pleasure garden, exploiting to the full the talents of the Moslem civil servants who ran his empire and made his fountains.[17]

Rudolf's own inclinations were scholarly. He invited Andreas Libavius the possessor of a fine chemical laboratory, and author of the first systematic book on Alchemy, to address his Court, where John Dee, Queen Elizabeth's map-maker and astronomer, rubbed shoulders with Cornelius Drebbel, enthusiast for perpetual motion. Here, too, came Kepler, with a telescope given him by Galileo, having refused a chair at Bologna in order to be free to work on the Rudolphine Tables.[18]

Elsewhere in the empire, mystical bodies dabbled in science. At Weimar, destined to have such a reputation in the following century, an Akademie des Palmbaumes or Fruchtbringende Gesellschaft (the very names indicated the hope), was founded by J. V. Andreae. In *Fama Fraternitatis* he outlined a plan for scientific investigation by a brotherhood of four men (later increased to eight), united 'to secure a general reformation' and 'discover the mysteries of nature'. Later, in his Utopia *Christianopolis* (1619), he drew the outlines more firmly for the laboratory 'dedicated to chemical science, and fitted out with the most ingenious ovens and with contrivances for uniting and dissolving substances'. Stood behind the treasury, Christianopolis was like Bacon's Solomon's house. Its citizens had 'a strong inclination towards the natural sciences', they maintained a pharmacy 'not only for the cause of public health but also with a view towards the advancement of education in general'. They also maintained a dissecting room for teaching the young 'the operations of life and the various organs, from parts of the physical body'; a hall of physics (which 'cannot be too elegantly described'), and an 'excavated place for mathematical instruments, a testimony of human acuteness and energy against our mortal chains'.[19] Andreae's Utopist vision was much influenced by the Danish astronomer Tycho Brahe for whom the King of Denmark had built a great observatory at Hveen. He relied so much on this that he wrote, 'I will not enumerate the instruments here, inasmuch as nearly all of them are understood from the description of the most eminent Tycho Brahe. A very few have been added and among these is a very valuable telescope recently invented.'

Another group was formed at Rostock: the Societas Ereunetica. Founded in 1622 by Joachim Jungius (1587–1657), a professor at the local university, it aimed at 'freeing all the sciences and arts which are based upon reason and experience from all sophisms; to reduce them to a state of demonstrable certainty; to propagate them by means of suitable instruction; and lastly to increase them by felicitious inventions'. When his own academy ceased to exist in 1624, Jungius went to Lubeck as Professor of Mathematics where he advocated experimental physics as opposed to astrology. His arduous campaign led Goethe to remark that had people followed his advice, the world would be a hundred years in advance of what it is.[20]

(6)

From Germany to England came three men who were to put these and other ideas into practice. Renaudot's idea of an Office of Address found an eager, industrious disciple in Samuel Hartlib,[21] a German merchant who arrived in England from Prussia soon after Bacon's *New Atlantis* (1627) was published. He, too, was a busy correspondent whose letters communicated intelligence on a wide front. Through his good offices the great Czech Comenius came to England in 1641. Together they planned to establish an 'invisible college'—a pansophic dream of long standing.

With yet another refugee Theodore Haak, Hartlib was given

a grant of £50 by Parliament in 1650, 'in regard of the many good services by them done by their correspondency in parts beyond the seas, and to enable them to continue it'. These many 'good services' were known to the savants who met during the Civil War to discuss 'the new philosophy' of Bacon. Dispersed during the protectorate, they used to assemble in the Oxford lodgings of John Wilkins, Cromwell's brother-in-law and a great collector of projects for mechanical powers and motions: submarines, flying machines, pulleys, reduction gears and automata all came within his province. To enable gentlemen to avoid 'the Delusions of any cheating Imposter' and common artificers to be 'advantaged by the right understanding of their Grounds and Theory', Wilkins published in 1648 *Mathematical Magick: or the Wonders that may be Performed by Mechanical Geometry*.[22]

With Henry Oldenburg (also a German and the tutor of Boyle's nephew), Wilkins acted as the secretary of the virtuosi who now met at Gresham College, where they were treated to various proposals to establish 'a Colledge for the promoting of Physico-Mathematicall Experimentall Learning'. Charles II was interested, and chartered them as the Royal Society of London two years later. A second charter extended their privileges and a third gave them lands in Chelsea, which they never obtained. It became, instead, the Pensioners' Hospital. Though unendowed, with members reluctant to pay fees, in ten years the society was considering national problems, like food supply, naval architecture and navigation, and the supply of timber. Its *Philosophical Transactions* were first published as a private venture by its first secretary, Henry Oldenburg. Housed at Gresham College from 1660 to 1710 (with a period at Arundel House 1665–93), it moved to Crane Court until 1778, then to Somerset House until 1857. From that time until the present day it has been at Burlington House, maintained by the Government though independent of its control.

(7)

Many of such early promoters were truly Utopian. Bengt Skytte (1614–83) son of the chancellor of the University of Uppsala, having visited Russia (in 1631), Hungary, Turkey and Britain, began, at the time the Royal Society was founded, to promote a scheme for a Sophopolis, or international learned society. He approached Colbert of France and finally, the Great Elector of Brandenburg, who issued a patent for its creation at Tangermünde on the Elbe in 1667.[23]

It was not on this large scale that such hopes were to be fulfilled, but rather through the anastomosing web of visits, correspondence and exchange of journals, specimens and papers. At first French scientists obtained their news of the Royal Society from Henri Justel, a former member of Montmor's group, whose work in disseminating English books and science over the continent of Europe was, in the opinion of a modern historian, 'not equalled before the eighteenth century, and only occasionally surpassed then'.[24] Justel experimented with a loud speaking trumpet invented by Sir Samuel Morland, 'master mechanic' to Charles II, and corresponded with G. W. Leibnitz who sent him a description of a coach invented by Erhard Weigel 'which could be changed into a boat or a tent, as was shown by experiment'. Another such 'intelligencer' was Claude Nicaise (1623–1701), a canon at Dijon who transcribed and relayed to various correspondents scientific news as others retailed gossip.

Such retailing was arduous work. Leibnitz, for instance, wrote 300 letters a year. Each fresh cabinet or academy increased the load and soon Sir William Petty was exploring systems of multiple writing to facilitate communications. Shorthand was used. The success of the *Gazette*, and that of Blaise Pascal's *Lettres écrites à un Provincial par un de ses amis* led, however, to decisive steps being taken to establish a scientific journal.

The first proposal was that of Mezeroy for a *Journal General de Litterature* to include news of the 'arts'. This came to nothing. In 1665 Pierre Perrier, Marquis de Crevan, a friend of Pascal's in association with M. de Sallo, issued a weekly *Journal des Scavans*, edited by Denis de Sallo, who had experience of transcribing other men's work. The first number, issued on 5 January 1665, was a landmark in thought, for it was the first scientific journal. Natural phenomena, new discoveries in machines, news from the universities and from the world of letters was given in print for the first time. It was later edited by the Abbé Gallois, a member of the Académie des Sciences, and after him by the Abbé de la Rogue. In its editing Chapelain also played some

26

part, both in finding contributors and writing articles. Its accounts of Perrault's dissections, Pecquet's medical work, Roberval's balance, Marriotte's hydrostatic work and Huygen's chronological mechanisms were supplemented by the work of Germans like Bausch and Sachs and by Englishmen like Henry Oldenburg. It was bought by Englishmen like Martin Lister.

One contributor to the first number was Henry Oldenburg who discussed it with the Royal Society. As a result an English counterpart was issued—the *Philosophical Transactions*, which, as evidence of its paternity, included three items from the *Journal des Scavans* in its first number. Unlike the *Journal* it was more philosophical. The *Philosophical Transactions* in turn influenced the publications of private French academies and conferences after 1670, especially as the *Journal des Scavans* appeared fitfully during its early years.[25]

3

<hr />

Academic Honeycombs

<hr />

(1)

NOBODY should hope to infuse sciences into men by means of
Lullian doctrines; Rosicrucian *Illuminationes Elias Philoso-
phorum* and other such rodomontades are commonly considered
a fool's game.' So wrote a former secretary of the Rosicrucians
in Hamburg: G. W. Leibnitz. Depressed because his fellow-
countrymen were the first to make inventions but the last to
use them, he appealed to nobles and princes to establish a society
like the Royal Society of London so that Germany could profit
from German inventions.

He followed up his *Memorandum on the Founding of a Learned
Society in Germany* (1669) by a four-year stay in Paris and
London. On his return to the service of the Duke of Brunswick
he published his notations of the calculus in 1684 and began to
argue that universities should emancipate themselves from
'monkish erudition' which lacked 'experience, activity and
reality'. He wished them to become centres of reconciliation
where 'savants and students should participate as much as they
can with other people and in the world'.[1] This 'entirely new
maxim' could best be fostered by a society of erudite Germans
issuing a biennial journal containing accounts of current advances
in mathematics, medicine, commerce and manufactures; co-
operating with French, Italian and English academies; co-ordi-

nating scientific research, and licensing the publication of books. This proposed society, he later thought, would accelerate the application of chemical and physiological discoveries to life, by including education, history, economics and what we would now call sociology within its scope of operations. Even children and prisoners could, he argued, furnish material for its investigations. So an 'appetite for curiosity' would be cultivated, the academy would become a bank of useful ideas, a centre of report and a promoter of 'trade and commerce in sciences'.

For forty-seven years Leibnitz tried to institutionalize this concept. He corresponded with scientists at home and abroad, immersed himself in the technological life of the day, designing calculating machines (which his mechanic Oliver tried to make), and pumps for the Harz mines. He even entered the political field, and tried to stop European war by suggesting that the King of France should 'Europeanize' Egypt.

He appealed to the Leopoldine Academy, the most active of the local scientific groups in Germany at that time,[2] to unite other German groups around them and become a truly imperial society sheltering and sustaining scientific research, surveying, sifting and solving problems affecting life. By doing so, Leibnitz urged, they would do more in ten years than humanity had effected in centuries.

The movement for such an imperial society got under way when Weigel suggested in 1694 that a group of consultants should be convened to reform the calendar. Profits were to subsidize further work in astronomy, mathematics and the arts. When this did become a burning issue in Brandenburg five years later, Leibnitz introduced an ingenious variation that the profits should be used to establish an observatory and a learned society.

So Leibnitz got his way and the Berlin Academy of Sciences took shape under his presidency. It provided for three interest groups: *Res physico-mathematicae*, *Lingua Germanica* and *Res literarae*. But it took a further ten years before it established itself. Not until 1710 were its first transactions *Miscellanea Berolinensia* published, and then in Latin. Poor Leibnitz, meanwhile, was saddled with the task of writing a history of the House of the Guelphs.

Leibnitz hoped that scientists in each of the capitals of

29

Europe would gather together to help one another. To help them do so he worked on a Universal Language (which he called a 'Universal Characteristic'), for all current knowledge to be read off by those anxious to apply it. The centre of this movement was to be Britain, followed three years later by Dresden and Leipzig (where Tschunkhausen was working on a mathematico-physical society). War cut short his plans, but Leibnitz, undismayed, outlined his plans to the Tsar in 1711 for technological discoveries and expeditions to Siberia. The Tsar in return gave him a pension, and fourteen years later, an academy was duly founded at St. Petersburg. But when he tried to interest Prince Eugene the Jesuits got in first and this particular academy was still-born.[3]

(2)

A year before the Berlin Academy was established, the French Académie des Sciences was reorganized. Under a formal constitution and a remarkably talented secretary, it was to meet every Wednesday and Saturday, with five public assemblies a year. Attendance was made compulsory (the threat of expulsion hung over any absentee). A hierarchy of grades was set up: ten honoraries, twenty pensioners, twenty associates and twenty assistants—a nomenclature not unfamiliar in the university world today.

The talented secretary was B. de Fontenelle, an able synthesizer of new knowledge; the weather man for the liberal climate of opinion that made eighteenth-century France the mecca of the cultural world. His forty-four-year tenure of office made him such a venerable figure that Voltaire depicted him as the secretary of the 'Academy of Saturnia' in *Micromégas*.

Fontenelle believed an *élite* should lead the thought of a nation.[4] This *élite* needed knowledge, and to provide it an exhaustive inquiry into all manufacturing processes was instituted. This inquiry was entrusted to Remy Antoine de Réaumur and it lasted for both their lives.

Published in a continuous series of 121 parts during the years 1761 to 1789 this survey of arts and crafts marks the emergence of modern technology. A similar passion for visiting, reporting and criticizing workshops, factories and industrial centres also animated D. Diderot to undertake another great French publication—the twenty-eight-volume *Encyclopaedia* which was issued between the years 1751 and 1772. Between old Réaumur and young Diderot little love was lost. Réaumur accused Diderot of copying from his work, sneered at his lowly origins, and castigated his use of science for political reasons.[5]

Réaumur was not the only one who criticized the political slant which Diderot gave to his articles. Even the publishers thought it provident to excise certain passages.[6] The considerable body of critical matter that survived excision was certainly well circulated throughout the country for a number of provincial academies had grown and were growing up. Like cells, these provincial academies covered the country, and in some cases Europe. Five were founded in the seventeenth, and nearly forty in the eighteenth century: Soissons (1674), Nîmes (1682), Angers (1685), Villefranche en Beaujolais (1679) and Toulouse (1684). Lyons (1700, 1724 and 1778), Caen (1705), the Société Royale des Sciences of Montpellier (1706), Bordeaux (1712), Rouen (1716, 1735, 1744), Périgueux (1718), Pau (1720), Béziers (1723), Marseilles (1726), Toulouse (1729), Montauban (1730), La Rochelle (1732), Arras (1738, 1778), Dijon (1740), Clermont (1747), Auxerre (1749), Amiens, Nancy, Châlons-sur-Marne (1750), Millau (1751), Besançon (1752), Bourg (1755), Metz (1757), Lille (1758), Grenoble (1772), Mulhouse (1775), and Agen (1776).[7]

Above them all was the Académie des Sciences, organizing competitions of various kinds. One of them was for the best manner of propelling boats without wind. Daniel Bernouilli proposed in 1753 a boat equipped with a vertical tube, with an issue pipe at the stern; water would be poured into the tube and, emerging from the pipe, would drive the boat forward. He also proposed a propulsion unit of paddle wheels turned by a 'pompe de feu'. Such a 'pompe' was actually used by the Comte J. B. d'Auxiron (1728–78) who obtained a fifteen-year concession in 1772 to use it on river boats. The Académie des Sciences appointed Jacques C. Périer (1742–1818) to evaluate it but unfortunately the vessel foundered. In 1775 Périer seems to have carried out an experiment on his own but his engine was too small. One of Auxiron's associates, the Marquis de Jouffroy d'Abbans, after experimenting with a Newcomen engine in a

31

boat on the River Doubs, successfully propelled his *Pyroscappe* up the Seine near Lyons for fifteen minutes on 15 July 1783. But in spite of submitting a model to the Académie des Sciences he never secured the support of the French Government. When, in 1780 d'Alembert and Condorcet (an associate with Diderot on the *Encyclopédie*), persuaded the Government to establish an Institute for the Study of Hydraulics at the Louvre, Gaspard Monge was appointed to direct it. Soon he was also examining potential officers for the Navy.

(3)

Ideas from the *Encyclopédie* circulated in Spain too, where the ground had been prepared by Conde de Penaflorida. Returning from France in 1746, this young Basque nobleman soon organized a *salon* at his house where mathematics, physics and current affairs were discussed. By 1767 the group obtained a licence from the Government enabling them to establish an official organization: the Sociedad Bascongada de los Amigos del Pais.

These 'friends of the Country' got permission to establish instruction centres for teaching languages and physics. They imported linen seed from Riga, offered prizes for technological improvements and generally enlisted popular interest in advancement through the 'arts'.

By 1789 some fifty-six of these societies had been founded, some in towns which did not have the resources to support them, simply because official policy smiled on them.[8] They owed much to the pioneer work of a Spanish disciple of Bacon: Benite Gerónimo Feyjóo y Montenegro, a monk who maintained that science did not necessarily clash with religion. The nine volumes of his *Teatro critico universal*, appearing between 1726 and 1739 and the other four of his *Cartas eruditas* elicited so many attacks that the king issued a royal order in 1750 prohibiting further criticism of his work, which ran *Don Quixote* close in the number of editions issued: fifteen before 1786.

Feyjóo's apostolate of experiment centred around medicine, and he was soon followed by others like Andrés Piquer, a professor at the University of Valencia. Their influence prevented the Inquisition's ban on the French *Encyclopédie* in 1759 from having too harmful an effect.[9]

(4)

Throughout the later part of the seventeenth and during the eighteenth century other schemes, suitably modified by the personalities promoting them and the circumstances surrounding their foundation, resulted in academies being established at Madrid (1713), Danzig (1743), Haarlem (1760), Trondhjem (1760), Brussels (1773), Lisbon (1779), Dublin (1782) and Vienna (1783).

In Italy another Neapolitan group, the Investiganti, began life in 1663 in the house of the Marquis of Arena who subsequently obtained a stock of instruments from the Cimento in Florence.[10] Its device was a setting dog, its motto, *Vestigia Lustrant*. A rival academy, the Discordanti, with a device of a seven-stringed zither, led to trouble and both were suppressed in 1670. The Investiganti had three Neapolitan offspring: The Spencierati or Incuriosi of Rossano (reformed 1696), the Palatine Academy of Medinaceli (founded 1698) and the Academy of Sciences (1732). The first lasted well beyond the gestation of the third, the second died in 1701, the third died in 1744.

Eleven other towns in Italy formed academies too: Bologna for mathematics (1692) and sciences (1712), Venice for medicine (1701), Mantua (1704) and Milan (1719) for sciences, Palermo (1745) for medicine, Florence (1752) for agriculture, Naples (1755), Verona (1780), Genoa (1783) and Padua (1792) for sciences. The eleventh is not in chronological order. It was at Turin and was formed in 1757 by a professor of mathematics at the Royal Artillery school there, J. Lagrange (1736–1813). Its first publication in 1759 contained several of Lagrange's papers. These brought him into touch with Euler, who nominated him for membership of the Berlin Academy. Seven years later, Lagrange moved, as we have seen, to Berlin.

(5)

Lagrange's move to Berlin indicates that technical ability was now purchasable by the State. From its first formal ceremonies held in the meeting hall of the observatory on 19 January 1711, the Berlin Academy was an embryo scientific civil service. Though none of its first fellows were up to Leibnitz's expections, nor was its endowment (for the income from the royal calendar monopoly was altogether inadequate), it excited the admiration of the English deist John Toland who after translating its ordinances and statutes admired its 'two firm and unshaken pillars, I mean most ample Salarys for the Teachers, and most easy Expenses for the Learners', and exclaimed 'What a mighty increase of Trade and Wealth will this Institution bring to the City of Berlin?'

The brothers Jablonski, who held the offices of president and secretary, quarrelled with Leibnitz, whilst other members had, because of the lack of accommodation and an absence of a laboratory, to work in their own homes. When the first volume of the *Miscellanea Berolonensia ad incrementum scientiarum* was published in 1710, twelve of the sixty articles were by Leibnitz himself and these in all three of the subject groups. In spite of, or perhaps because of, this, Leibnitz was denied his salary, and soon the academy found itself paying rent for its observatory.[11]

Though King Frederick William I despised it and dismissed Leibnitz's friend Christian Wolff from the chair of mathematics and natural philosophy at Halle in 1721 appointing three of his Court fools as presidents, he was by no means averse to fostering its interest in medical science. His collegium medico-chirurgicum, founded in 1724, became the leading school of science and medicine in all the German states.

His successor, Frederick the Great, recalled Wolff to Halle, and began to coax foreign talent to Berlin. He lured Leonard Euler from the St. Petersburg Academy in 1744 and when Euler left twenty-two years later, he recommended Lagrange to Frederick, who promptly as the 'greatest King of Europe' invited the 'greatest mathematician' from Turin (where he was a professor), to the military school in Berlin.[12] Lagrange stayed for twenty-one years (from 1766 to 1787), swelling the proceedings of the academy with his papers and writing his *Mécanique Analytique*. When Frederick the Great died he accepted a pension and the advice of Mirabeau to return to Paris.

Frederick the Great gave the Berlin Academy in 1746 new statutes and a new president. Pierre Louis de Maupertuis was, not like Jablonski, a theologian, but a practical mathematician, astronomer and geographer, and above all, a veteran of the battle of Mollwitz. Two days before Maupertuis became president the army chaplain, J. P. Sussmilch (1707–77) was elected to the academy for advocating application of the statistical method in estimating the industrial and scientific wealth of a nation in a book with the curious title *The Divine Order* (1742).

The president was, like his royal master, an autocrat. Having in earlier days made forays to Lapland to measure degrees of longitude, he now ventured to look for a unifying formula for all the laws of nature. Fumbling with the 'law of least action' (p = mvs.) where action (p) = mass (m) × velocity (v) × distance (s), he professed to find in it a proof of the existence of God. Really he was stumbling on the threshold of quantum mechanics. Voltaire laughed at him in his *Diatribe du docteur Akakia, Médecin du Pape* (1752),[13] a lampoon against Maupertuis for persuading the academy to accuse a fellow-academician of forging a letter of Leibnitz. Though Voltaire liked neither accused nor accuser, he felt strongly about the persecution of an intellectual. He said so in such terms that Frederick II had his pamphlet publicly burnt by the hangman, and sent the ashes to Maupertuis. It certainly cured Voltaire of his earlier hope of playing Aristotle to Frederick's Alexander. 'If he had more daring,' wrote Voltaire in his notebooks, 'he would have destroyed the house of Austria and the Christian religion.'[14]

The secretary, J. H. S. Formey, was equally contentious. When Rousseau's *Émile* appeared, he wrote a counterblast. Life might be quantitative in eighteenth-century Berlin, but it was also quarrelsome.

The real role of the Berlin Academy was to make up for the shortcomings of the barren north German plains. Having no colonies, the laboratory of the Berlin Academy under Andreas S. Margraf (1709–82) recovered sugar in beetroot in 1746 and showed that a constituent of alum, alumina, is contained in clay. In 1760 he took over the class for experimental philosophy and directed it for twenty-two years, until 1810.

(6)

Other academies were founded at Erfurt in 1753 for the 'Useful Sciences' as well as at Leipzig (in 1768) and Munich (in 1759).[15] At Dresden a collegium-medicio-chirgicum had been founded in 1748. German universities, too, were founded, like Göttingen in 1734 and Erlangen in 1743. These in turn harboured academy founders. The great systematizer Albrecht von Haller (1708–77) laboured from 1738 for seventeen years in a

35

specially built theatre at Göttingen and founded in 1751 the Königliche Gesellschaft der Wissenschaften. Author of 13,000 scientific papers, Haller was a learned society in himself; being a physiologist, poet, botanist and novelist. With his *Elementa Physiologiae Corporis Humani* (1757–66) we reach modernity. At Göttingen, too, J. F. Blumenbach (1752–1840) did seminal work in medical ethnology. Shape of skull, facial configuration and colour of the skin he established as criteria in classifying human types. He introduced the category 'Caucasian' to describe the white race because a female Georgian skull was the most symmetric.

Indeed a veritable ground-swell of enthusiasm for technical training flowed in Germany. Johann Georg Leib's *Probe, wie ein Verbesserung Land und Leuten* (1705) had urged the establishment of an academy to improve manufactures whilst at Halle a pupil of Weigel's, Jean Christopher Semler, had put forward a plan for a 'mechanical school'. With A. H. Francke a move was made to introduce the principle into the schools of Halle where he was an inspector. But he found little support and the scheme was abandoned in 1709 and not revived until thirty years later. At Erlangen J. G. Cross and at Leipzig G. H. Zincke were also active promoters of similar ideas.

Frederick the Great utilized this ground-swell to encourage the foundation of an Economical-Mathematical Realschul in Berlin where J. J. Hecker was to help pupils 'to apply under various circumstances what they had learned of science and mathematics in the school'. Inspired by the survey of the French Académie des Sciences of arts and crafts, J. G. Busch opened an academy at Hamburg in 1767, concentrating on the commercial aspects of technology. Here F. von Stein, Goethe's friend, and Alexander von Humboldt were pupils and from here F. Ch. Wurms went to open a similar institution in Wilhelmsdal in 1785. Maria Theresa opened, on his plan, another in Vienna in 1770.

Farther south, at Freiberg in Saxony, where the mines had been attracting students like the famous Russian Lomonosov as early as 1739, a mining school had been growing up. Now, in 1766 it was officially recognized. A. G. Werner (1749–1817) was later appointed to its staff. Dogmatic and stimulating, he attracted students by avoiding speculation and stressed the importance of observing facts. From these facts he formed the idea that the sea had the decisive role in the formation of rocks: 'Neptunism' his successors called it.

To Werner's 'Neptunist' school at Freiberg came Russian, Scandinavian, Spanish, Polish, Portuguese and Neapolitan students. Britain was represented by the son of James Watt. Many of these students returned to their own countries to found similar institutions. Andrei Deriabin became director of a Russian mining institute in 1773. Fausto El Huyar set up one in Spain in 1782 and Mexico in 1792. Prussia followed suit with a mining school at Clausthal in 1775 and France established the École des Mines in 1781 where under B. G. Sage, scholarships were provided for sons of miners and peasants who had reached the age of 16.

This movement was given a name: 'technology'. The word, significantly enough, was coined by Johann Beckmann (1739–1811), a former student of theology, who turned to mathematics and the natural sciences, visiting the Netherlands, Russia, Sweden and Denmark. Impressed by what he had seen, he initiated lectures on agriculture, mineralogy, market research and financial administration at Göttingen University under the generic title of 'technology'. He wrote a textbook on the subject in 1777 which ran to six editions by 1809. Beckmann also developed into a historian of inventions, and his book on this subject was still being issued in England as late as 1846.

(7)

Technology had found its clerisy in the academies—220 of them by 1790. These academies were in many cases no more than groups of like-minded investigators, often furtive, often masking (as in the case of Freemasons), their real designs with some ritual. A shrewd Scot, who abandoned a career in the Church (had been an army chaplain), to become a professor of chemistry, then of mathematics at Edinburgh, remarked in 1767 that man should only be studied in groups, not as individuals.[16] Collecting, measuring and examining everything they could see or lay hands on, these academicians devised telescopes and microscopes, experimented, travelled and wrote.

Though living in secular nation states and involved in the improving of guns, powder or mines, commerce and medicine, or in making palaces, fountains, dyes and medicaments, they communicated with each other by letter and journal. These journals constitute one of the major ecumenical forces of the seventeenth and eighteenth centuries. Seventy-five per cent of the 220 academies and societies associated with science and technology issued such printed works in the form of collections,[17] transactions or prize essays.

Though such groups appeared at the same time and in the same places as the botanic gardens, they were in every sense, discrete. And they became more discrete as they wrote about, as well as to, each other. Their self-consciousness was further enhanced by others' need of them. 'The pundit's faith in his own mission,' said Karl Mannheim, 'lasts only so long as he holds the key to the secrets of the universe, so long as he is the then king order of other strata. His presumptuousness ends when he encounters the commanding world view of another group.'[18]

In the eighteenth century theirs was truly a commanding world view. Fäy has described them as constituting 'an international general staff endowed with a strong *esprit de corps*'.[19]

Linked by bonds of Freemasonry and language (Latin or French was still used in their publications), their membership transcended nationality. Benjamin Franklin for instance, was a member of more than twenty societies in 1785, whilst the Berlin Academy of the same year included five Germans, five Swiss, four Huguenots, three French and one Italian.

Yet the politics of science were evident too. Voltaire returned from England in 1729 imbued with the Newtonian system and commended it to his fellow-countrymen. But his book was publicly burnt. The directors of the Paris Observatory, the Cassinis, challenged it. Maupertuis, also, was sceptical for a time but was convinced by the findings of an expedition to Lapland (1735) and his own participation in another in Peru (1736) which, by measuring the degrees of longitude in those places convinced him that the earth did flatten at the poles. Euler at Berlin and St. Petersburg applied the Leibnitzian and Newtonian calculus to astronomical problems, while Lagrange at Turin, Berlin and Paris carried Newton's work into mechanics, eliminating God from the celestial system, which he regarded as an autonomous machine.

(8)

These academies undertook the first real international co-operative work in science. A typical example was the organization, both in 1761 and 1769 of observations of the transit of Venus. In 1761, 120 observers were organized in 62 separate stations and 8 years later 138 observers were organized in 63 stations. Only in 15 cases were the same stations used for both events.[20] For thanks to the invention of the achromatic object glass, this was followed by an outburst of observatory founding: Stockholm (1750), Prague and Göttingen (1751), Vienna (1756), Oxford (1771), Geneva and Mannheim (1772), Lilienthal (1779), Dublin (1785), Slough (1786), Leipzig (1787), Breslau, Kazan and Palermo (1790), Cracow and Golba (1719) and Madras (1792). It was from Lilienthal that F. W. Bessel came to take charge of the new observatory at Königsberg in 1813.

Though France and Britain were at war for an aggregate of sixty years during this period, scientists in those two countries never ceased to communicate with each other. Masonic enthusiasm for diffusing knowledge of the useful sciences and the *beaux-arts* linked them together. Thus the Chevalier Ramsay, impressed by the Club de l'Entresol (formed in 1724 by Bolingbroke in the Place Vendôme), fostered Freemasonry in France. Subsequent French visitors to England became Masons. English Freemasons, like J. T. Desaguliers translated works by French engineers like Marriotte in 1718 and Vaucanson in 1742, and was himself awarded a prize by the Academy of Sciences at Bordeaux. The secretary of the Society of Agriculture, Sciences and Arts at Aix, Jacques Gibelin (1744–1828), translated Kirwan's *Minerology*, Franklin's *Autobiography* and the works of Joseph Priestley. One French Mason in England, Helvetius, on returning to France, founded the lodge 'Les Sciences' with La Lande, which embraced all scientist Masons in Paris at that time. He wanted to expand the lodge, but died before he could do so. Fortunately La Lande was able to help organize the Grand Orient de France, and this gave birth to the famous Nine Sisters Lodge on 5 July 1776. Les Neuf Soeurs, as it was called, was composed of exceptional people who had published work in the sciences or the arts, or patronized such publication. It was divided into nine sections, each under a commissioner, who were to subsidize further publications. Within two years it had 180 members and an annual intake of twenty a year. Apart from its ritualistic activities it provided lectures on various subjects. When Benjamin Franklin became its master he took a lead in establishing the Société Apollonienne or Musée de Paris for the publication of books and production of lectures.[21]

The Musée de Paris, instituted on 17 November 1780 proved too humanistic for many and so on 11 December 1781 a rival Musée was established under Pilâtre de Rozier, the aeronaut. After Pilâtre's death in 1785 in a balloon, it was rechristened the Lycée de Paris when it widened its curriculum to include the humanities. Amongst the professors were Condorcet and La Croix (Mathematics), La Monge and Deparcieux (Physics) and Fourcroy (Chemistry). After 1802 it became the Athenée. After the Restoration it became the Athenée Royale with G. Saint-Hilaire, Benjamin Constant and Auguste Comte on the staff. It closed in 1848.

One of the most active promoters of Anglo-French co-operation was J. Hyazinthe de Magellan (1722–90), a French tutor in England. On one hand he kept Lavoisier abreast of work done in England whilst on the other he kept English provincial groups supplied with news of French scientific work. His correspondence went as far afield as Berlin and St. Petersburg. French chemistry also found an able popularizer in England in William Nicholson (1753–1815) who translated the works of Fourcroy and Chaptal and began to issue his famous journal of *Natural Philosophy, Chemistry and the Arts* in 1797.

Publications of the various academies were exchanged, travelling between the two countries was continued and election to membership of their various societies continued. As Sir Gavin de Beer has remarked: 'these principles were constantly upheld by men of science on both sides, without any suggestion that such action was reprehensible or derogatory to their sense of patriotism; and this good feeling is all the more remarkable because in general there was little love lost between the ordinary people of the two nations'.[22] Armies and navies might fight, but the letters of protection by Franklin, Jenner or Sir Joseph Banks carried untold weight for the scientist who bore them. What many of these travellers were after we shall now see.

4

Glands of the Plantocracy

(1)

THE enormous potential of the colonies as plantations was envisaged by the ebullient publicist-botanist, John Hill, whose
tussle with the Royal Society was partly due to their reluctance
to adopt his large views. He castigated its Fellows as 'butterfly
hunters', 'cockle shell merchants' and 'medal-scrapers', thereby
losing any chance he might have had to being elected to fellowship. This attack, though it led to a reform in their publications
—they ceased to be published by the secretary, but by the society
as a whole[1]—resulted in his exclusion from the Chelsea Physic
Garden. So he began his own garden near what is now Lancaster
Gate.

He also advised, at the suggestion of Lord Bute, various
colonial governors on the cultivation of their islands.[2] For he
held strong ideas on the economic importance of botany. His
Idea of a Botanical Garden in England (1758) and *The Usefulness
of Knowledge of Plants illustrated in various instances* (1759),
probably led Bute to recommend him as Superintendent of the
Dowager Princess of Wales' gardens at Kew—an appointment
not confirmed. In the latter year Hill began the issue of what
was to be a series of twenty-six folio volumes—his famous
Vegetable System.

Blind as Bute might be to the American colonies' rights, he

had a keen eye for the aesthetic and economic importance of plants.[3] America, declared her first great botanist in 1767, 'has furnished England with a greater variety of trees than has been procured from all other parts of the world for more than a thousand years past'.[4] The chief furnisher was John Bartram, appointed botanist to King George III in 1765.[5] He filled the royal gardens with plants garnered from his travels between the Great Lakes and Florida, while son William journeyed even farther to stock the gardens of English duchesses.[6]

For thirty years, from 1736 to 1766, the English correspondent of Bartram and James Logan,[7] Peter Collinson, bought trees for various noblemen like the Prince of Wales, the Dukes of Richmond, Norfolk and Bedford, the Earl of Jersey and Lord Petre. Lord Petre had so many that Collinson said 'on visiting him one cannot help thinking one is in North American thickets, there are such quantities'. Pines, maples and a dozen types of oak were included. As another remarked, 'in this manner more kinds, especially of the hardy trees of North America, became naturalised in British parks and gardens'.[8] Collinson virtually trained his customers in botany, laying out his own botanical garden at Mill Hill (now occupied by the well-known public school of that name) in 1749. Among the fifty or so plants he introduced were three species of azalea (the first to be cultivated here) and five species of phlox.[9] As a friend of Linnaeus, he tried to convince him that swallows did not hibernate under water. As a friend of Benjamin Franklin he acted as his agent in London for some thirty years sending him books (like Newton's *Philosophy* and Miller's *Gardener's Dictionary*) and apparatus and communicating, where necessary, on his behalf with the Royal Society.

To speed up the exchange of the vegetable products of various countries, Collinson's friend, John Fothergill had a garden at Upton in Essex, second only to Kew, and protected, according to one report, 'by the amplest buildings which this or any other country had seen'. Begun in 1762, it had more scarce and valuable plants than any other garden in Europe, royal or private, where seeds and plants from China, Siberia, the East and West Indies and Africa flourished, including some sixty-eight specimens of mesembryanthemum. Sea captains, travellers and collectors worked for him, and to help them he printed *Directions for taking up Plants and Shrubs and conveying them by*

Sea. At Upton, Fothergill had a tea tree from China at a time when that beverage was only coming into common use. He persuaded Wesley to stop drinking hot water and sugar, and to take tea—after Wesley had been denouncing tea for twelve years. Fothergill also hoped to introduce the breadfruit and the mangosteen into the West Indies.

Most of the plants in Fothergill's greenhouses went on his death to those of John Coakley Lettsom at Grove Hill, Camberwell, hitherto specializing in the mangold-wurzel or 'root of scarcity'. Lettsom hoped it would supplement the potato and he boiled the leaves for eating at his own table.[10] His very enthusiasm for it seemed to prejudice others against it.[11] The wealth of plants afforded by North America is reflected in the names given to them by grateful botanists. Claytonia was called after John Clayton (1693–1773), who was botanizing at the advanced age of 77; Kuhnia after Adam Kuhn (1741–1817), who studied with Linnaeus in Uppsala; Mitchella after John Mitchell (1687–1768); Marshallia after Moses Marshall, one of Linnaeus's correspondents, Bartonia after Benjamin Smith Barton (1766–1815), a noted botanist.[12] But the aptest I like is Bigelowa, called after the first native botanist to systematize the flora of New England—Jacob Bigelow (1786–1879), the Professor of *materia medica* at Harvard, who in the intervals of publishing his *American Medical Botany* (1817–20), lectured on the application of science to the useful arts. His lectures, published in 1829, bore the significant title of *The Elements of Technology*. The appearance of this word in America marked the institutional flowering of another concept that was to dominate the minds of the nineteenth century.[13]

(2)

The second great 'plantation' was the West Indies where a botanical garden was laid out at St. Vincent, near Kingston, in 1763, at the prime instigation of the Royal Society of Arts. This society had been formed nine years earlier, to meet the urgent need for a substitute for madder (a shrubby climbing plant the roots of which are used for dyeing). 'It can claim', assert its two most recent historians, 'not merely to have encouraged (botanical) gardens, but to have been the first to have publicly proposed their establishment'[14] by offering premiums

for fostering the growth of cochineal, cinnamon, man-
goes, vegetables, silk, nutmegs, breadfruit, senna and cashew
gum.

On becoming a royal establishment under the Secretary of
War the botanical garden at St. Vincent received an annual
Government subvention of £1,200. After ten years the society
accorded a medal to its director, Dr. George Young, for having
so many turmerics, cinnamon, mango, logwood and nutmeg
trees in full growth. Under his successors it became 'the finest
tropical experimental station in the world'.[15] Specimens grown
there were widely distributed and the West Indian flora was
immeasurably enriched.

The Jamaican plantocracy flourished with it. Sugar exports
tripled in value between 1734 and 1770, while coffee planting,
begun in the latter year, had preoccupied 686 plantations by the
end of the century.[16] Planters' wealth became so powerful that
Edward Long, the island's first historian, had to publish his
work anonymously in 1774.

Other attempts were made to introduce new plants, and
botanic gardens became the rage. The receiver-general, Hinton
East, had one in St. Andrews; Matthew Wallen another on
Cold Spring plantation. Both men were also responsible for a
public garden being laid out at Bath in 1775, East's also coming
under State control after his death,[17] and acquiring cinnamon,
mango and nutmeg trees from a captured French vessel.

Yet another garden was formed by the Government of
Jamaica in 1775. After inquiries, John Hope (who was himself
laying out a new botanic garden at Edinburgh), recommended
Thomas Clarke who served as curator for ten years from 1777
to 1787. His successor Thomas Dancer (1755–1811) resigned
in 1804 because he could not get more support, though his
Observations respecting the Botanic Garden were adopted by the
House of Assembly. Subsequent quarrels with the Governor
led to the property being neglected. By 1818 many of the plants
were removed to Trinidad and the Government grant was
stopped.[18]

The accession of these Jamaican plants, together with medi-
cinal ones from Demerara, enabled a private botanical garden,
already existing in the Diego Martin valley, near Port of
Spain, Trinidad, to flourish. It had been founded by a member

of the Legislative Council, Mr. Beggorat, for the acclimatizing of foreign trees.

So many new crops were introduced that the natives on the islands could no longer grow enough food for themselves. So to feed them, a botanical offensive was launched. From West Africa came the ackee in 1778, from Mauritius (via a captured French ship) the mango, and from Tahiti, in 1793 the bread-fruit. The importance of the transport of the breadfruit by Captain William Bligh at the second attempt has been over-shadowed by the dramatic failure of the first, when the crew of his ship *Bounty* mutinied, for the breadfruit was planted in the Government botanical gardens at Bath, in St. Thomas, and in others. Cheap starch for the labourers in the plantations was now available.[19]

(3)

Launcher of these and other botanic offensives was Sir Joseph Banks, a squire in England's own larder county of Lincolnshire. King George III recognized his interest in botany by merging the royal gardens at Richmond with others at Kew in 1773 and giving Banks the general supervision of them. '—this was of the utmost importance', wrote a recent New Zealand historian, 'not only to the two men, but to British botanical development; it was significant to the empire, not only of Britain, but of science.'[20] For from Kew were mounted operations which were world-wide.

Banks had no sooner begun to take his duties seriously at Kew before some American colonists unceremoniously dumped tea into the harbour at Boston, and a war, long brewing, erupted. Fearful of the safety of the dumps of ammunition amassed to quell the American rebels, the British Government asked the Royal Society to suggest a good lightning conductor. The Royal Society recommended pointed ones. Pointed ones were accord-ingly fixed, but when one dump at Purfleet exploded in 1777, it was recognized that these conductors had been originally de-vised by the rebel Benjamin Franklin. So the Government adopted 'blunt' conductors, the king fitting them to the royal palace.[21]

Since the President of the Royal Society could not see his way clear to support blunt conductors, even after a royal request, the king suggested his resignation, and in his place was elected Sir Joseph Banks.

Banks's election in 1778 led to a minor civil war breaking out in that body. The mathematicians and physicists preferred one of their own number, in this case Alexander Aubert, whose three private observatories at Austin Friars, Highbury and Lewisham were considered to have contributed more to science than Banks's weekly receptions at Soho Square. Though their candidate was defeated, the mathematicians and physicists did not forget, and five years later when Banks dismissed Dr. Charles Hutton the Professor of Mathematics at Woolwich from the foreign secretaryship of the society, they took action. With the secretary and a former secretary—Doctors Maty and Horsley— supported by the physicist J. H. de Magellan, the mathematician Francis Maseres, and the Director of the Royal Observatory, Nevil Maskelyne, a case was presented to the society. Entitled *An Authentic Narrative of the Dissensions and Debates in the Royal Society* (1784), Banks refused to accept it. So Maty resigned, and Banks, with great skill secured the appointment of his own nominee.[22]

The mathematicians who had such a major influence on the development of British navigation, were now overruled by those who could find food and vegetable products. The doctor-poet John Wolcot shrewdly attributed to Banks the apocryphal couplet

> The turnpike road to people's hearts, I find,
> Lies through their guts, or I mistake mankind.[23]

In his new office, Banks faced another problem. The continuance of the war against the American colonists had by now filled up the transit gaols and hulks with convicts waiting transportation there. A new dump for them was urgently needed and[24] Sir Joseph Banks suggested that the House of Commons should seriously consider the place named by himself and Captain Cook some nine years earlier when together they sailed round Australia—Botany Bay—where the climate was mild and escape difficult.[25] His suggestion was ultimately adopted, when, on 13 May 1787, the first prison ships set sail to Australia, and deposited their human cargo at Port Jackson just north of Botany Bay.

Banks was also very interested in the opening up of Africa's botanical resources. After the African Association was formed in 1788 and two expeditions under Sweidiaur and Houghton had been sent out, Banks recommended Mungo Park, who set out from the Gambia in 1795. Four years later, addressing the African Association, Banks expressed the hope that Park had

> opened a gate into the interior of Africa into which it is easy for every nation to enter and extend its commerce and discovery from the west to the eastern side of that immense continent.

He wanted to send a military force to establish posts there. In the meantime he sent his unique and unofficial corps of botanical angels. The Cape of Good Hope, North America and the Canaries were combed by Francis Masson (1741–1806), who died, significantly enough, in Canada; Brazil, Australia and New Zealand by Allen Cunningham (1791–1839), whose brother Richard became colonial botanist for New South Wales, only to be murdered by the natives; China and north-western America by Archibald Menzies (1754–1839).[26] For them specimens were all-important. Whilst dining with the Spanish Governor of Chile, Menzies noticed his dessert was garnished with seeds. He promptly slipped them in his pocket, and getting back to the ship, planted them in a greenhouse he had built on the quarter-deck. They took root, with the result that by the time the ship returned to London, he had five monkey-puzzle trees.

These angels virtually redistributed the vegetable products of continents. David Lockhart, for instance, who went to the Congo became, in 1818, Superintendent of the Botanic Garden at Trinidad—a post he held for twenty-eight years.

And wheresoever they went they stimulated the formation of more botanical gardens. At the Cape of Good Hope that querulous Mancunian, George Caley, evoked a suggestion by Sir John Barrow in 1800 that a garden should be set up there,[27] a suggestion amplified by P. M. A. Broussonet in 1802.[28] Twelve years later Banks was recommending Allan Cunningham and James Bowie as collectors of plants for it.[29] As a reward for combing China with David Lang, William Kerr was appointed Superintendent of the newly founded Botanic Gardens in Ceylon.[30] A later superintendent of this garden, George

Gardner, collected many thousands of plants in Brazil.[31]

Certainly the Ceylon botanic garden opened up the island to coffee, cinchona, tea, cardamoms and rubber.

'The rush for land,' remarked an observer, 'was only parallelled by the movement towards the mines of California and Australia, but with this painful difference, that the enthusiasts in Ceylon, instead of thronging to disinter, were hurrying to bury their gold.'[32]

Coffee became a staple export of the colony—over a million hundredweight being exported by 1875. Later, when disease attacked the crops cinchona was introduced, then tea, then rubber. Cocoa, cardamoms and coconuts also throve.

Some of these 'angels' were true experimenters: the East India Company used to send Banks seeds of hemp and flax for 'apportioning' to them.[33] They also discussed with him the provision of food, not for humans, but for the cochineal insect. A committee of secrecy was promised £500 for a satisfactory specimen of the food (Nopal), £1,000 for the insect, and another £1,000 for a successful transfer from Banks's garden to India. Unfortunately the secret leaked.[34]

(4)

Under stimulus from the Government the East India Company now established its own botanic garden at Calcutta. After the Secretary of State for War in 1787 had pointed out that the French were forestalling the British in the introduction of new plants into their colonies,[35] the company appointed Colonel Robert Kyd (1746–93) as its superintendent, and bought 300 acres of land near his property at Sibhur Howra, near Shalimar Point, for a botanic garden.

Kyd wanted to grow teak for the British Navy, as well as cotton, tobacco, tea and coffee. Banks was very anxious that the garden should be 'for utility and science, not a place of retreat for officials', and asked that lists of plants 'useful in medicine and manufacture' should be sent to him.[36] Kyd brought sago trees from Malaya[37] and mulberries from China, but the presidencies delayed to forward him necessary articles and only gave him a scanty allowance of silk worms. His plans for making salt by evaporation in the Bay of Balasore were also turned down with some contempt by Lord Cornwallis.[38]

Little wonder Kyd died at the early age of 47. His successor William Roxburgh (1751–1815) came from another botanic garden at Samulcotta near Coconada and tried to get plants from America and the West Indies for the garden, especially nutmeg, cloves, cinnamon, indigo and madder. Roxburgh was the first to give a systematic account of the plants of India and sent his son, John, to the Cape and the Moluccas (where he also hoped gardens would be established), to collect seeds.[39] Roxburgh's successor (in 1815) was the Danish botanist, George Wallich, under whose long superintendency plants were successfully collected by wrapping them in paper treated with arsenic to protect them from insects. Eight thousand specimens were sent to leading botanical institutions of Europe. Wallich lost part of the botanical garden in 1820 when it was decided to build Bishop's College upon it.

Wallich should have been succeeded by William Griffith whose explorations of Burma and Afghanistan led to him taking charge from 1842 to 1844. But unfortunately he died at the early age of 35 in Malacca.[40] He was, however, just in time to help Sir Joseph Hooker's three-year survey of the states of Sikkim, Nepal, Eastern Bengal, Chittagong, Silhet and the Khasia Hills. In return Hooker paid a warm tribute to the Calcutta garden:

'They have', he wrote, 'contributed more useful and ornamental tropical plants to the public and private gardens of the world than any other establishment before or since.'[41]

Not only had they played a part in the introducing of Indian tea, but from here cinchona trees were acclimatized and planted in the Himalayas, thus giving the Indians a cheap available supply of quinine. Jute, sugar cane and mahogany also came into India via the gardens.

Other botanic gardens were established at Saharanpur in the Upper Ganges and at Madras. At Saharanpur, Addiscombe trained John Royle (1799–1858), served as superintendent from 1823 to 1832. Royle advocated the cultivation of cinchona in India. His successor, Hugh Falconer (1808–65) served on the Committee for Tea Culture that was formed in 1834 to initiate experiments in growing Chinese tea. Their attention was then drawn to wild tea-growing in East India Company territory stretching from Sadiya to the borders of Yunnan. This enabled

49

Chinese importations to be discontinued and Falconer was able to superintend the first blending of Indian tea.[42] Falconer was then appointed as Professor of Botany at the Calcutta Medical College in 1848 and adviser to the Government of India on vegetable products.

These gardens literally enabled the products of continents to be switched. Cinchona, laboriously collected by C. R. Markham (1830–1916) from the eastern Andes, were first grown here, enabling a plentiful supply of native quinine to be continuously available.[43] Rubber plants grown at Kew from seeds romantically shipped by Sir Henry Wickham in 1876 from Santarem on the Amazon were matured in Ceylon; from them have developed the vast cultivated plantations in Malaya and the East Indies, Burma and Southern India.[44] Paradoxically enough the Brazilians themselves took up the cultivation of coffee.

(5)

Meanwhile in England the role of the botanic garden drew from Erasmus Darwin, the Lichfield doctor, a famous eulogy. Issued in two parts: Part II *The Loves of the Plants* (1789) and Part I *The Economy of Vegetation* (1791), it remains in the words of Darwin's latest biographer, 'unique as the only best selling English poem on a scientific subject'.[45]

So much science and technology is written into it that the very title is misleading. Darwin himself confessed its purpose was 'to enlist imagination under the banner of Science; and to lead her Votaries from the looser analogies, which dress out the imagery of poetry, to the stricter ones, which form the ratiocination of philosophy'. Scarcely a plant peeps through Part I, instead contemporary scientific theories are not only dilated upon, but in many cases shrewd anticipations are laced with shrewd assessments of various discoveries. His on the present and future of transport have a St. Simonian ring. Thus on Dr. Brindley's canals:

> So with strong arm immortal BRINDLEY leads
> His long canals, and parts the velvet meads . . .

or on the steam engine:

> Soon shall thy arm, UNCONQUER'D STEAM! afar
> Drag the slow barge, or drive the rapid car;

Or on wide-waving wings expanded bear
The flying-chariot through the fields of air.
—Fair crews triumphant, leaning from above,
Shall wave their fluttering kerchiefs as they move;
Or warrior-bands alarm the gaping crowd,
And armies shrink beneath the shadowy cloud.

or on submarines:

Led by the Sage, Lo! Britain's sons shall guide
Huge SEA-BALLOONS beneath the tossing tide;
The diving castles, roof'd with spheric glass,
Ribb'd with strong oak, and barr'd with bolts of brass,
Buoy'd with pure air shall endless tracks pursue,
And PRIESTLEY'S hand the vital flood renew—
Then shall BRITANNIA rule the wealthy realms,
Which Ocean's wide insatiate wave o'erwhelms.

'I know not how steam engines come among the plants,'
wrote James Watt to Darwin, 'they are neither plants, animals
nor fossils, otherwise they would not have escaped the notice
of Linnaeus. . . . However, if they belong to *your* system, no
matter about the Swede.'[46]

Both Erasmus Darwin and Watt were members of a group
in Birmingham that was technocratic rather than plantocratic.
Twelve others, besides themselves, were members and also like
themselves, were pioneers in some industrial process or other.
The real botanist among them, William Withering, planted
Darwin's own botanical garden.

The Lunar Society of Birmingham was not the first of these
provincial groups in England.[47] At Spalding some gentlemen
met to discuss Steel's *Tatler* and in three years had formed into
a society, meeting once a week under the leadership of a local
antiquarian. Others took shape at Stamford, (1721), Peter-
borough (1730), Lincoln, Wisbech and Doncaster, and farther
south, proper agricultural societies were formed, like the
'Society of Gentlemen' at Odiham, which took a great interest in
horse breeding.[48]

Erasmus Darwin himself went on to form the Derby Philosophical Society in 1784.[49] Others at Liverpool (1779)[50] Manchester (1781)[51] Leeds (1783),[52] Leicester (1788) [53] and
Newcastle (1793)[54] though owing much to medical men, uni-

tarians and booksellers focused intelligence on technical and social problems of the day. Indeed several of them sustained early colleges of science and formed audiences for itinerant lecturers who circulated rather like travelling preachers. By the end of the Napoleonic War so many had developed that the Vicar of Liverpool, Abraham Hume, set about writing a history of them. He well might. They were the 'sects' of a new religion.

(6)

The gardeners now began to organize themselves nationally. A self-educated gardener who had risen to be Philip Miller's successor at Chelsea and had devised a tree plaister which earned the official thanks of the House of Commons, William Forsyth put forward the idea of a horticultural society in 1801.[55] He was joined by John Wedgwood but their proposals were too broad and generalized for academic botanists like T. A. Knight[56] whose *Treatise on the Culture of the Apple and Pear* (1797) was based on extensive experiments at Elton (near Ludlow). So when the Horticultural Society did take shape, it was on Knight's plan: 'somewhat on the lines of the many existing agricultural societies' according to Banks. The Royal Horticultural Society owed much to John Lindley, its assistant secretary from 1822 to 1841, who managed its gardens. According to Professor Keeble he was 'in no small measure responsible for its very existence'.[57] Lindley subsequently founded the *Gardener's Chronicle* and edited it for the next twenty-five years, thereby disseminating the results of recent research to make horticulture a popular pursuit.

For the society's own garden at Chiswick, David Douglas sailed round Cape Horn to the mouth of the Columbia River on whose banks he found the musk in 1826. Raised at Chiswick, musk was first described and illustrated by John Lindley in 1828.[58] Its scent stimulated the Council of the Society to propagate it by cuttings, and so popular did it become that it was universally cultivated in England,[59] until its scent mysteriously disappeared in 1911.[60] Douglas also introduced the Californian poppy,[61] the Oregon grape, the red flowering-currant and the fir still known by his name.

Another of the Society was Robert Fortune who visited China for them in 1842, sending home the double yellow rose, the Japanese anemone and the fan-palm (*Chamaerops fortunei*) now named after him. Fortune's success was due to his employment of 'Wardian boxes' which he also used to bring 2,000 tea plants and 17,000 sprouting seeds from China for the East India Company to plant in North West India in 1848. His reports made him a significant disseminator of knowledge about the Far East in Britain.[62]

(7)

If the middle-class towns were forming literary and philosophical societies, the labourers were cultivating gardens. 'You see', wrote William Cobbett (himself a seed farmer for a time in Kensington in the late 1820's), 'in almost every part of England that most interesting of all objects, that which is such an honour to England, and that which distinguishes it from all the rest of the world, namely, those neatly kept and productive little gardens round the labourers' houses.'[63] In the same year, the Duke of Wellington and Mrs. Arbuthnot found, on visiting Blenheim, that the Duke of Marlborough was 'gardening mad'.[64]

These gardens registered the ubiquity of Banks's angels, who had brought back over 7,000 new varieties to Kew alone.[65] The Banksia rose—the tea rose—the first wisteria (which arrived at Kew in 1818 from China), dahlias, petunias, calceolarias, lupins, pentstemons and garden ribes adorned the gardens of rich and poor.

Banks's vision of Kew as the great plant exchange, advisory centre and spearhead of botanical exploration, persisted too, when his former assistant librarian, Dr. Lindley, was appointed chairman of a parliamentary commission in 1838 which recommended that a National Botanic Garden should be established to control and co-ordinate the work of the various gardens in the British dependencies like Calcutta, Bombay, Saharunpur, Mauritius, Sydney and Trinidad. The scope envisaged for Kew by Lindley's Commission indicates the tremendous importance attached to planning scientific advance in those days:

The wealthiest and most civilized country in Europe offers the only European example of the want of one of the first proofs of wealth and civilization. There are many gardens in the British colonies . . . costing many thousands a year; their utility is much diminished by the want of some system under which they can be regulated and controlled. There is no unity of purpose among them, their objects are unsettled, and their powers wasted from not receiving a proper direction, they afford no aid to each other, and it is to be feared, but little to the countries where they are established: and yet they are capable of conferring very important benefits on commerce, and of conducing especially to colonial prosperity.

Lindley recommended that these 'lesser establishments' should be arranged about a 'National Botanic Garden' whose chief should control them and 'acting with him and through him with each other, recording constantly their proceedings explaining their wants, receiving supplies, and aiding the mother country in everything useful in the vegetable kingdom: medicine, commerce, agriculture, horticulture and many branches of manufacture would derive considerable advantage from the establishment of such a system'. Nor did the imperial theme end here, for Lindley concluded that the garden would 'undoubtedly become an efficient instrument in refining the taste, increasing the knowledge, and augmenting the rational pleasures of that important class of society, to provide for whose instruction is so great and wise an object of the present administration'.[66]

At Kew, experiments were carried out for Charles Darwin who at the age of 33 had retired in 1842, after an epic round-the-world voyage as a botanist, to a country house in Kent. His very immobility and invalidism caused him to rely on Joseph Hooker to compile lists and statistics relating to the ways in which plants were distributed, transported, fertilized and hybridized. He would also go over to Darwin's house to be 'pumped' (the verb is Darwin's) on various botanical points.

'I learn more in these discussions,' Darwin said, 'than in ten times over the number of hours reading', while Darwin's son acknowledged that 'without Hooker's aid Darwin's great work would hardly have been carried out on the botanical side'.

This great work was *The Origin of Species*.

(8)

Such intensified exploitation of the vegetable resources of the British possessions set the pace for other countries. A garden for all plants used in the 'arts' was the aim of every country. Spain imported a student of Linnaeus's in 1751 to improve botanical studies and created a garden at Madrid in 1755. Four others were later laid out in other towns while by 1778 the King of Spain was reported as wishing to establish a botanic garden to grow 'all the plants of the world'. Certainly King Carlos III bought a private collection to form a Cabinet of Natural History, and gave his royal support to promising youths for overseas study and to scientists for research in natural history in the New World. Indeed the botanical expeditions to Mexico and the offshoot that reached Guatemala in the 1790's exercised 'the most profound and traceable influence' on that blaze of restlessness that consumed all the Spanish colonies.[67]

Of the Spanish botanists, the one who left the greatest impression was Dr. Jose Celestin Mutis (1732–1808). Spending the last third of the eighteenth century at Bogota, nominally as physician to one of the viceroys, but actually subsidized by the King of Spain to the extent of 10,000 pesos a year, he made more than 3,000 folios of designs. With his corps of fifteen engravers and water-colourists he was the nucleus of a scientific corps, for in addition to collecting plants, he built an observatory at Bogota in 1802. Bogota became so science-conscious that when visited by the German savant Alexander von Humboldt a public holiday was declared.[68] Suitably impressed, Humboldt wrote, 'After that of Banks in London I have never seen a botanic library as big as that of Mutis.'[69] Aime Bonpland, Humboldt's companion on this five-year survey, collected over 6,000 plants hitherto unknown and some years later he returned to South America bringing with him a number of useful European fruits and plants.[70]

Other European countries saw virtues in botanic gardens other than aids to exploiting overseas possessions. The Danish Government was asked by G. C. Oeder in 1754 to establish a botanical garden in Copenhagen, in order to produce better foresters and botanists. Oeder cited Peter Collinson, Philip Miller, Albrecht von Haller and Bernard de Jussieu in support of his claim. He got his garden and it ran successfully until 1770.[71]

At the same time the gardens at the Schonbrunn in Vienna were laid out by Adriaan Stekkhoven from Leyden, and from Leyden too came Richard van der Schat to act as head gardener. A third Leyden botanist, N. J. Jacquin (1727–1817), was dispatched to the West Indies and Central America to obtain new plants and specimens for the Schonbrunn. Jacquin left Vienna in 1763 to become Professor of Chemistry at Chemnitz, returning seven years later as Professor of Botany and Director of the Garden. He was made a baron in 1806: a fitting tribute to an imported scientist.[72]

Iceland, too, had its garden at Reykjavik in 1779 founded by the Iceland Company of Denmark whose director Andreas Holt was a friend of Sir Joseph Banks.[73] These, together with others like the Botanic Society of Gorenski in Russia, the Botanische Gesellschaft in Ratisbon and Gerard Devisme's botanic garden in Lisbon[74] joined the informal international exchange of ideas, assisted by journals like the *Magazin pour l'Histoire Naturelle de la Suisse* founded in 1787 by the apothecary J. G. A. Hoepfner (1759–1813).

Even in Ireland the spirit of improvement stirred when the Royal Dublin Society 'for the improvement of husbandry manufactures and other useful arts and sciences' was helped by the Government to open a botanic garden at Glasnevin 'to increase and foster a taste for scientific and practical botany'. The Government made annual maintenance grants as well as individual grants for particular purposes, but left the management of it to the Dublin Society until 1877.[75]

A botanical garden was laid out at Weimar by the general factotum of the Duke, J. W. Von Goethe, who had already taken up mineralogy and geology to understand the problems posed by the ducal mines of Ilmenau and obtained a full-time research assistant in J. C. W. Voigt to help him to do this. Voigt was sent to Freiburg to study mining.[76]

Prime mover of the garden was W. H. S. Bucholz—a chemist —and the first in Weimar to experiment with hot-air balloons. Bucholz was also a leading member of a small literary and philosophical society in Weimar which later met weekly at Goethe's house. Amongst the members was a young doctor, Christopher Hufeland, who became Professor of Medicine at the University of Jena and started the first German medical journal, later moving to Berlin, as the first dean of the medical faculty there. His friend, A. J. G. K. Batsch, who looked after the botanical gardens at Jena, helped found a natural history society (Naturforschende Gesellschaft) at Jena in 1793 which first brought Goethe and Schiller together.[77] 'All Goethe's friends', Schiller remarked on his first visit to Weimar in 1787, 'would rather collect plants or study mineralogy than involve themselves in empty demonstrations.' So would Goethe: round his deathbed hung a geological map of England by de la Beche.

(9)

The most comprehensive and extensive of all the botanical gardens of this time was that established by the Dutch in Java at Buitenzorg. Significantly it owed much to an American, Thomas Horsfield, who had been botanizing extensively in Java before the island was returned to the Dutch.[78] The British Governor's advice—that if the Dutch were to obtain the islands after the peace of 1815 they should maintain the improvements introduced—was remembered, and the Buitenzorg garden obtained a Kew-trained curator, James Hooper.[79] With its laboratories, experimental botanic and mountain gardens, Buitenzorg was the growing centre of the Javanese economy. Here were planted the seeds of the cinchona tree for which Charles Ledger had looked for years. Collected for him by the Indian Manuel Icamanatu at the cost of his life in 1864, they were successfully developed by L. C. Bernelot Moenz the Director of the Cinchona Plantations of the Government of the East Indies. By 1939 Java was producing from 85 per cent to 95 per cent of the world supply of quinine, some 750 tons, used widely for alleviation of malarial, influenzal and cardiac complaints.[80]

PART II

✧✧✧

The Epiphany of the Technocracy

5

◇◇

From Physiocracy to Physicism

◇◇

(1)

ENGLISH ideas penetrated, via the Jardin du Roi and the Académie des Sciences, into France,[1] where Francois Quesnay (1694–1774) founded the so-called group of Physiocrats who believed in government according to a natural order inherent in society. His significantly named *Maximes Générales du Gouvernement Économique d' un Royaume Agricole*, laid down

> That the sovereign and the nation never forget that land is the only source of wealth, and that it is agriculture which multiplies it. That the economic government occupy itself only in favouring the productive outlays and the commerce of agricultural commodities, and that it leave alone the sterile outlays.[2]

Acceptance of these maxims involved reconstituting the structure of the kingdom and its policy-making bodies. They wished to jettison the idea of trade balances, the exploitation of office by people with no policy other than their own advantage, protectionism and income differentials. Above all a sovereign authority must impose its will in the interests of all in an agricultural kingdom. These interests would include 'large farms exploited by rich farmers'[3] and free commercial intercourse between provinces, then restricted by tolls.

The physiocrats advocated that the economy be tended by an

authoritative planning government and would no doubt have been pleased to know that their concept of 'growth' would become so popular.

But, like many political philosophers, they ignored the implications of what was going on in their own time. The Jardin du Roi was not concentrating on a *Royaume Agricole*, nor preoccupying itself with plants and medicaments, but was becoming the world's greatest chemical school where new industrial processes were being incubated by a dynasty of chemists. From being a simple 'gland' of the plantocracy it was becoming a complex identification centre for nutrients of an industrial state.

The particular secretion of this gland was chemistry. The process had been going on for a century or more since William Davisson, the first professor of chemistry at the Jardin, lectured to, amongst others, British royalist exiles, one of whom recorded his 'excellence in Alchemy', rating him 'above all the men now living in the world, whereof by his wonderful experiments he giveth daily proof although his learned books published in the native tongue did not evidence it, meriteth well to have his name recorded in this place and after him'.[4] William Davisson's successor Nicasius le Fevre was invited over to England with Charles II, becoming apothecary to the Royal Household and given a laboratory at St. James's Palace. He became an original Fellow of the Royal Society.[5]

Their successors at the Jardin broke out new paths in chemistry. The *Cours de Chymie* (1675) of Nicholas Lemery (1645–1715), was one of the earliest books based on experimental work in a laboratory, and passed through a dozen editions in his lifetime, being translated into Latin, English, German, Italian and Spanish. It publicized the manufacture of sulphuric acid by burning brimstone with nitre: the first inorganic catalytic process to come into general use.[6] That the term 'plant' should be used today for a chemical engineering works has a fine historical implication.

By the eighteenth century G. F. Rouelle had as his pupils Antoine-Laurent Lavoisier, Proust, Cadet and Diderot, to whom he showed that salts were produced by the combination of acids and bases.[7] His brother H. M. Rouelle isolated urea from urine regarding it as the nutritive principle of vegetables taken as food which had changed its nature by digestion and circulation. Like-minded, these pupils themselves established other chemical schools. B. G. Sage (1740–1820) founded a chair of minera-logical chemistry at the mineralogical museum in 1768; here Rome de l'Isle and F. A. Chaptal were trained. He also per-suaded the Government to establish a school of mines in 1787.

(2)

Yet another of Rouelle's pupils P. J. Macquer (1718–84)[8] compiled a *Dictionary of Chemistry* which was a favourite book of Erasmus Darwin and of his friend Josiah Wedgwood. Trans-lated into English in 1771 by yet another friend, James Keir, a former army physician in the West Indies who had returned to make glass at Stourbridge and manage Boulton and Watt's works at Birmingham, it inspired Keir to set up with a brother officer an alkali works of his own at Dudley.

Such profitable industrial applications of their subject were not lost upon Macquer's own demonstrators. A manufacturing laboratory for making amongst other commodities, sal ammoniac from urine and salt was set up by Antoine Baumé (1728–1804). Other manufacturing laboratories followed. Soda (required for the manufacture of hard soap and glass) was obtained either by burning seaweed (kelp), or plant ash from Spain (barilla) but the possibility of obtaining it from salt heated with sulphuric acid was worked on by Father Malherbe, Lord Dundonald and Nicholas Leblanc (1742–1806) led to the devising in 1787 of the process known by Leblanc's name. Three years later, it was put into production.

Such industrial enterprises were multiplied after Revolu-tionary wars broke out, and further accelerated the move away from vegetable products. Ironically enough an unsuccessful applicant for Macquer's chair at the Jardin in 1784, C. L. Berthollet (1748–1822) was invested with the responsibility for organizing French industry during the Revolutionary wars. Other chemists were given similar tasks—Guyton de Morveau (1737–1816), for instance, was asked to develop the use of balloons, which needed hydrogen, and was made responsible for the reorganization of French industries after the Revolution broke out. He had been running a saltpetre works since 1778 and the first French soda factory since 1783.

Macquer's pupil and successor A. F. de Fourcroy (1755–1809) was appointed a member of the commission which recommended the founding of a medical school in Paris (and others later in Strasbourg and Montpellier). Fourcroy became a professor in the medical school, still keeping his original post at the Jardin du Roi, which now became the Museum of Natural History.[9] He subsequently, in 1802, assumed responsibility for public instruction for some eight years. Fourcroy played an integral part in making the French supply of saltpetre safe. Education and explosives had a real link then as now: Fourcroy brought Jean Antoine Chaptal (1756–1832) to Paris to direct a gunpowder factory in 1793. Chaptal subsequently became Minister of the Interior in 1800–4, and a very wealthy industrialist as a result of his own chemical factories in Rouen and Montpellier.[10] Fourcroy was also one of the moving spirits in the creation of the institution which took over the teaching of chemistry when the Jardin du Roi was converted to the Museum of Natural History in 1793: the École Polytechnique.

(3)

Created to provide engineers for the Revolutionary armies, the École Polytechnique was a formidable supplement to the forty-five-year-old École des Ponts et Chaussées.[11] Both were State supported, but whereas the École des Ponts et Chaussées provided builders of bridges and roads only, the École Polytechnique supplied officers with a basic training in pure science.[12]

It began as a Central School of Public Works housed at the Palais Bourbon in Paris, with subsidiaries (*écoles centrales*) in each provincial capital to feed industry and the armies with technical personnel. Its descent from the École des Ponts et Chaussées was symbolized by its first director, J. E. Lamblardie (1747–97). To provide teachers for the *écoles centrales*, the École Normale was established at the same time; this was later to train such distinguished scientists as Louis Pasteur, a pupil (1843), and later (1857), its director.

After 1794 its students, admitted by competitive examinations, were stretched for two years by the best French mathematicians, physicists and chemists of the day. Two years of basic science were topped by a third devoted to engineering.

Textbooks, so necessary for the large classes in mathematics, physics and chemistry were written by the lecturers and were so good that other countries adopted them. The discoveries of these teachers (and their pupils) were disseminated by the issue of the *Journal de l'École Polytechnique* and the *Correspondence sur l'École Polytechnique*, both indicating the intensity of their preoccupations. As a modern historian of science has said, 'in collaborating in the most direct way in the national life, the scientists acquired a new prestige; while the interest which they brought to technical questions was reinforced by the success of their work'.[13]

Clustering round the École Polytechnique were the luminaries of Europe. Monge's own talent as a geometer was reinforced by mathematical analysts like Lagrange (1736–1813), S. F. Lacroix (1765–1843) and A. L. Cauchy (1789–1857) Modern chemical nomenclature was popularized by C. L. Berthollet (1748–1822) and J. L. Gay Lussac (1778–1832). The steam-engine was improved by the thermodynamic research of Sadi Carnot (1796–1832), son of the founder. Advances in the theory of light by D. J. F. Arago (1786–1853) and Augustin Fresnel (1788–1827), in electricity by A. M. Ampère (1775–1836), were to provide data for the prime movers that were to supersede it. The theory of the turbine was to be brilliantly illuminated by J. V. Poncelet (1788–1867) a graduate of 1810, and later commandant of the school.

Its physico-centric curriculum (students studied mathematics, physics and chemistry exclusively) produced a new type of man, 'appearing', according to Professor Hayek, 'for the first time in history'.[14] Having never learned to interpret human life or growth in terms of mankind's literary past (since their training did not include history, literature or languages), they tended to see life in scientific terms. As its self-appointed spokesman Count Henri de Saint Simon (1760–1825), expressed it: 'we must examine and co-ordinate it all from the point of view of Physicism'.

'Physicism' according to St. Simon would need a new physical 'clergy' to both interpret and organize society on scientific lines. This, he argued, would lead to European Federation and a Common Parliament. St. Simon influenced Augustin Thierry (1795–1851) who in turn influenced Karl Marx. St. Simon's ideas on the importance of the engineer were enlarged upon by Barthelemy Enfantin (1796–1864), who wrote:

> The Ecole Polytechnique must be the channel through which our ideas will spread through society. It is the milk which we have sucked at our beloved School which must nourish the generations to come. It is there that we have learnt the positive language and the methods of research and demonstration which today secure the advance of the political sciences.[15]

St. Simonians were the first technocrats: apostles of the religion of industry. Machines, according to St. Simon, eliminate human drudgery; and his followers became evangelists for the engineer. Especially was this seen in Britain, where a schoolmaster lamented that 'the sciences which Bonaparte encouraged (chiefly for the sake of raising engineers, gunners, surgeons, and all other descriptions of people who assist in sieges and works of slaughter), are becoming the fashionable study to the exclusion or at least the comparative neglect of, polite literature and culture'.[16]

Polytechnicians entered, almost as of right, the French governing *élite*, most notably F. P. C. Dupin (1784–1873) as councillor of State and Minister of Marine, known as much for his theorem (Dupin's indicatrix) as for his application of scientific techniques to economics—displayed in his *Forces Productives des Nations de 1800 à 1851* (1851).

Surviving rough treatment by Napoleon[17] (who put the students under strict discipline in barracks), and temporary dissolution by the Restoration in 1816, the Polytechnique survived to produce graduates who were so valuable in civil life that a duplicate institution, the École Centrale des Arts et Manufactures was formed by several former polytechnicians and bankers as a private venture in 1828.

(4)

The social orientation of science under the National Assembly and its successors was symbolized by the introduction of the metric system. A commission on weights and measures to which Gaspard Monge rendered valuable service began to measure the arc of the terrestrial meridian as a standard of measurement in 1790. Following its report the metre, gram, litre and franc were established by the Republic in 1794 on 1 July and by 1800 were in standard use.[18]

The need to produce nitrates for gunpowder and alum for glass, dye works and soap making,[19] preoccupied Fourcroy, who took over the nine-year-old *musée* and transformed it into the Lycée des Arts on 7 April 1793. This, it was hoped (and by none more than Lavoisier), would become a central society of the arts and sciences, fostering the application of arts to industrial processes. 'Purified' of its Royalist members (including Lavoisier who was executed for being a taxfarmer), it became the Lycée Républicain.[20]

Since engineers were needed in greater numbers than the École des Ponts et Chaussées or l'École de Génie could supply them, Colonel C. G. Desaudray established in 1791 the Bureau de Consultation des Arts et Métiers, to make awards to inventors. Within a year it was housed in part of the Palais Royal. Several monthly public meetings were held in 1793 to present awards for notable discoveries and to educate the public in the implications of science. To provide it with funds, shops were built in the front of the Palais Royal. But the rents were meagre and the response to an appeal even poorer, even when the Government was approached for money to establish classes in arts, crafts and agriculture in the evenings and holidays. Yet from exiguous resources Desaudray managed to publish a *Journal du Lycée des Arts* and his collaborator a *Magazin Encyclopédique*. When the Palais Royal was burnt down on 15 December 1798, the society lost ground, but revived as the Athénée des Arts for the encouragement of inventors. It held public meetings until 1869.

A greater need was to speed up manufactures. Here A. T. Vandermonde (1735–96) undertook to make experiments in what was virtually production engineering. He was given a laboratory in 1793 and in the following year a Benedictine priory—St. Martin des Champs—was put at his disposal. Here he collected every automatic device he could lay hands on, most notably the automata made by Macques de Vaucanson (1709–82). Known as the Conservatoire des Arts et Métiers, this collection was an enormous stimulus to J. M. Jacquard (1752–1834) in the perfection of his famous loom.

To provide scientists with a central body (for the Academy

of Sciences and of the other academies of Inscriptions and Belles-Lettres and Fine Arts had been dissolved), the Société Philomathique (formed in 1788 by frustrated young scientists who could not get elected to the academy), offered a convenient forum until the Institut de France was established.[21]

(5)

Such massive concentration on science was fascinating to St. Simon. The emerging sacerdocy of scientists impressed him.

> 'One does not create a system of social organisation', he wrote, 'one perceives the new alignment of ideas and interests which have been formed, and indicates it, that is all. It is not I who have formulated the project of a constitution of which I discovered the foundation, it is eight centuries of European History.'

The true constitution maker, he continued, is not a king but a 'social' scientist who studies events and discovers the law of their development:

> This recognition, or, if one wishes, this legitimation of the preponderant forces which exist in a society at all the important epochs of civilisation, is what one calls its constitution, which, without that, would be but a metaphysical revery.'[22]

To recognize the direction of history was not enough, he had to hurry it along. During the American War of Independence he had suggested to the Viceroy of Mexico a plan for a Nicaraguan canal, and later, on returning to Europe he urged a similar scheme to connect Madrid to the sea. During the Revolution he expended a fortune made in speculation with Church lands by entertaining scientists, hoping to become the Newton of the New Social Order.

In 1798 he began his quest for a physico-politics which would become a new religion and by 1803 had issued the first of his many works: *Lettres d'un habitant de Genève*, proposing to replace the anti-Christian outlook of the eighteenth-century encyclopaedists by a cult of Newton.

Here again he was in line with history, for during the Revolution the Paris churches had become Temples of Reason and Robespierre's Culte de l'Etre Suprême still survived. Many of the cults of those days, like theophilanthropy (whose creed was 'the good is all that tends to preserve and perfect man'), were supported by the State. St. Simon, perhaps disturbed by Napoleon's concordat with the Pope in 1802, asked his readers to subscribe to a new social order which would have its head-quarters at Newton's tomb. Subscribers, men or women, would be allowed to elect the three greatest mathematicians, physicists, chemists, physiologists, writers, painters and musicians in the world. The President of the Royal Society of London was to be head of the fund in the first year, afterwards the largest sub-scribers. All scientific and artistic genius was to be helped by this fund.

Property owners, said St. Simon, were to sustain scientists but not make them dependants. Class interest demanded it, the whole of society needed it. Property owners were also to support scientists since science increased their power over nature. St. Simon's vision of the new religion of Newton was of mankind, redeemed by science, reorganizing the world not in the name of chastity and continence, but in that of creative talent and brotherly love.

The religious basis of this technocracy was, of course, Bacon's who also looked for science to redeem man's lot from labour. It was also Voltaire's, who called for the redeemed European to convert the Asians and Africans to the new religion. But Napoleon preferred to legitimize his power through a concordat with the Pope, so St. Simon's role for him as founder fell to the ground.

Even more Baconian was St. Simon's *Essai sur l'organisation sociale* (1804), a blueprint for a State ruled by a Parliament of Improvements consisting of thirty elected scientists and fifteen partnered artists and industrialists. Though the relative position of scientists and industrialists in his ideal policy was to perplex St. Simon for the next twenty years, he became progressively disenchanted with the idea that scientists should be elected by the uneducated masses. As he eliminated popular voting he became more enamoured of the necessity of recruiting his intellectual *élite* by co-option.

As St. Simon himself descended in social status (he was actually a copyist until rescued by a former servant), his ideas expanded. He began to outline a system of the sciences which was to be the prelude of a new encyclopaedia. At first he pestered the official scientists in the Bureau of Longitude to take him into their work. When they refused, he accused them of being sub-servient to English science. Then he pestered Napoleon to convene an international assembly of scientists devoted to 'general science' each of whom would prepare a plan for a general encyclopaedia, and then judge each other's. But Napoleon was no kinder than his scientists.

Another theme that was to preoccupy those who were to try and reconcile the implications of science with belief was also explored by St. Simon. For, failure as he was during these years, his ideas were crystallizing and in his manuscript *Mémoire sur la science de l'homme* (published after his death) and even more in his *Travail sur la Gravitation Universelle* of the same year (1813), he stressed the need of *one* principle, that of gravity, to integrate the disparate and unrelated scientific laws that were steadily accumulating. What St. Simon was looking for was a monistic principle to explain the universe, and that principle was at first that of Newton. Monism was, as we shall see, to preoccupy a number of later nineteenth-century St. Simons.

A third strand in St. Simonism, as in other technocracies, was its authoritarian nature. Disillusionment with the Bourbon restoration led him to look for salvation through industry. He successfully modified his dictatorship of the competent from scientists and property owners to scientists, businessmen and bankers. As his 'temples of Newton' assumed greater functions —teaching, research and worship—it became increasingly difficult to visualize what would be the name of the religion practised therein. 'Physicism' demanded a kind of universal numeracy which even St. Simon, optimist as he was, could not but regard as Utopian. Still searching for a symbol of the Unity of Nature he stumbled on the idea of God, and two months before he died published *Nouveau Christianisme* (1825), with its theme that one should love one's neighbour as oneself, and work for universal terrestrial happiness. For this new Christianity he proposed a priesthood, a creed and a theology.[23] Like most founders of new religions, he is not to be held responsible for the excesses of his disciples.

(6)

For disciples he had, especially among bankers. Lafitte gave him 10,000 francs a month to publish his review *L'Industrie*, whilst other bankers like the Pereires, Vibal Roux the Governor of the Bank of France and the economist Jean-Baptiste Say helped support him. Even more significantly, he evoked support from scientists like Cuvier and Olinde Rodrigues, a teacher at the École Polytechnique, who introduced his ideas to a mystical engineer student Prosper Enfantin.

These disciples publicized his doctrines. *Le Producteur* (1825–6) was the first of several journals which aimed at fostering 'the union of scientists, industrialists and artists as the only means of rescuing society from its present state of crisis'. In its successors, *L'Organisateur* (1829–31) and *Le Globe* (1831–2) and in the lecture courses organized for the same and three main principles emerged—Universal Association, the peaceful organization of industry and the production and redistribution of wealth according to qualifications and service. These principles became, in the mind of Prosper Enfantin, the dogma of a new religion.

Enfantin, with Olinde Rodrigues and St. Amand Bazard as St. Simonian co-priests emphasized the creative role of the State in expanding industry. St. Simon conceived of the canal across the isthmus of Panama and Enfantin canvassed one across Suez. In a series of lectures from 1828 to 1830 the St. Simonians indicated that science both stemmed and extended the religious idea that nature was orderly, and so, as science had grown, so had religion until, of course, with St. Simonism, science and religion phased and fused.

Founded in 1829 with departmental (or diocesan) branches in the provinces, the St. Simonian church erupted, in true ecclesiastical fashion, into sectarian controversy. Enfantin and Bazard were soon at loggerheads and Enfantin withdrew with his supporters to a St. Simonian monastery at Ménilmontant, near Paris, where they donned, as symbols of mutual interdependence, waistcoats that buttoned at the back, and in the intervals of observing their unique religious rites, searched for the 'mère suprême' to join Enfantin. That 'mère suprême' was never found: Enfantin got married and became secretary of the Paris to Mediterranean Railway.

'Social communication' was the real gospel of the St. Simonians. Fournel first conceived of the project of a Suez Canal. Enfantin's followers were commissioned to construct a Nile Dam.

In France itself, the transport system was in the words of Dr. Evans: 'the work of these Romantic polytechnicians, carried out in the face of government opposition'.[24] And behind railways there were the St. Simonian bankers, the Pereire brothers, whose Crédit Foncier and Crédit Mobilier were to lubricate so many French industrial enterprises.

Converts to this businessman's socialism sprang up all over Europe. In Germany Heine dedicated his *De l'Allemagne* to Enfantin; Goethe's *Second Faust* betrays evidences of the redemptive potential of technology; whilst the native town of Karl Marx, Trèves was a centre of such propaganda.[25] In England, Carlyle translated Saint-Simon's *Nouveau Christianisme*.[26] John Stuart Mill was presented 'for the first time' with 'the natural order of human progress' and acknowledged that, thanks to the Saint Simonians,

> 'my eyes were opened to the very limited and temporary value of the old political economy which assumes private property and inheritance as indefeasible facts and freedom of production and exchange as the *dernier mot* of social improvement.' He added: 'as long as their public teachings and proselytism continued, I read nearly everything they wrote'.[27]

Four years after Charles Duveyrier came with Gustave d'Eichthal (a correspondent of Mill's), on a mission to England he wrote *L'Ingénieur ou la mine de Charbon* (1836), a drama in praise of the engineer.

(7)

One polytechnician who possessed ideas of his own as well as being possessed by St. Simon's was Auguste Comte. Comte was a polytechnician through and through: though he was expelled from the École Polytechnique in 1816 for taking the lead in demanding the dismissal of one of the tutors, he spent the rest of his life trying to get back there—as a professor. He even asked Guizot to create a chair for him in the history of the positive sciences and sincerely thought he would become director of the school in 1840. His disappointment led him to preface the sixth volume of his *Philosophie Positive* with an account of his persecutors, of whom Arago the physicist was the chief.

Comte was especially affected by his work with St. Simon to

whom he attached himself in 1818 whilst working out the outlines of his system which first appeared in a 191-page pamphlet *Plan des travaux scientifiques nécessaires pour réorganiser la société* (1822) and was later elaborated in the six volumes of his *Cours de philosophie positive* (1830–42).[28] Positivism as he saw it was knowledge based on science, as opposed to theology or metaphysics.

Comte hoped for 'a religious alliance founded on a system of management'. This would grow through the development of order and by a 'disciplining of the forces of man'.[29] In growing it would foster 'the incorporation of the proletariat', by getting them 'to accept the fatalism which sanctions and directions their nobler aspirations, noticeably in opposition to the absolute fatalism which originally the profane domain could not but suggest'.[30]

This managerial Church State was described by Comte as 'sociocracy', and defined as 'a western religion' as opposed to 'essentially oriental' theocracy.[31] The sociocratic State would repair the injustice of the last three centuries to Catholics for Comte despised Protestant sects as reactionary, incomplete faiths 'which could not attain any real coherence' since 'they attributed to every believer the infallibility they deny to the Pope', thereby stimulating 'pride and vanity to a degree bordering on madness', and 'impelling the intellect to aberrations without limit on questions which are really insoluble'.[32]

Positivists should, he argued, organize 'a noble league . . . of all theologists who are adequately influenced by the urgent need of a reconstruction of spiritual discipline. Every soul that feels the urgency of always making morals paramount over politics and of subordinating material activity to culture of the sympathies, may, whatever its belief, concur in the religious reconstruction.'[33]

The special worship of the Virgin, argued Comte, might soon be transformed so as to prepare Catholic nations for the universal adoration of Humanity.[34] In this, the Positivists would be assisted by women and regenerated Jesuits. For the Jesuits had, in Comte's opinion, made an effort to return to the principles of chivalry by reviving the worship of the Virgin. As 'the necessary precursor' of Positivism, Roman Catholicism was so acceptable to Comte that he argued that 'it would be desirable at the present day, both for public good and for private happiness that all should remain Catholic until they become Positivist, avoiding scepticism entirely'.[35]

If Catholics were to Comte the precursors, Communists were the agents or 'active auxiliaries' of Positivism. Positivism, as a systematization which aims at subordinating politics to morals, in order to initiate the true social existence' could not come about, in Comte's opinion, 'without the energy of the nobler communists'. Indeed in Comte's view:

> . . . communism will be able to co-operate as much as Catholicism in aiding conservatives to inaugurate definitively the organic transition. The two together will be useful in proclaiming two includable problems, the one political, the other religious, each of which can only be effectively stated by virtue of some solution or other, till such time as the close connections between them gives the victory to the only doctrine which has solved them.[36]

The official sanction of the disease of the West was, to Comte, universal suffrage. Modification of the suffrage would, in his opinion, win over the 'proletary communists'. 'Sound policy', he argued, 'will obtain more help from Communists than from individualists' since 'the latter tend in the direction of the indefinite dispersion of wealth, the former lend their influence to its absolute concentration.[37] Here Comte put his finger on the real trend. To him Communists 'state the social problem, though with a solution as narrow as it is subversive, and are therefore open to demonstrations drawn from the indivisibility of human existence, in which material advance cannot be regulated apart from the spiritual order',[38] whilst individualists 'confine themselves to disputing the possession of power without disciplining its exercise otherwise than by anarchical restrictions'.[39]

(8)

Physiocracy was thus transformed into Physicism. As with Quesnay so with Comte, 'Planning' was the watchword: 'Nothing can excuse the metaphysical school of economics for systematically resisting the intervention of human wisdom in the various departments of social action', wrote Comte. As with the physiocrats there was the single-minded concentration on the ultimate goal. 'I am working to establish doctrines, not institutions', he told a friend, 'when the former take shape, that is to say in about sixty years time, we can think about the latter . . . I am not exactly saying "my kingdom is not of this world" but the equivalent in terms of our epoch.'

'Thanks to Comte', a modern sociologist has pointed out 'the idea of historical stages of thought has in fact become a basic assumption of social eidos.' On the one hand we may agree with the critics of positivism that it was seriously misleading to represent the study of society as about to advance into 'its final and definitive state'. But on the other hand we may still consider that a 'third stage' of social eidos has resulted from the high prestige of science itself.[40]

Comte was, I think, the first writer to place such uncompromising stress on the social character of morality . . . Perhaps he can even be said to have invented the idea of society in the abstract, as a force beyond ourselves.[41]

6

◇◇◇◇◇◇◇◇◇◇◇◇◇◇◇◇◇◇◇◇◇◇◇◇◇◇◇◇◇◇◇◇◇◇◇◇

Materialists and Monists

◇◇◇◇◇◇◇◇◇◇◇◇◇◇◇◇◇◇◇◇◇◇◇◇◇◇◇◇◇◇◇◇◇◇◇◇

(1)

ENGINEERS in the German states were doing, in a smaller way, what Lamblardie and Monge were doing for France. J. A. Eytelwein (1764–1848) took the lead, and in 1799 organized the *Bauacademie* in Berlin, becoming its director and Professor of Engineering Mechanics. It soon developed as a nursery of land surveyors, civil and hydraulic engineers. This through stages, was to develop, along with another institution in the capital, into the famous technical institute of Charlottenburg.

A polytechnic was also organized in Prague in 1806 under F. J. Gerstner (1756–1832), a professor of mathematics, who remained its director and Professor of Mechanics until 1832. A Bavarian Polytechnic Association was formed in 1815 on the model of the Société d'Encouragement pour l'industrie nationale. A polytechnic institute was also founded in Vienna in 1815 whose director Johann Joseph von Prechtl (1778–1854) initiated a collection of machines, acquiring 3,378 of them in eight years.

Cut off from many chemical products by the blockade from 1806 to 1812, patriotic German chemists turned their attention to synthesis. Goethe, as a government official, was responsible for fitting out a laboratory for J. W. Döbreiner at Jena, who, with W. H. S. Bucholz (1734–1798), worked on the possibility of using water gas as an illuminant, and experimented on alloys of manganese, silicon and iron. They produced sugar (from alcohol and carbon dioxide, with platinum sub-oxide as a catalyst) and sulphuric acid (from sulphur dioxide also using a platinum catalyst).

Goethe also encouraged A. N. von Scherer (1771–1824) a member of the Naturforschende Gesellschaft at Jena. To improve his chemical and technological knowledge Goethe secured him a trip to England and Scotland. On his return, Scherer gave lectures in chemistry at Weimar in a large hall and began to edit a journal, *Allgemeines Journal der Chemie*, in 1798. Two years later he was appointed Professor of Physics at Halle. Scherer was, however, a restless soul and after a time migrated to join the medico-chirurgical academy at St. Petersburg where he edited many journals.

Elsewhere in Germany, laboratory instruction was being firmly established. It was made obligatory at Göttingen, under Frederick Stromeyer, the discoverer of cadmium, who taught the Englishman Edward Turner. Breslau, where Goethe's nominee J. E. Purkin was Professor of Physiology, was not so forward: Purkin had to establish a laboratory in his own house. Later Landshut and Jena followed suit. This was of course a prelude to the later triumphs of Liebig.

(2)

After the Napoleonic War, the Association for the Promotion of Industrial Knowledge was established in 1819. Through five committees—industry and trade, accounting, mathematics, physics and chemistry, art and architecture—it worked to increase efficiency and promote new methods. Such was the theme of the opening address of its founder Peter Beuth on 15 January 1821 to 145 of the 367 members who turned up to hear him. For those who didn't, Beuth issued a series of intelligence reports on the technical progress of West European industry and agriculture, through its *Transactions* (*Verhandlungen*) which began to appear in the following year.

Aptly enough it obtained a former industrial exhibition building in the Klosterstrasse large enough for a laboratory. It became a repository for models so many and various that within five years it overflowed into extended premises, becoming known as the House of Industry. This name it amply justified, for amongst those associated with it in one capacity or another were J. F. W. Tappert (1766–1831), a leading cotton spinner, the iron founder F. A. J. Egells (1788–1854), the locomotive engineer August Borsig (1804–54) and the shipbuilder Ferdinand Schichau (1814–96).[1]

As prime mover of this association, Peter Beuth, though anxious to see science taught in the *gymnasia*, advocated the establishment of a new type of school—a vocational or *Gewerbeschule*—linked to a local technical institute (*Gewerbeinstitut*). To show how it should be done he and his associates opened a technical institute in November 1821 with thirteen pupils between the ages of 12 and 16, to whom they taught mathematics, chemistry and machine drawing and for which they were paid by the Government. In twenty years the number of students had reached three figures. The Association stimulated the formation of similar bodies at Stuttgart (1819), Cassel (1821) and Chemnitz (1830) and *Gewerbeschulen* at Magdeburg (1819) and Berlin (1824).

A second, less official, crusade was launched by Lorenz Oken (1779–1851) a professor at Jena who resigned his chair in 1819 because *Isis*, his two-year-old monthly journal of literature and science, was threatened by the censor. He was anxious to found a Parliament of Scientists, and by 1822, managed to attract thirty like-minded souls to Leipzig where they founded the *Deutsche Naturforscherversammlung*, a yearly meeting of 'the cultivators of science and medicine from all parts of the German fatherland'. Subsequent and successive meetings, held at university towns like Halle, Würzburg, Frankfurt, Dresden and Munich, were more successful: official hostility melted, so that by the time they met in Berlin—in 1828—they were lavishly received and entertained. So many now attended the meetings that it was found convenient to group them into sections, according to their professional interest, and by 1830 the chairman could say

> whereas in former times men regarded the inquisition of nature as a pleasant but useless employment, and as a harmless pasture for idle heads, they have of late years become daily more convinced of its influence upon the civilisation and welfare of nations, and the leaders

of the public are everywhere bestirring themselves for the erection of establishments to promote its advancement and extension.[2]

(*3*)

Of all the establishments to promote the advancement and extension of science to which the chairman referred in 1830 none were more characteristic than the new universities of Berlin (1810) and Bonn (1817): both German variants of the École Polytechnique. The polytechnic fever had been first caught by Alexander von Humboldt. 'I work at the school, I sleep there: I am there all night, all morning, I share the same room with Guy-Lussac', he wrote to a friend.[3] Alexander's enthusiasm for research was shared by his philologist brother Wilhelm who played a major role in founding the University of Berlin in 1810 to offset the loss of Halle to the French. Berlin established the research role of the university: students were to co-operate in discovering new knowledge rather than to receive instruction. Humboldt took the initiative in securing a Government grant for the new university at Berlin, and envisaged it assuming functions hitherto discharged by the Berlin Academy of Sciences. Indeed when the University of Berlin opened its doors in the palace of Prince Henry, the Polytechnic can be said to have had a step-child. Subsequently, German universities continued to derive great strength from the German variants of the poly-technic that took shape as *technische Hochschulen*.[4]

One of those who came to Berlin from Halle at Humboldt's invitation was J. C. Reil (1759–1813). Goethe's psychiatrist (he once listened to Goethe for a fortnight and only prescribed a sedative), Reil was a pioneer in the humane treatment of the insane, rejecting the harsher methods of his day. He had started at Halle the *Archiv für die Physiologie* (1795) and it passed into the hands of Johann Friedrich Merkel the younger at Leipzig (with whom he had collaborated in 1807). Reil worked on histology of nerve fibres, and had some notion of metabolism. One of his successors both at Berlin and as editor of the *Archiv* was Johannes Peter Müller (1801–58), who virtually refounded it as *Müllers Archiv* (1834–58).

A pupil and Professor of Anatomy at Bonn, Müller worked out, and elaborated after being called to Berlin in 1833, the outlines of modern embryology. Bringing to bear the principles

79

of psychology, elaborated by Reil and his successors, the chemistry of Liebig, and the techniques of microscopic observation, he worked out the anatomy of cartilaginous and glandular tissues in his *Handbook of the Physiology of Mankind* (1833–40).

This in turn was used by his Berlin pupil Theodor Schwann (1810–82) who, working in Berlin from cartilages, went on to the ovum and back to the adult tissues to show that plants and animals are composed either of cells, or of substances thrown off by cells, which though they have to some extent a life of their own, are yet subject to that of the organism as a whole. These concepts of the cytoblast (now called the protoplasm) and of the process of metabolism have profoundly affected subsequent thought.

To replace a number of older German universities swept away by the Napoleonic wars, Breslau (1811), Bonn (1818) and Munich (1826) were founded. These set, with Berlin, a new pattern for universities in that research, according to the strictest definition of that term, became their driving force. They were specifically unlike the Napoleonic *Université Impérial*, for whereas in France the central university had to control all the schools of every grade in every province, in Germany the only obligation of the university was to research. German universities provided increasing cadres of intellectuals from 1831 to the end of the century: Berlin (1,821 to 6,151), Breslau (902 to 1,522), Halle (810 to 1,605), Greifswald (208 to 779), Königsberg (421 to 778), Bonn (795 to 1,780), Münster (261 to 479), Braunsberg (24 to 54), Göttingen (865 to 1,227), Marburg (331 to 1,040), Kiel (275 to 645), Munich (1,556 to 3,905), Würzburg (445 to 1,343), Erlangen (278 to 1,026), Tübingen (806 to 1,306), Heidelberg (661 to 1,142), Freiburg (474 to 1,141), Leipzig (1,145 to 3,413), Jena (501 to 763), Giessen (355 to 717), Rostock (95 to 449), Strasbourg (470 [1871] to 1,075). The total increase was from 13,029 to 32,336, or from 395 per million to 599 per million of the population. In this increase the greatest was in the faculty of philosophy which prepared teachers for secondary schools as well as technologists, mathematicians, politicial economists and pharmacists. It began with 2,395 students in 1831 and rose to 11,497 by 1899, or an average of 83 per million to 213 per million.[5]

(4)

Meanwhile Beuth's *Gewerbeschule* at Berlin had become a nursery of chemists. The first was Friedrich Wöhler (1800–82), one of the founders of organic chemistry, who left Berlin in 1831 for another *Gewerbeschule* at Cassel, and only left Cassel in 1836 for the chair of chemistry at the University of Göttingen.[6] He was succeeded at Cassel by an equally illustrious chemist, R. W. Bunsen (1811–99). Other distinguished organic chemists who found in the *Gewerbeschule* of Berlin a spring-board for further progress were Adolf Baeyer (1835–1917) who rebuilt the famous laboratory where other famous chemists like Victor Meyer (1848–97) made their names.

More importantly, ability hitherto denied access to the universities was tapped by Justus Liebig (1803–73). As Karl Vogt wrote

> The majority of those who had their names on the list of the laboratory students had not come by the usual educational route through the gymnasium and had not passed their leaving examination (*Maturitätsprüfung*). Liebig was engaged in a continual and embittered struggle with the university pedantry which demanded the leaving certificate and indeed the classical one as the indispensable prerequisite for admission to the university and its institutes to which, to be sure, the laboratory also belonged.[7]

Liebig had been introduced by Alexander von Humboldt to Guy-Lussac, and on returning to Giessen in 1824 as Professor of Chemistry, he modelled it on Guy-Lussac's laboratory, and only took students who were enthusiastic, whether or not they had been to the *Gymnasium*. Structurally Liebig's laboratory was a modest affair, considering it trained sixty or so graduates a year. Originally in the wing of the Giessen barracks, it was rehoused as

> a work-room with a colonnade at the front. Scant space for about twelve workers was found at the tables set under the windows. In the middle there was a large stove on which and in which crucibles and retorts could be heated. Behind the hall there was a room crammed full with equipment and supplies; behind this a second room where the apparatus for glass-blowing was kept and where the anvils for fashioning platinum crucibles and also the balances were set up. Opening into the corridor which led into the latter room

81

was Liebig's own work-cabinet and a small private laboratory in which there was room for two, or at the most, three persons. Above the laboratories were the very limited quarters of Liebig's private dwelling. That was all there was. Coal was used for heating since gas was still unknown. So were friction matches. Fire was obtained by means of asbestos dipped in strong sulphuric acid.[8]

From 1832 onwards the discoveries of its students began to appear in the *Annalen der Pharmazie* (after 1840 the *Annalen der Chemie und der Pharmazie*), originally a journal known as the *Magazin der Philosophie* edited by Liebig and Geiger. When Geiger died, Liebig replaced him by Wöhler. Through this journal the public heard of the astonishing products of organic analysis techniques; including chloroform, chloral and metaldehyde. It carried the discoveries of non-university scientists too. In 1842 for instance it published the first announcement, by J. R. Mayer (1814–78), a physician of Heilbronn, of the principle of the conservation of energy.

Just as Liebig's students stoically bore the anhydrous formic acid which he put on their arms, so they carried the mental stigmata of Giessen to the corners of the civilized world. To England, his translator, Lyon Playfair (1818–98), returned to campaign for more scientific training and Sheridan Muspratt to found the Liverpool Chemical College. To Russia N. I. Zinin returned to lay the foundation of organic chemistry at the University of Kazan.[9] To America Wolcott Gibbs returned to the Rumford chair of chemistry at Harvard and Lawrence Smith to kindle an enthusiasm for chemistry at Louisville University.[10]

But perhaps the greatest example of the impress of Giessen was the establishment, by private subscription, of a College of Chemistry in Hanover Square for which Liebig was asked to nominate a director. Two of his nominees turned it down. The third, A. W. Hofmann (1818–88), obtained two years' leave of absence to accept. Hofmann stayed for nearly twenty, and during this time he more than earned the £700 a year which he ultimately obtained. His pupils, W. H. Perkin, F. A. Abel, W. de la Rue, E. C. Nicholson and C. B. Mansfield created the coal-tar dye industry.

Liebig's friend Wöhler built up the laboratories at Göttingen where he was professor of chemistry from 1836 to 1857. Eight thousand students passed through his hands, to make it, in the course of fifty years, as famous as Giessen. Under his successors Victor Meyer and Otto Wallach (the latter a pupil of his) the tradition of hard work and intensive research continued.

A third chemical nursery was established by R. W. Bunsen (1811–99) in Marburg (1839–51) and Heidelberg (1852–89). At Marburg a roll of distinguished names testifies to his stimulus: Herman Kolbe (his successor), F. A. Genth, Edward Frankland and John Tyndall. It was for Bunsen that the Government of Baden built a new laboratory in Heidelberg for which Bunsen devised his famous burner. Heidelberg took the place of Giessen after 1852, for when Liebig moved to Munich he lost interest in research. Here Kekulé was a young researcher, later to happen upon the fundamental idea of the quadrivalency of carbon and the linkage of its atoms.[11]

(5)

Though they proudly appended their names to papers on atoms of carbon, scientists furtively withheld them from tracts on man in society. Lorenz Oken might return to university work after the success of his parliament of science, but the ever-present threat of suspension hung over the most brilliant of professors.

Consider the case of Wilhelm Weber (1804–90). Called to the chair of physics at Göttingen in 1831 he had, in collaboration with that prince of mathematicians K. F. Gauss (1777–1855), helped found the system of electrical measurement generally used today. Later with his electro-dynamometer and earth inductor he was to measure electrical energy with an accuracy not known before. In doing so he found that it was propagated with the speed of light. In 1833 he and Gauss introduced the electromagnetic telegraph by signalling to each other.

Yet, for opposing the King of Hanover's adoption of a constitution in 1837, Weber lost his appointment for five years. Although the units of current, voltage and resistance which he established were ratified by an International Congress at Paris in 1881, not one of them was, at the time, named after him. This was probably due to the fact that he did not accept an invitation to attend the congress. Today that omission has been rectified.[12]

Anonymity was necessary before a natural scientist at Erlangen could publish some thoughts on death and immortality in 1830. After establishing himself with a life of Bayle (1838) the anonymous writer, now identified as Ludwig Feuerbach, claimed that Christianity had 'long since vanished, not only from the reason, but from the life of mankind'. In *Das Wesen des Christentums* (1841) Feuerbach saw God as an outward projection of man's inward nature: a correspondent of some acutely felt need—a myriad rather than a trinity. Translated into English by George Eliot the novelist in 1853 his ideas influenced 'materialism'.

Idolized by the German revolutionary party in 1848 they evoked the disgust of Karl Marx, who hurriedly scribbled down in his notebook, for later elaboration 'he (i.e. Feuerbach) does not grasp the significance of "revolutionary", of "practical-critical activity" '. He then added

> The materialist doctrine that men are products of circumstance and upbringing and that, therefore, changed men are products of other circumstances and changed upbringing, forgets that circumstances are changed precisely by men and that the educator must himself be educated.

He then concluded

> The standpoint of the old materialism is 'civil society', the standpoint of the new is *human* society or socialised humanity.[13]

For holding similar ideas Karl Vogt (1817–95) was dismissed from the University of Giessen and Jacob Moleschott (1822–93) from the University of Heidelberg. Having suffered in the same way, F. K. C. Büchner (1824–99) forsook academic work altogether and became a medical practitioner. This is why his book, *Kraft und Stoff*, became one of the most popular works of the age, for he possessed the common ear to such an extent that we shall see his ideas agitating students in Russia.

These three so annoyed Engels by the 'shallow and vulgarised materialism' preached on their 'tours', their ignorance of 'a science of the processes of the origin and development of these things and of the inter-connection which binds all these processes into one great whole',[14] that he described them as 'vulgar pedlars'. They used 'all the advances of natural science . . . only as proof against the existence of a creator of the world . . . (as) . . . it was quite outside their scope to develop the theory any further'. Engels considered that 'Feuerbach was unquestionably right when he refused to take responsibility for this materialism; only he should not have confounded the doctrines of these hedge-preachers with materialism in general'.[15]

(6)

Materialism was a natural philosophic by-product of the heavy emphasis on the production of engineers, chemists and architects. Both industry and the provincial rulers of Germany cultivated *technische Hochschulen* at the expense of the universities, since the universities, being tucked away in medieval towns, were less amenable to industrial pressures.[16]

From the time Nebenius of the Grand Duchy of Baden established the first *technische Hochschule* at Karlsruhe in 1825, they became a familiar feature of all the German State capitals. Munich (1827), Nürnberg (1829), Dresden (1828), Stuttgart (1829), Cassel (1830), Hanover (1831), Augsburg (1833) and Brunswick (1835) were followed by others outside Germany like the *technische Hochschule* at Zürich in 1855 where Einstein was to be a pupil.[17]

At Karlsruhe the first professional body of German engineers —the *Verein Deutscher Ingenienure*—took shape, helped by one of its professors, F. Grashof (1826–93), himself a former student at the *Gewerbeinstitut* at Berlin.[18] The existence of electromagnetic waves, and their remarkable similarity to light waves was proved by another professor at Karlsruhe in 1886: Heinrich Hertz (1857–94).[19] A third professor, Fritz Haber (1868–1934), working with Fritz Bunte, synthesized ammonia.

The importance of this discovery was recognized by the Badische Analin und Sodafabrik (later I. G. Farben) which sent its own scientists, Karl Bosch (1874–1934) and Mittasch to Karlsruhe to investigate. They found that an iron catalyst could be substituted for Haber's rare osmium, so endowing Germany with enormous potential for manufacturing fertilizers, as well as explosives.[20]

Nor was the Karlsruhe *technische Hochschule* alone in its distinction. One of its professors, O. Mohr, designer of some of the first steel truss bridges in Germany, was himself a former pupil of the Hanover *technische Hochschule*. Hanover also produced A. Wöhler (1819–1914) whose work on the fatigue strength of metals was put to effective use in the development of German railways. To Hanover also came Ludwig Prandtl in 1890 whose brilliant use of soap-film to solve torsion problems led to him being invited to the University of Göttingen in 1904 where he worked on hydro—and aerodynamic problems with wind tunnels.

In these *technische Hochschulen* were cradled the prime movers that were to supplant the steam-engine.[21] At Munich in 1878 Rudolf Diesel (1858–1913) heard of the poor efficiency of the steam-engine and decided to devote his life to the more efficient unit of propulsion that goes under his name. The internal combustion engine was pioneered at Karlsruhe in 1867 by Eugen Langen (1833–95) working with Nikolaus Otto (1832–91) and, at Stuttgart, Gottlieb Daimler (1834–1900) acquired the knowledge that was to enable him to build one that moved at high speeds.[22]

The success of these institutions prompted an English deputation to investigate. They were told that their capacity far exceeded the demand for places, on the authority, no less, of von Helmholtz and Werner Siemens.[23] The English were especially impressed by the *technische Hochschule* at Charlottenburg, Berlin. This was natural for Berlin was a special institution. Created in 1876 by the amalgamation of the *Bauakademie* (founded in 1799) and Beuth's *Gewerbeschule* (founded in 1824), it secured (in 1899) in common with other *technische Hochschulen*, the power to award the *Dip-Ing* and *Dr.-Ing*: the equivalents of university degrees.[24] It was from a lecture room at Charlottenburg that Adolf Slaby and Count Georg Arco transmitted the first radio message in Germany to a water tower some distance away. This was followed two years later by the discovery of the cathode-ray tube by Ferdinand Braun (1850–1918) at Strasbourg. Slaby's and Arco's work was taken up by the Allgemeine Elektrizitäts-Gesellschaft (A.E.G.) whilst Braun's was adopted by Siemens-Halske. Subsequently in 1903 these two firms established the Wireless Telegraphy Company, later known as Telefunken. And Telefunken was to conduct massive research on electronics on its own initiative. It was, incidentally, the advances in radio that enabled Germany to direct, with such success, a submarine campaign in both World Wars.

(7)

So rewarding were raids on Nature's pantry that business corporations built industrial research laboratories.[25] They were forced to do so by the sheer size of their firms.

University-trained chemists were being hired after 1868 by Lucius and Bruning of Höchst near Frankfurt-am-Main (founded in 1863) and the Badische Anilin und Soda-Fabrik of Ludwigshafen (founded in 1865). That they became the two largest dye factories in the world is perhaps the best commentary on the success of their policy. Lucius himself directed the university-trained chemists of the research departments of the first firm, whilst August Clemm (a pupil of Liebig) directed the research team of the second until 1868, when he found it better to hire a distinguished chemist, in this case Heinrich Caro, to handle the research side whilst he and his brother Carl concentrated on the commercial.

Caro became the guiding genius of the Badische Anilin und Soda-Fabrik. Travelling to England in 1876 he secured from D. N. Witt the secret of making chryoidine and from P. Griess the secrets of the azo compound helianthin. He co-operated with the University of Munich and with Adolf Bayer effectively synthesized indigo: a task that took twenty years.

The Badische Anilin und Soda-Fabrik was also fortunate in Caro's successor: Alwyn Mittasch (1869–1953) who founded their research laboratories at Oppau, acting as director from their inception in 1918 to 1933. During this time (1925) the firm became the Interessen-Gemeinschaft Farbenindustrie (I. G. Farben). Mittasch began with six and ended with 150 scientists in his research group, making Ludwigshafen a training school for hundreds of chemists who occupied a wide variety of posts. As befitted a former pupil of Rudolf Knietsch and Carl Bosch, he worked on catalysis. 'Chemistry without catalysis,' he remarked, 'would be a sword without a handle, a light without brilliance, a bell without sound.'[26] Many startling advances in biochemistry came from his leadership.

A third firm, that of Friedrich Bayer of Elberfeld, offers a good example of the growth of a research laboratory. It hired Dr. Schonfeld in 1864, and later, others, of whom the best was Carl Duisberg, to do pure research on university lines. The chemists so employed on research and development grew from 15 in 1881 to 24 in 1885, 58 in 1890, 90 in 1815 and 104 in 1896. Housed in a laboratory costing one and a half million marks, designed specially so that the twelve research men could see and talk to each other from U-shaped niches, and staffed with glass blowers, dyers, analysts and technicians, Duisberg's research division instituted a bi-monthly seminar in 1886, a training programme, and, in 1904, a teaching programme. The libraries of Kekulé, Victor Mayer and Sir Henry Roscoe were bought to swell its stock. By 1896 it had investigated no less than 2,378 colours, of which 37 had reached the market.[27]

The great chemical city-states sustained at Höchst, Ludwigshafen and Leverkusen, by these three companies recruited hundreds of qualified men to concentrate on the exciting (and dangerous) adventure of building new compounds. Following one another's work with ardour, they lit on colours with menacingly ambivalent purposes: Congo red (discovered by Bottiger in 1884), uses the same materials and processes as T.N.T. or tear gas (brombenzil cyanide), while the techniques of producing sulphur black (R. Vidal, 1894) were, with slight variations, capable of producing another explosive—picric acid. These German research chemists knew of phosgene (Kern, 1883) and mustard gas (Victor Mayer, 1886) long before they were used on the battlefield. Pleasanter aspects of their work were the production of pharmaceutics like antipyrin (Knorr, 1883) and sulphonal (Baumann, 1886); flavourings like vanillin (Tiemann and Haarmann, 1876); or musk (trinitrobutyltoluene).

(8)

Barriers between academic and the industrial scientists, disturbed by the *technische Hochschulen*, were broken by Werner Siemens, the great electrical manufacturer. His works at Charlottenburg were probably the most advanced in Europe. He told the Royal Academy of Sciences in 1874 that 'scientific knowledge and method are now no longer confined to the narrow circle of the professional scientist, but exert their fructifying influences over larger circles of the community.'

Siemens's close ally in this was the Professor of Physics at the University of Berlin, Hermann Helmholtz (1821–94), the great enunciator of the principle of the conservation of energy, who had refused the chair of experimental physics at Cambridge in 1871. Originally a Prussian army surgeon whose research work in physiology earned him chairs in that subject at Königsberg (1849), Bonn (1855) and Heidelberg (1858), Helmholtz worked closely with Werner Siemens from 1883 to 1887 to establish the Physikalische-Technische Reichsanstalt at Charlottenburg.[28]

In this institution the marriage of the research of pure physicists and the needs of industry was to take place and, as chief celebrant of the nuptials, Helmholtz became its director.[29] It excited the admiration of British observers: The Mathematical and Physical Sciences Section of the British Association heard Sir Oliver Lodge say at Cardiff that 'the further progress of physical science in the somewhat haphazard and amateur fashion in which it has hitherto been pursued in this country is becoming increasingly difficult, and that the quantitative portion especially should be undertaken in a permanent and publicly supported physical laboratory on a large scale'.[30] Lodge insisted that such an institution would not weaken but strengthen existing private laboratories. His words had their due effect, and ten years later the British established their own National Physical Laboratory.

As the official German representative at the Paris Conference of 1881 on the nomenclature of units of electrical energy, before resigning his university chair to become president of this great physico-technical institute, Helmholtz also excited the admiration and imagination of Max Planck (1857–1947), who though he confessed that Helmholtz was a boring lecturer yet regarded him as 'the very incarnation of the dignity and probity of science' and wrote that 'a single word of approval, let alone praise from his lips would make me as happy as any worldly triumph'.[31] Planck's career in Berlin from 1889 onwards, stimulated by a correspondence with Nernst of Göttingen and Ostwald in Leipzig, resulted in the promulgation of the quantum theory in physics. This suggestion that an elementary quantum of action should be fitted in to classical physics, opened up a new era in natural science, an era which in the hands of Niels Bohr and Erwin Schrödinger was to give us atomic theory.

(9)

By 1905 Emil Fischer, Walter Nernst and Carl Duisberg realized that the universities could not afford the research facilities and expensive equipment needed for modern research. They therefore decided to found a chemical counterpart, an organization similar to the Physikalische-Technische Reichsanstalt. Funds were forthcoming from industry but the Government in 1908 refused to be responsible for its administration and supervision as its founder had desired.

At the centenary celebrations of the University of Berlin in 1910 Leibig's grandson, Adolph von Harnack, a theologian, stressed the need of supplementing university research. His idea was that advocated over a century before by Wilhelm von Humboldt: richly endowed institutes should be established under eminent scientists, invested with freedom to choose their work and staff. The Emperor Wilhelm II was moved to establish the Kaiser Wilhelm Gesellschaft zur Förderung der Wissenschaften in 1911 as a parent body for the institutes. These grew rapidly: seven were set up before the war, eight during it, and another fifteen after it, so that by 1926 there were thirty, covering most fields of endeavour. Of these, perhaps the most notable was the Kaiser Wilhelm Institute for Physical and Electro-Chemistry, built, equipped and maintained by Leopold Koppel, a wealthy industrialist, who insisted that Fritz Haber should be its director. Haber had only been in action for two years when the First World War diverted his energy.[32] Not only was he able to direct the German chlorine attack at Ypres, but after the war he spent much time and ingenuity trying to recover gold from the sea to repay Germany's war debt.[33]

(10)

For a theologian to promote an 'establishment' of science was no stranger than for scientists to establish a church. For this is what had been happening since Wöhler's time if not before. His synthesis of an organic element out of inorganic components helped to destroy the idea of a life force as a source of metabolism in the human body. Julius Mayer for instance, in a paper refused by all the scientific journals and issued as a pamphlet in 1845, showed that the ultimate source of energy in earth was solar: assimilated by plants, this was the foundation of life on earth. His idea was given greater prominence when, two years later, Helmholtz published an essay on the conservation of force, which gave mathematical validity to the idea of the indestructibility of energy. Much affected by Helmholtz's omission of his name in 1847, poor Mayer had a nervous breakdown and though Helmholtz later made adequate amends, this did not satisfy one of Mayer's followers, the philosopher Eugen Dühring, who bitterly attacked Helmholtz.

Now Dühring (a non-scientist) was much more obsessional, and in 1874 published a complete philosophy of the universe based on it. To him 'energy' was such a basic form of explanation that he was prepared to explain everything, even the constitutions of states by it. This brought down on him the wrath of another German, living in Manchester, Friedrich Engels, who pointed out that Dühring's simple monistic explanation took no account of evolutionary, dialectical processes. In a series of articles published in the Leipzig paper *Vorwärts* in 1877 Engels used an analogy which Sir Joseph Banks would have appreciated:

> If we take an artificially cultivated ornamental plant, for example, a dahlia or an orchid: if we treat the seed and the plant which grows from it as a gardener does, we get as the result of this negation of the negation, not only more seeds, but also qualitatively better seeds, which produce more beautiful flowers, and each fresh repetition of this process, each repeated negation of the negation increases this improvement.[34]

The 'negation of the negation' was ignored by Dühring, and by an even more enlightened scientist, Ernst Haeckel, who had become Professor of Zoology at Jena some sixteen years before Engels wrote his *Anti-Dühring*. Haeckel accepted the evolutionary idea of the struggle for existence (which Dühring had rejected in favour of the idea of a free society where all power relationships were abolished and all human relationships were socialized). For his work on animals, sponges and amoeba evoked rapture. His exposition of Darwinism at a scientific congress in 1863 did much to ensure its reception in Germany. Enthusiasm was Haeckel's main trait. He came to believe that progress was inevitable, 'a natural law which no human power, neither the weapons of tyrants nor the curses of priests, can ever succeed in oppressing'.[35] Further scrutiny of the unicellular objects to which he was dedicated, led him to extrapolate upwards, up through man and the universe to God, and to conclude that there was one universal principle: energy. In a number of lectures to scientific societies and in books, he expounded this notion, attracting those veteran materialists Vogt (who, having lost his chair at Giessen for his views, had migrated to Geneva) and Büchner (who never had a chair, but was living on his reputation as the author of *Kraft und Stoff*). With them and some younger materialists like A. Brehm (a naturalist), F. von Hellwald (a geographer) and G. Jäger (of the hygienic theory), Haeckel now began to talk about uniting the natural with the mental sciences, to acquire a uniform view of life which could be propagated in schools.

This brought down on Haeckel the criticism of the physiologist Rudolf Virchow, who, though he had also suffered dismissal after the 1848 revolution for his scientific views (he had been a medical officer in a Silesian industrial area) and was an opponent of Bismarck, now accused Haeckel of 'socialism'. This led the Prussian Minister of Education to ban Darwinism (and indeed biology) from the schools. The socialists having heard Haeckel denounced as a socialist by Virchow, a liberal-minded professor at the University of Berlin, adopted Haeckel for themselves. With Haeckel came his principle: that energy was a fundamental principle of life.

With the socialists came others. Haeckel, wishing (for he was now 65 years old) himself out of history with a succinct statement of his views, published *The Riddles of the Universe* (*Die Welträtsel*) in the last year of the nineteenth century. It was an astounding success, being read all over Germany and translated into many languages. Very simply, it said that progress in science had not been accompanied by any similar progress in social organization.

Die Welträtsel was a tocsin. A league of monists (*Monistenbund*) was formed to promote his ideas. It began with study circles and ended with religious ceremonies. 'Sermons' were delivered on its behalf and against it. Politician-scientists like Reincke attacked it in the Prussian Parliament, and in opposition, another league of scientists was formed called the *Keplerbund*.

(11)

An archetype of these new saints of the specialisms round

whom the institutes were built was bearded, fresh-faced Wilhelm Ostwald (1853–1930), Professor of Physical Chemistry at Leipzig, founder and editor of the first journal devoted to it.[36] At the age of 48 he appeared at the Society of German Scientific Investigators and Physicians in September 1895. Like some new father at a Christian council, he delivered a searing attack on the engineers' universe of Kant and his followers, who held that reality was composed of matter. This, Ostwald maintained, was an illusion. Matter was really energy in different forms. From this he passed to a new science of the sciences. Believing that civilization only improved as man acquired understanding and perfected his control over energy, Ostwald regrouped the sciences into three divisions, those of order (e.g. logic and mathematics), those of energy (e.g. physics and chemistry) and those of life (in which he included psychology and 'culturology').

'Culturology' or 'instrumental interpretation' was from now on Ostwald's main concern. Lecturing on the implications of energy in the intervals of founding the Elektrochemische Gesellschaft (1894) and his Institute of Physical Chemistry (1897), he built up monistic philosophy so vigorously that he became President of the German Monists League. As the first exchange professor between Germany and the U.S.A. (which he visited in 1903, 1904 and 1905) he had ample opportunity to compare his views with those of William James and John Dewey.[37]

Retiring to his country house, 'Energie', Ostwald busied himself with schemes for an international body to organize and integrate intelligence and culture, in an international language. His majestic Sunday sermons revolved about his formula for life:

$$G = K(A - W)(A + W)$$

where G = happiness, A = energy expended usefully in the accomplishment of work and W = energy dissipated in the overcoming of resistance.

7

Emergent Operationalism in England
1815-61

(1)

'MEN OF SCIENCE' grew in numbers after the French wars. From the depths of Dorchester gaol, Thomas Carlile suggested that they might 'amend and moralise' the human passions. If they could, he was sure that 'the money now extorted by the priesthood' would be 'willingly given for the erection of Temples of Science and the support of competent professors in the Arts and Sciences'.[1]

But scientists were far more concerned to 'amend and moralise' their own profession. The chief amender and moralizer was the Lucasian Professor of Mathematics at Cambridge, Charles Babbage, leader of a campaign to secure that elections to the Royal Society should be by merit. The president shelved a report favourable to Babbage's ideas and rigged the election of councillors to keep it so. So Babbage took his case to the world at large in some *Reflections on the Decline of Science in England and on Some of its Causes* (1830). 'It must be the devout wish of every friend to science', editorialized *The Times* on 8 May 1830, 'that his serious accusations should be either satisfactorily refuted or effectively remedied.'

Neither the refutation nor remedy was forthcoming. The president nominated the Duke of Sussex as his successor, and against determined opposition by Babbage and others not only got his way but secured a place for himself on the council. Babbage was so furious that, with the other professionals, he gave his support to a scheme for a Parliament of Science on the lines of the German Naturalists group convened by Oken some nine years earlier.[2]

The other professional scientists who promoted the idea of a deliberating assembly of their fellows were J. F. W. Johnston, a chemist, and Sir David Brewster. Both had seen the German assembly in 1830, and with the help of others they convened the British Association for the Advancement of Science at York in 1831.[3] Thereafter it met annually. Within two years it began to live up to its name by compensating labour and paying the expenses of research apparatus: half the total subscriptions were earmarked for this purpose from 1848 onwards. One beneficiary was J. P. Joule, a former pupil of John Dalton's in Manchester. As a recent American writer remarked: 'All those reforms which it had been hoped to introduce into the constitution of the Royal Society were here embodied.'[4]

But when the British Association itself threatened to become 'popular', voices were raised in protest, notably that of Dr. Whewell, Master of Trinity College, Cambridge, who watched with alarm 'its increasing use by various persons for purposes which it cannot recognise, and which I doubt whether we ought knowingly and with foresight to further'. 'What kind of institution do we become,' he asked, 'if we allow ourselves to be made an ambulatory meeting for agitators in assemblies, when both *eminent* and *notorious* men (Dr. Chalmers and Robert Owen) address a miscellaneous crowd on the sorest and angriest subjects. If we cannot get rid of these characters, most assuredly I shall be disposed to make my connexion with the Association as brief as I can.'[5]

(2)

One 'sore and angry subject' was the growing gap between the facts of creation as stated in Genesis and the facts of life as discovered by geologists. Before he died in 1829, the Rev. Francis Egerton, F.R.S., eighth Earl of Bridgewater tried to span it. He believed that science not only confirmed, but corroborated the story of creation and to encourage other scientists to publicize similar views he left £8,000 for the President of the Royal Society (the same man who discouraged Babbage's attempt to keep the society professional), the Archbishop of Canterbury and the Bishop of London to assemble a formidable team; among them scientists like Dr. Kidd, William Whewell, P. M. Roget, W. Prout, W. Buckland and Sir Charles Bell. But not all of them could fulfil the Bridgewater expectations, expecially the Rev. William Buckland, who much to his fellow-clergymen's dismay, came down on the side of geology as opposed to genesis.[6]

Amateur field investigations to discover the ages of rocks were mounted. So many clergymen and naturalists of all persuasions began to chip and hammer in the wake of the railway engineers and the mining prospectors that in 1835 the Government established a Geological Survey which initiated a survey of the solid geology of England and Wales that was to take fifty years to finish. Not only did this benefit the mining, civil and mechanical engineers, but it was of enormous use in farming, water supply and sanitation.

The Geological Survey was a major landmark in three respects. It was the first Government-sponsored survey of natural resources, it was a model for other countries to follow, and it was a nursery of geologists who were to make similar surveys in underdeveloped areas.[7]

(3)

Geological strata were a tractable problem: social strata were not. Wrestling with the training of 'refractory hands' for a machine civilization, only too acutely aware of the need to ascertain 'the different talents of men', and their need to 'identify themselves with the unvarying regularity of the complex automaton',[8] Dr. Andrew Ure of the Andersonian Institution of Glasgow[9] (now the University of Strathclyde) precipitated a walk-out by his class in 1823 who promptly formed themselves into a Glasgow Mechanics' Institute.

Ure's views did not impress the Glasgow mechanics, but they certainly much impressed that veteran polytechnician, Baron Dupin. Having heard him in 1817 and 1824, Dupin returned to France to start similar classes. By 1825 his example was being followed in some fifty-nine other French towns. Dupin's actions were cited by the *London Mechanics' Magazine* in 1823 as warranting the formation of a Mechanics' Institute in London.[10]

Similar feelings in Manchester and Leeds led Benjamin Heywood and Edward Baines to found mechanics' institutes in these towns. Others followed, so bent on affording free instruction in science that by 1835 one member was complaining 'many of us are already saturated with as much as of what is called science as we can carry'. The 'science' which attracted the mechanics and froze the generosity of the employers was political, so many variations of the institute idea were essayed in the interest of social sedation. Nevertheless over a quarter of the 500 institutes in England were to be found in Yorkshire and a ninth in Lancashire where, in the fullness of time they developed into technical colleges.[11]

Other variants of the French polytechnic were essayed in London by a contributor to the *Mechanics' Magazine*, the Yorkshire squire-scientist, Sir George Cayley. Supported by several industrialists he established a polytechnic in Regent Street. If the mechanics were difficult to handle in mechanics' institutes, the industrialists proved difficult to handle in the polytechnic. Cayley complained:

> Mr. Nurse, the great builder, furnished the largest half of the capital and he and his friends (all for money, with science as the means) will have the main say at such a meeting . . . However, we wanted more *science* and we wanted a sub-committee to carry on matter between the meetings of directors . . . We have laid out a good round sum of money, and the place, by its laboratory, its theatre and splendid gallery, is well adapted for the display of scientific discoveries, and were it truly in scientific hands, so that scientific discoveries were thrown off here hot from the brain and before they had become public property by publication, sufficient novelty would be produced to excite public attention and to make it pay. We much want a good scientific board confined by no aristocracy of orthodox men who sit like an incubus on all rising talent *that is not of their own shop*.[12]

A second venture of Cayley's was the Adelaide Gallery, an English version of the Conservatoire des Arts et Métiers, which might also be called an early version of the National Physical Laboratory. It stood near the site of the present National Gallery. Here, Telford conducted hydraulic experiments and Charles Wheatstone tried to determine the velocity of electricity. A similar institution took shape in Manchester, under William Sturgeon (late of Addiscombe), the electrically minded friend, associate and counsellor of James Prescott Joule. And Joule was to be the co-operator and fellow-worker of William Thomson (later Lord Kelvin), a former pupil of the Glasgow Mechanics' Institute.

(4)

The use of the Adelaide Gallery by Telford and Wheatstone for tests is but one indication of the further boost to technological research that followed the winning of the operational trials of various types of engines at Rainhill in October 1829 by George Stephenson's model with its steam blast and multitubular boiler. The network of lines grew, enlisting scientists and engineers as consultants: 'full up to the eyes with good sense' if Trollope is to be believed. Mathematicians like Eaton Hodgkinson, physicists like Charles Wheatstone and engineers like C. B. Vignoles, all were needed to solve problems concerning the building of lines as well as the operation of others already built.

Operational trials continued and indeed were raised to a higher level by the would-be reformer of the Royal Society, Charles Babbage, who served as a consulting engineer for Sir Isambard Brunel, devising the 'cow-catcher', the speedometer and the dynamometer car. Babbage's belief in the labour-saving quality of machines preceded the railways however, for he devised a machine which would compute tables by machinery which he (like a true railway engineer) called an engine. The Government built him a workshop where he employed Joseph Whitworth as his foreman. Though Babbage's engines were later abandoned, Whitworth obtained such an insight into the niceties of fine machinery that he became the pioneer of the thread that bears his name. So too, Babbage's operational studies of the Post Office showed that the cost of collecting, stamping and delivering a letter much exceeded its carriage, so he suggested that the differential carriage rate be established and a flat rate of charges should be imposed. This was later taken up by Rowland Hill when he introduced the Penny Post.

A third example of Babbage's application of scientific method was his publication of the first study of the theoretical aspects of actuarial calculation, whilst the 'life-tables' compiled on his principles were widely used until, thanks to the use of his own difference engine, they were superseded.

Aware of the work of the eighteenth-century French engineer Perronet on the manufacture of needles, Babbage also wrote on *The Economy of Machines and Manufacturers* (1833). Lord Bowden and others have hailed him as a pioneer of operational research, citing his observation: 'Let it not be feared that erroneous deductions may be made from recorded facts. The errors which arise from the absence of facts are far more numerous and more durable than those which arise from unsound reasoning respecting true data.'[13]

Like Babbage, Peter Barlow was a professor (at the Royal Military Academy at Woolwich), but worked on a research grant by the Board of Longitude to study the problems of induced magnetism posed by the increasing use of iron in ships.

For ships and railways also fostered the use of scientific experts by the State on various royal commissions evoked by problems of their regulation. Here applied scientists were on tap if not on top, when questions of bridges and gauges demanded expert solutions. And as the towns mushroomed, other experts on sanitation were called in like Dr. Southwood Smith of London, Dr. James Kay of Manchester and Dr. Thackrah of Leeds.

(5)

The railways also did much to crystallize the professional status of the engineer. In the year before the Rainhill trials, the institution of Civil Engineers asked Thomas Tredgold to define the term 'civil engineer' so that a charter could be obtained. Tredgold replied:

> Civil engineering is the art of directing the great sources of power in Nature for the use and convenience of Man; being that practical application of the most important principles of natural philosophy which has, in a considerable degree, realised the anticipations of Bacon, and changed the aspect and state of affairs in the whole world.[14]

But when, eighteen years later, George Stephenson was refused admission to the institution unless he submitted some evidence of his capacity on paper, the leading railway engineers of the day formed the Institution of Mechanical Engineers in 1846. This was the second major professional engineering union to take shape in England. A third, the Society of Engineers, evolved from a private engineering school at Putney House, established in 1834. This was later to absorb the Young Engineers Scientific Association (in 1861) and the Civil and Mechanical Engineering Society (in 1910).

But whilst astronomers, geologists and mathematicians had their associations, mere 'cultivators of science' lacked even a name if they were not 'applied'. William Whewell confessed he would think himself a goose if he 'were to be tempted to give practical men advice about railroads and fisheries'.[15] 'We need very much to describe a cultivator of science in general', he wrote. 'I should incline to call him a scientist.'[16] The name stuck, Whewell investing it with substance by introducing the natural sciences tripos at Cambridge.

Perhaps the most symbolic act of his mastership of Trinity was to put a statue of Bacon in the ante-chapel of Trinity.[17] Whewell himself had close relations with the Admiralty who, in 1835, gave him the equivalent of a research assistant to help him with his work on tides.[18] He also persuaded them to allow G. B. Airy to lecture.[19] He told Quetelet, the eminent Belgian statistician, in 1839:

> We are endeavouring to induce our Government to send out an expedition towards the South Pole to determine the present population of the Southern Magnetic Pole and also to establish several permanent magnetic observatories in order to observe the simultaneous changes discovered by Gauss and his friends.[20]

When the Government gave what was then the unprecedented sum of £1,000 a year to the Royal Society, Whewell revealed, in a private letter just how potent scientists had become as a pressure group:

> Some persons, I find, doubt whether the old practise of applying the screw of opinion in the scientific world to government on each special occasion was not better that this perennial stream of bounty . . . though often very creditable indeed to the spirit of the government and the nation . . . I am not quite sure that I like the responsibility of handling, or directing the handling, of Parliamentary money.[21]

(6)

For 'the screw of opinion in the scientific world' was to be applied with even greater intensity in the decade that followed by members of both Houses of Parliament who had formed a Parliamentary Committee of the British Association in 1849 to look after 'the interests of science and to inspect various measures from time to time likely to affect such interests'. Prime movers in this were the President of the Royal Society (the Marquis of Northampton), Lord Rosse (who four years previously had built a great telescope at Parsonstown in Kings County, Ireland), Lord Adare, Philip Egerton and Sir Charles Lemon with Lord Wrottesley as chief spokesman.[22]

Within two years the committee had grown so large that it was limited to six in the House of Lords and six in the Commons. The Lords group included the Duke of Argyll, Lord Cathcart, Lord Enniskillen and the Earl of Harrowby (as well as Lords Rosse and Wrottesley), whilst the Commons group had Sir Robert Inglis, Sir John Johnstone, J. H. Vivian and James Heywood (in addition to Sir Philip Egerton and Sir Charles Lemon).

Some of these were active 'members for science' in other respects too. James Heywood successfully moved in April 1850 for a Royal Commission on Oxford and Cambridge:[23] a logical result of his own admiration for the French polytechnics.[24] But he was not so successful with an equally important motion six years later when he moved for a Select Committee 'to inquire what public measures could be adopted to advance science and improve the position of its cultivators'. He acknowledged the way in which the Government had responded to the example of the German school of mining at Freiberg by founding the School of Mines in Jermyn Street, and how the American oceanographer Maury, by inducing American skippers to keep logs of tides and oceanographic phenomena, had led the Board of Trade to establish a Marine Department.[25] But this, to Heywood, was not enough. He asked for the establishment of an Order of Merit for scientific men to counterbalance the decorations awarded to generals and admirals, and of a Board of Science, possessing 'at once both authority and knowledge'.[26] His supporter, William Tite, M.P. for Bath, argued that 'the Royal Society might not be in itself sufficient to answer the questions that constantly arose in connexion with science', and that 'an even larger body in the nature of a Council of Science was required'.[27]

But both the Government and men of science were not yet ready for this. The Government persuaded Heywood and Tite to withdraw their motion whilst they consulted with the most eminent scientific men as to the exact nature of the measures which they might think desirable to be adopted, and submit them in a substantive motion to the House. The council of the British Association also remarked that 'the idea of such a Board had yet to receive the sanction of other men of science'.

The extent to which the State should help science was widely debated. Sir David Brewster, one of the original founders of the British Association wanted a Royal Institution on the French model with 'a class of resident members enabled to devote themselves wholly to science', whilst the Queen's chief scientific adviser, Sir George Airy, preferred 'the initiative to be left to private associations'. Yet significantly enough, Airy agreed that 'when any branch of science has been put in such a form that it admits of continued improvement under a continued administrative routine that administration should be undertaken by the Government'.[28] There the matter rested.

(7)

Science had a powerful patron in the Prince Consort, himself a pupil of Quetelet.[29] His disciples, like Lyon Playfair, wanted to brace and lace the mechanics' institutes by a great industrial university at South Kensington. They secured the Science and Art Department by an Order in Council on 25 February 1856. This was a logical outgrowth of the Art Department, originally founded in 1835, as the 'Council of the School of Design', under the Board of Trade, which after a searching examination by a Select Committee of the House of Commons in 1849, had become the Department of Practical Art. As this was not what the scientific moralists of the Great Exhibition hoped for, a Department of Practical Science was grafted to it in 1853 under Playfair himself. Three years later it became the Science and Art Department.[30]

During the forty-six years of its existence it was, for all practical purposes, identified with John Donnelly. Donnelly joined the Department in 1859 as an inspector, on the invitation of Henry Cole, the first secretary and by 1874 he became Director of Science, and by 1884 administrative Head of the Department. It was he who organized the system of payment by results (which began in the Department in 1859). It was he, too, who organized the first technological examinations in the country in 1871. It was his partnership with T. H. Huxley that secured the establishment of the Royal College of Science. Huxley supported him through thick and thin.

Grants on results were used as intelligently as possible. It is easy to criticize the system but it should not be forgotten that it had four very important aspects. Without some sort of guarantee, no Victorian Parliament, whatever its political complexion, would undertake to vote much money for education. Nor would students, without some positive incentive, brave the overt hostility of their employers (who were, in many cases, convinced that technical education spelt an end to trade secrets) to attend classes. Teachers for scientific subjects were impossible to obtain, and incentives were needed for them to improve their qualifications while they taught. Lastly, by nibbling at South Kensington grants, school boards (created in 1870) trespassed gaily in the field of higher education which they would never have entered if they had depended solely on the long-term vision of middle-class ratepayers.

'South Kensington' pupils were to shape the future. One such was Sir Richard Gregory, who was to dominate scientific journalism in the first half of the twentieth century. Another was Gilchrist Thomas, who helped the British steel industry by enabling steelmasters to eliminate the phosphoric loading of British iron and a third was H. G. Wells who reached out to capture, irritate and stimulate two generations by his scientific romances.

(8)

Above all, seed-beds of scientists were needed. William Tite, M.P., wanted some thirty colleges for special sciences, helped by a State grant of from £18,000 to £27,000 a year.[31] Of these special sciences, chemistry (in the coal age) was to Sir Humphrey Davy, 'most important' and he proposed to establish a chemical laboratory under the aegis of the Royal Society.

Since the Royal Society itself was, when Davy died in 1829, locked in a controversy of its own, little was done until 1844, when Dr. John Gardner hit on the idea of combining the idea of an English Giessen with a 'Davy College of Practical Chemistry'. A prospectus put out in 1842 illustrated the direction of his thoughts. 'The college', it ran, 'will be mainly devoted to Pure Science; at the same time, to meet the exigencies of this country, and to adopt the latest improvements in the continental schools, an appendage will be provided, devoted to the Economic Arts, where enquiries to Pharmacy, Agriculture and other Arts may be pursued.' Since space at the Royal Institution was limited, temporary buildings were taken in Hanover Square. Liebig suggested A. W. Hofmann as principal. He justified his choice training a generation of chemists, like Abel, Bloxam, Galloway, Rowney, Nicholson and de la Rue. Subsequently special buildings were erected in Oxford Street.[32]

The rise of public examinations for apothecaries (after 1815) led, amongst other things, to the establishment of the University of London in 1827 with strong medical schools and the foundation of the Chemical Society in 1841. Pupils of the German chemist Liebig flowed into England. Two of them, A. W. Williamson and W. A. Miller, were Professors of Chemistry at the University of London; another, Joseph Henry Gilbert, established on the estates of J. B. Lawes at Rothamsted an Agricultural Experiment Station in 1843; a fourth, J. C. A. Voelcker, had become a professor at Cirencester Agricultural College and a fifth, James Sheridan Muspratt, founded a college of chemistry in Liverpool.[33]

Another new college, founded by John Owens in Manchester, opened in March 1851, where two pupils of another German chemist, Bunsen, taught: E. A. Frankland and H. E. Roscoe.[34] They were followed by a third, Carl Schorlemmer, who organized the first department of organic chemistry in the country, and was to be a great friend of Marx and Engels.

As a translator of Leibig's agricultural treatises, Lyon Playfair won great respect amongst the agricultural interest in England during the thirties and forties. Problems posed by sanitation, the potato famine and the best kind of steam coal for warships, all led to his being consulted, so much so that Dr. Foote comments: 'his role is a unique one and he would have been the last to claim that this activity was typical of the relationship between scientists and governmental administration'.[35]

(9)

The self-appointed prophet of science to the mid-nineteenth century was H. T. Buckle. He told a friend, 'I want my book to get among the Mechanics' Institutes' and the people . . . there are they whom I am now beginning to touch and whom I wish to move.'[36] His 'book' was the *History of Civilisation in England* which, appearing in two volumes in 1857 and 1861, showed that man was wholly a part of the nature about which modern science was discovering so much. He too was a friend of Quetelet and claimed to have discovered laws of progression in history.

'I pledge myself', he wrote, 'to show that the progress Europe made from barbarism to civilization is entirely due to its intellectual activity . . . In what may be called the innate and original morals of mankind, there is, so far as we are aware, no progress.'

Buckle was not the only Positivist influencing students in the new scientific institutions set up at this time. Neil Arnott, an original member of the Senate of the University of London was one,[37] Sir Charles Wheatstone, the Professor of Experimental Physics at King's College, London, was another. Wheatstone, in fact, was credited with being the first to bring Comte's work to England. A. W. Williamson, Professor of Chemistry at University College, was a firm disciple; and so was John Stuart Mill, to whom Comte's *Cours* was 'very nearly the grandest work of the age'. Mill introduced it to Sir John Herschel, the astronomer.

Yet Comte's advocacy of broad perspective over specialization and of science as superior to the humanities seems to have exerted little influence in England. Indeed a recent investigator considers that the reason why 'positivist educational ideas as such made almost no discernible impact', was due to the weakness of 'the anticlerical incentive for educational reform' as compared to France.[38]

The general diffusion of scientific ideas was, however, considerable. From the 133 volumes of Dionysius Lardner's *Cabinet*

Cyclopaedia to the *Penny Cyclopaedia* of the Society for the Diffusion of Useful Knowledge they permeated down through every level of society, and were reinforced by a veritable hagiography by Samuel Smiles, whose *Life of George Stephenson* (1857) and *Lives of the Engineers* (1861–2) were to offer to the secular Victorian world a picture of the past that was more relevant than that offered by that more traditional hagiographer, Sabine Baring-Gould, some twenty years later.

As a former railway engineer and subsequently an economist, it was left to Herbert Spencer to exploit his constitutional inability to sleep to become the ideologue of British scientism by ingesting, in true Positivist fashion, a large number of ideas which he synthesized into cosmic laws. He put forward in the Positivist journal *The Leader* (of March 1852), the argument that all animals and plants developed from homogeneity to heterogeneity and coined the phrase 'the survival of the fittest'. In the popular mind this phrase expressed deep convictions. Yet his ideas had a Germanic basis. He so admired Feuerbach's English translator, the novelist George Eliot, that people thought he was going to marry her.

As Spencer's *System of Synthetic Philosophy*, announced in 1860, rolled off the presses, with brief intermissions, until 1893, it flooded the world from America to Japan. In so many words it said, 'Science is organised knowledge.'[39]

8

The Laws and the Prophets

◇◇◇◇◇◇◇◇◇◇◇◇◇◇◇◇◇◇◇◇◇◇◇◇◇◇◇◇◇◇◇◇◇◇◇◇◇

(1)

B Y 1860 in England the habit of regarding the orderly recurrence of natural phenomena as the uniform results of corresponding conditions (or the generalized statements of such conditions and their consequences) as scientific laws was generally accepted. As laws they often conflicted with statements set out in the first five books of the Old Testament (the Pentateuch), or with other generally accepted relationships.

This conflict (or dialectic) was often resolved, in the lay mind at least, by middlemen of ideas, brokers discounting their overtones or else playing them up. For the layman was so seized of the need to know these scientific laws (which might well affect their livelihood) that 'attendance at lectures by eminent scientists became as obligatory in the manufacturing towns as was attendance at church or chapel in the country'.[1]

The religious analogy is an apt one, for these scientific discoveries had implications, which teased out, were a kind of secular hermeneutic. The exegetes of the unravelling book of nature had by now plenty of warrant for their confidence, since in 1860 the personnel of the high court or clearing house of such laws, the Royal Society, was equally balanced between professional scientists and amateurs and from now on the balance steadily tilted towards the professionals.[2] Moreover the number of professional societies (as opposed to local literary and philosophical societies) was increasing, each of them functional rather than territorial in purpose, each with its journal and forum for validating yet more laws. And, as expertise accumulated, the local literary and philosophical societies surrendered first their functions, then their libraries, to functional training schools, which by the seventies became university colleges. The journals of these professional associations increased from about a dozen in 1860 to about seventy in 1900, whilst general scientific and technical journals increased from just over forty to over one hundred and thirty in the same period.

Such professional associations nourished and were nourished by what has been called "the dogmatism of mature science", a dogmatism strengthened by the steady growth of education in science, an education which Thomas S. Kuhn sees as 'far more likely to induce professional rigidity than education in other fields, excepting perhaps, systematic theology'.[3]

One can see the type in the fictional Swithin St. Cleeve, a scientist who 'took words literally'. 'There is something in the inexorably simple logic of such men' wrote his creator, Thomas Hardy, in *Two on a Tower* (xx 334) 'which partakes of the cruelty of the natural laws that are their study'.

(2)

A classic example of the way in which such a 'law' was promulgated occurred at this very time. Late in the eighteenth century, the Reverend Thomas R. Malthus, a professor at the East India Company college of Haileybury propounded his theory that whilst population was increasing geometrically, food was only increasing arithmetically.

His book powerfully affected naturalists. Reading him in October 1838 'for amusement', Charles Darwin was convinced 'that under these circumstances favourable variates would tend to be observed and unfavourable ones to be destroyed'. The result of this would be the formation of new species. Here then, Darwin exclaimed,

> I had at last got a theory by which it would work; but I was so anxious to avoid prejudice that I determined not for some time to write the briefest sketch of it. In June 1842, I first allowed myself the satisfaction of writing a very brief abstract of my theory in

pencil of 35 pages and this was enlarged during the summer of 1844 into one of 230 pages, which I had fairly copied out and still possess.

The abstract was subsequently *The Origin of Species*.

Re-reading Malthus whilst bedridden with fever in the Moluccas, another naturalist, Alfred Russell Wallace, found that:

> These checks—war, disease, famine and the like—must, it occurred to me, act on animals as well as man. Then I thought of the enormously rapid multiplication of animals, causing these checks to be much more effective in them than in the case of man; and while pondering vaguely on this fact there suddenly flashed upon me the *idea* of the survival of the fittest—that the individuals removed by these checks must be on the whole inferior to those that survived. In the two hours that elapsed before my ague fit was over, I had thought out almost the whole of the theory: and the same evening I sketched the draft of my paper, and in the two succeeding evenings wrote it out in full, and sent it by the next post to Mr. Darwin.[4]

When Darwin received it he remarked: 'if Wallace had my MSS sketch, he could not have made a better abstract'.

On the advice of Lyell and Hooker a joint paper was presented to the Linnaean Society in July 1858, and Darwin pressed ahead to finish his *Origin of Species*. This finally dissipated the catastrophic theory—that each new geological era began with new creations of living things—and strengthened the idea of uniformity in the record of nature. The idea of change—gradual change—had been partly, and more or less unconsciously acquired from the Newtonian conception of change in mechanics. Newton, conceiving change as a continual process, invented the differential calculus to describe it. Darwin crystallized it as the popular concept of evolution. 'The Intellectual Development of Europe considered with reference to the Views of Mr. Darwin',[5] was the theme of an address delivered at Oxford in 1860 by a professor in an American university.

This professor, J. W. Draper, had been one of the earliest chemistry graduates of the University of London. He was the author of a *Treatise on the Forces which Produce the Organization of Plants* (1844), as well as of the leading physiology textbook of the day (containing the first microphotograph ever published). His theme was that increasing understanding of the world would only be won by studying the mechanical and physico-chemical processes of life processes. When expanded three years later into *A History of the Intellectual Development of Europe*, it proved almost as big a best-seller as *The Origin of Species*.

Draper's address was described by one hearer as 'all of a pie of Herbert Spencer and Buckle without a seasoning of either'.[6] The bishop in whose diocese the paper was delivered, rose to his feet to demolish him, delivering what was intended to be a *coup de grâce* by asking one of Draper's supporters whether it was through his grandfather or grandmother that he claimed descent from a monkey. The supporter was T. H. Huxley, a polemicist of distinction, who more than adequately defended himself by replying that he preferred 'a simian ancestor to one who plunged into scientific questions with which he had no real acquaintance only to obscure them'. Deference to bishops was going out of fashion.

Samuel Butler wrote in his notebook:

Science is daily more and more personified and anthromorphized into a god. By and by they will say that science took our nature upon him, and sent down his only begotten son, Charles Darwin, or Huxley, into the world so that those who believe in him, etc., and they will burn people for saying that science after all, is only an expression for our ignorance of our own ignorance.[7]

Others teased out the implications of the Darwinian revelation. After visiting Leslie Stephen, Thomas Hardy recorded that their conversation 'turned upon theologies decayed and defunct, the origins of things, the constitution of matter, the unreality of time, and kindred subjects'. So too Grant Allen envisaged a Darwin's Day—20 December—when an imperfect child would be executed. Allen's 'long looks forward'—as in *The British Barbarians* (1895)—were greatly to influence that secular prophet H. G. Wells,[8] and foster the emergence of the predictive fantasy.

(3)

Delighted to see that Darwin had rediscovered among animals and plants 'his own English Society with its division of labour, competition, opening up new markets, inventions and Malthusian struggle for existence', Karl Marx wrote to Lassalle:

> Darwin's book is very important and serves me as a basis in natural science for the class struggle in history. One has to put up with the crude English method of development, of course. Despite all deficiencies not only is the death-blow dealt here for the first time to 'teleology' in the natural sciences, but their rational meaning is empirically explained.

For this reason, Marx wished to dedicate his own book *Das Kapital* to Darwin, but Darwin declined. When the second German edition appeared in 1875 he sent Darwin a copy. Darwin replied:

> I thank you for the honour which you have done me by sending me your great work on Capital: and I heartily wish that I were more worthy to receive it by understanding more of the deep and important subject of political economy. Though our studies have been so different, I believe that we both earnestly desire our extension of knowledge, and this is sure to add to the happiness of mankind.

Such exploitation was, however, the lot of the followers of Darwin and Marx. Both were Bible makers and both attracted helpers as well as prophets. Darwin's children worked on worms for him, and his daughter Emma read the manuscript of the *Descent of Man*. Marx's wife copied Engel's letters for publication, and his disciples—'the scum of international communism' as Leibnicht described them—sat at desks in the British Museum delving into the records of the human struggle for existence.[9]

By calling attention to the slowness of the evolutionary process, Darwin armed the true Conservatives with arguments against reformers, planners and liberals of all kinds. He also appealed to the Right because he stressed the importance of breeding (the only way to get rid of undesirable members of society, argued Herbert Spencer, was to let the law of survival have free play).[10] Thirdly he appealed to the Right because his thesis of progress from undifferentiated homogeneity to differentiated heterogeneity provided a scientific justification for inequalities of class and race. Indeed some pursued the argument farther, and pressed for conscious attempts to apply the laws of nature—substituting human for natural selection and breeding only the best.[11]

As C. B. Davenport put it:

> Man is an organism—an animal, and the laws of improvement of corn and of race horses hold true for him also. Unless people accept this simple truth and let it influence marriage selection, human progress will cease.[12]

This argument could also be extended to prove that the race must be kept pure, and an added justification for maintaining the privileged position of successful races.

Darwinism was just another kind of anthropomorphism, according to Patrick Geddes. By confusing what was happening in the Galapagos Islands and Peru[13] with the processes of life in Manchester and Birmingham it presented a picture of 'unbroken evolutions under uniform conditions which pleased everyone—except curates and bishops'. 'It was', as Henry Adams said, 'the very best substitute for religion; a safe, conservative, practical, thoroughly Common-Law deity.'[14]

Marxism was its very obverse: a near chiliastic hymn to a technological apocalypse. Marx became the Bible of the Left because he preached the redemption of labour by technology, and in this sense can be said to have foreseen automation. For as he said in a by now familiar passage:

> As soon as the working machine can perform without human aid all the movements requisite for the elaboration of raw material so that nothing more than supervision is needed, we have an automatic system of machinery.[15]

Marxism had its sacred books, its authoritative scripture, its heresies, its eschatology. God was dialectical materialism. Observing that they used the word determinism with all the overtones of St. Augustine and Calvin, Crane Brinton remarked, 'For them the overtones are those of science. This system, they insist, is a scientific one which is why it must be true.'[16]

Marx was obliquely endorsed from New Zealand. In an essay on 'Darwin among the Machines' by Samuel Butler, subsequently refined and enlarged as a satirical novel *Erewhon* (1872), Butler pictured a land where machinery had been abolished just because it:

would so equalise men's powers and so lessen the severity of competition that many persons of inferior physique would escape and
transmit their inferiority to their descendants.[17]

Man, argued the Erewhonian Book of the Machines, might so
degenerate that his whole body might become 'purely rudi-
mentary . . . man himself being nothing but soul and mechanism,
an intelligent but passionless principle of mechanical action'.

(4)

A near-Erewhonian apocalypse haunted those custodians of
the nation's industrial health after the poor showing of British
exhibits at the Paris Exhibition of 1867. Led, if not goaded, by
Colonel Alexander Strange, the veteran Indian engineer-officer,
and his ally Norman Lockyer, editor of the newly-founded
scientific journal *Nature*, the British Association helped secure
the appointment of a Royal Commission under the Duke of
Devonshire to investigate scientific instruction in Britain. This
commission proposed that a separate ministry 'dealing with
science and education as a public service' should be established.[18]

Though this particular proposal had to wait eighty-eight years
for supplementation, the Duke of Devonshire showed how the
needs of the time had impressed him by giving £6,300 to Cambridge University for a teaching staff of experimental physicists.
After some debate, the university accepted his offer and established the professorship that still bears his family name—
Cavendish. The first professor, J. Clerk Maxwell complained, 'I
have no place to erect my chair but move about like the cuckoo,
depositing my notions in the Chemical Lecture Room in the
First Term, in the Botanical in Lent and in the Comparative
Anatomy in Easter.'[19]

Maxwell was not the only Englishman who felt like a cuckoo.
Others saw that the nests where Britain had so absent-mindedly
laid her iron eggs could now be defended by a technical expertise
of their own—and that perhaps it would be as well to establish
hatcheries of technological talent on the American or German
model.

The two leading journals of the profession in Britain, *The
Engineer* and *Engineering*, both founded by an American, Zerah
Colburn, kept transatlantic examples before their readers, whilst
the by-no-means dormant disciples of the Prince Consort, like

John Scott Russell, called attention to the 'wonderful organisation of the culture and discipline, of the Prussian people . . .' which has produced such a result'. As a marine engineer and friend of the late Prince Consort, he showed his loyalties by proposing in 1869 a great national institute (with a hundred chairs), federated with fifteen local colleges (each with twenty-five chairs).[20]

The theme of 'more science' was orchestrated by public meetings like that organized in November 1872 by Sir Benjamin Brodie, the Professor of Chemistry at Oxford and Mark Pattison, the Rector of Lincoln College. Pattison considered that there was 'but one possible pattern on which a University as an establishment for science, can be constructed, and that is the graduate Professoriate. This is sometimes called the German type.'[21] Even more forcefully, more publicly and more persistently Matthew Arnold pointed out that 'It is in science that we most need to borrow from the German universities. The French university has no liberty, and the English universities have no science; the German universities have both.'[22] As G. M. Young put it, 'the great Victorian omission had to be made good, and the executive class educated up to the level of the demands now making on it in a trained and scientific world'.[23]

Alarmed by the intimations of British industrial mortality that were only too visible at the Paris Exhibition of 1867, aware of both German and American responses to this need of a trained executive class, local industrial initiative erupted in the shape of eleven new colleges—all to become universities—at Newcastle (1871), Aberystwyth (1872), Leeds (1874), Bristol (1876), Sheffield (1879), Birmingham (1880), Nottingham (1881), Cardiff (1883), Bangor (1884), Reading (1892) and Southampton (1902).[24]

Developing dialectically with their regions, these colleges were multipliers of chemists and physicists, usually in the Manchester mould: men like Sydney Young, who left Manchester for University College, Bristol in 1882 to work on hydrocarbons from petroleum, or his friend Arthur Smithells who left for Yorkshire College, Leeds, in the following year to do work with the South Yorkshire coal industry. At Leeds, too, T. E. Thorpe directed Dugald Clerk to study the fractionation of petroleum oils (enabling him to pioneer the two-stroke engine), and

Archibald Barr founded the first engineering laboratories in Great Britain. Barr's partnership with William Stroud was to lead to the devising of the famous height-finder that bore their names.

(5)

A new breed of industrial draghound was also emerging. Since W. H. Perkin's isolation of aniline purple in 1857, they were in full cry, chasing new elements, new combinations of elements and new uses for the combinations. Expertise in experiment coupled with a flair for exploitation were the marks of this new species: the technical manager. Examples abound: Henry Deacon, who discovered a new method of obtaining chlorine whilst managing his chemical works at Widnes; Walter Weldon, a journalist doing the same thing; John Glover, product of the local mechanics' institute at Newcastle upon Tyne revolutionized the manufacture of sulphuric acid, whilst at his sugar refining works at Victoria Docks; and J. A. R. Newlands who arranged chemical elements into groups having similar properities.[25]

Now, to the needs of the chemist were added those of the electrical engineer. The link between them was Joseph Wilson Swan who devised lamp filaments (and inadvertently started the manufacture of artificial silk), at the same time as the lessons of another Paris Exhibition—that of 1878—were being brought home. For the streets of Paris had been illuminated by electric candles, devised by a former engineer in the Russian Army, Paul Jablochkoff. They much impressed English pioneers like Professor Sylvanus P. Thompson and Colonel R. E. B. Crompton, who followed suit: the former as an adviser, the latter as a contractor, whilst American initiative in the form of the Anglo-British Electric Light Corporation began operations at Charlton in 1879. All these and others too, found an opportunity to show their wares at the Crystal Palace Exhibition in 1882.

Meanwhile, ostensibly surveying American technical education, William Mather was so impressed by the Edison dynamo that he returned with European rights to manufacture it at Salford. He started an electrical department at his works under Dr. Edward Hopkinson, whose improvements to the Edison dynamo made it possible for Mather's firm to obtain the contract for the first London Tube in 1889.

The rapid progress of this new source of power in turn demanded physicists and electrical engineers.[26] Two English engineers teaching at the Yedo Technical College in Japan— then the world's leading centre of electrical teaching and experimentation in electrical engineering—were tempted back to England to teach at the first polytechnic to be founded by London's City Guilds—the Finsbury Technical College. Together they invented the surface-contact system for electrical railways, helped by Sylvanus P. Thompson, one of their colleagues. Finsbury became a place 'where every young man of promise, every engineer with ambition was attracted from Germany, America and elsewhere' since 'new discoveries and inventions were the order of the day'.[27]

At a second institution, founded three years later at South Kensington, H. E. Armstrong (1848–1937), a former pupil of Kolbe at Leipzig, established the first, and for a time the only, chemical engineering school in the country. Armstrong also played a great part in helping Rothamsted to keep abreast and ahead of current agricultural research. At a third polytechnic founded by the Goldsmiths Company at New Cross one of Armstrong's pupils, W. J. Pope, made such a name that Cambridge University invited him to fill the chair of chemistry where he created four other chairs in the subject (physical, theoretical, colloid and metallurgical). Needless to say another of Armstrong's pupils, T. M. Lowry, was appointed the first of these.[28]

(6)

This new class of managers were alive to the need for efficiency and new knowledge. William Mather had, as early as 1874 organized, under the auspices of the Society for the Promotion of Scientific Industry, an exhibition in Peel Park, Salford. Subsequent trips to Russia where technical education was rapidly progressing, led him to a life of busy political service to further his ideas.

Here we also detect the fitful beginning of the industrial laboratory. W. H. Perkin fitted up one for his sons at Sudbury: two became professors of chemistry and the third an industrial chemist at Leeds. J. Clerk Maxwell did much of his work in the attic of 8 Palace Gardens, Kensington. There was Lord Rayleigh's private laboratory at Terling where it has been suggested that 'the Cavendish tradition was started'. There was also the private laboratory of R. E. B. Crompton the noted electrical engineer, at 'Thirplands', his Kensington home.[29]

In one of his fancy waistcoats (worn to emphasize the importance of dyes), H. E. Armstrong commended the excellence of German industrial laboratory in his evidence to the Cowper Commission of 1894. He might well do so, for when the United Alkali Company established an industrial laboratory in 1892 it was put under Ferdinand Hurter, a product of Heidelberg and Zürich. When Guinness the brewers established a laboratory they invited W. S. Gosset (1876–1937) to continue his experiments on barley with E. S. Beaven. Similarly William Rintoul joined Nobel Explosives at Ardeer as chief chemist.

Other types of industrial laboratories appeared. John Dewrance (1858–1937), who in 1882 obtained an ingot of aluminium by electrolysis, founded one which developed into a two-acre factory with a pier on the Thames. Dewrance took out more than 100 patents, and was chairman of Babcock and Wilcox from 1899 until his death.

Yet another laboratory was set up in the works at Sheffield where young Robert Hadfield worked.

'Steady, methodical investigation of natural phenomena is the father of industrial progress', observed John Brunner. He should have known for with Ludwig Mond, he had founded the great firm that bore their joint names. He was speaking to the Society of Chemical Industry in 1889, eight years after it was founded.[30]

Of the 'new men' produced by the 'new' colleges, two indicate the type. John Cadman, a graduate of the Durham College of Science, served as an assistant inspector of mines before working on the petroleum resources of Trinidad. On becoming Professor of Mining at Birmingham University in 1908 he instituted a degree course in petroleum technology and with Sir Oliver Lodge (then principal), worked on the fractionation of oil. His Birmingham students played their part in the rapid rise of the petroleum industry and his university laboratories did the necessary analyses for the Royal Commission on Persian oil which resulted in the British Navy abandoning coal for firing. During the First World War Cadman became Chief Technical Officer and later Director of the Petroleum Executive and afterwards the chairman of Anglo-Iranian. His build-up of Abadan was to become a major political issue after 1945.[31]

The second, F. S. Kipping, graduated from Manchester in 1882 and served the Manchester Gas Department before taking the high road to Munich and von Baeyer. Becoming Professor of Chemistry at Nottingham in 1897 he worked on the attachment of organic groups to silicon, a discovery that was taken up by Staudinger, W. H. Carothers, the Corning Glassworks Team, the Mellon Institute of Pittsburgh and General Electric, not by a British firm. Today it has been greatly exploited for electrical insulators, water-repellants and varnishes.[32]

Indeed the reciprocality of technical innovation and oligopoly in industry is well illustrated by the rise of Lever Brothers. From the establishment of Port Sunlight in 1889, a bi-monthly meeting of the chemists Winser and Scott took place. The laboratory was the breeding ground of the complex dealing with problems of oil and glycerine, devising 'Lifebuoy' (1894) and soapflakes (1899). And in the quarrel between Winser and Smith, which led to Smith's dismissal, one can see the politics of science in miniscule.[33]

(7)

The corporate muscles of this rapidly expanding corps of scientists were flexed by the need to protect society from the dangers of unplanned industrial growth. Of the many case histories clamouring to be cited, we must be content with three: the doctors, the chemists and the electrical engineers.

The doctors, as usual, had set the precedent by overcoming their reluctance to enter politics in 1856 by converting their twenty-four-year-old Provincial and Medical Association into the British Medical Association. They played their part in securing the codification of over a hundred separate and often local acts into the great Public Health Act of 1875, thereby providing the basis of British sanitary legislation for the rest of the century.[34]

Strengthened by two further acts in the same year—one protecting the public from impure food and drugs, and the other requiring town councils to appoint Medical Officers of Health and empowering them to purchase slums for rebuilding—local

118

authorities could now enlist experts to assist in decision-making. Local Government Acts of 1888, 1894 and 1929 led to the employment of further experts who found corporate strength in the Institution of Municipal Engineers (1873), the Society of Analytical Chemists (1874), the Royal Society of Health (1876) and the Institution of Water Engineers (1896) and of Heating and Ventilation Engineers (1897).

Such experts often formulated the public will, as in the case of the growing alkali industries, whose emission of noxious hydrochloric acid fumes poisoned smell and sight for miles around. Following a Select Committee of the Lords in 1862 an Act for the more effective Condensation of Muriatic Acid gases in Alkali Works passed in 1863, obliging firms to condense 95 per cent of their waste gas, and appointing an inspectorate of five. The vigour and vigilance of these five secured further legislation eleven years later to cover emission of sulphurous and nitrous fumes as well. Further noxious vapours resulted in a Royal Commission in 1878 on which sat two chemists and a chemical engineer, which inspired yet further legislation in 1881 with an enlarged inspectorate. This inspectorate brought into existence 'a new type of Civil Servant', the technical expert. Here England led, and other countries followed.[35]

The third case concerns the conflict between the vested gas interests and the surgent electric light concerns and between the public and the private echelons of the latter. To obtain an unbiased view of these two feuds the Government appointed a Select Committee under Sir Lyon Playfair which recommended that 'it might be expedient to give to the municipal authorities a preference'. An Act of 1882 accordingly reached the statute book. It so deterred private companies from stepping in where municipal authorities were dilatory that the Institution of Electrical Engineers (as it was to become in 1888) gestated an organization for its repeal. Including Colonel Crompton, a deputation waited on the Government, but not until a Conservative ministry were private companies allowed, by a subsequent Act, a more lengthy security of tenure. The part played in the politics of electric lighting was a material factor in transforming the Institution of Telegraph Engineers into the Institution of Electrical Engineers.[36]

(8)

That the State should, in all its actions, be guided by the best scientific advice possible was the basis of Francis Galton's and Karl Pearson's work. Pearson wanted to subordinate class needs and group cries 'to the standpoint of the efficiency of the herd at large'. This efficiency, in Pearson's view, could best be achieved under Socialism, possibly under a dictator.[37] 'You cannot', he added, 'get a strong and effective nation if many of its stomachs are half fed and many of its brains untrained.'

The 'herd' needed training. As Francis Galton (Darwin's cousin), reasoned, its members could be inherently more intelligent than its progenitors. Each generation should, therefore, be better educated and better still, better bred. Such breeding needed the study of what he called 'Eugenics' which 'had strong claims to become an orthodox religious tenet of the future' since it 'co-operates with the workings of nature by securing that humanity shall be represented by the fittest races'.[38] Galton wished to issue eugenic certificates to those qualified to breed. To collect information for these he created a chair in the subject at the University of London. Naturally Pearson occupied it, and from it dilated upon 'the failure of the old economic system' before 'sweeping industrial and commercial changes which are now in progress'.[39] Pearson denied the validity of class war or revolution, preferring to preach that socialist society needed not religion but 'a rational motive of conduct' which he defined as 'service to society'. As he said, 'Socialism, despite Haeckel, despite Herbert Spencer, is consonant with the whole teaching of modern science.'[40] One of his lectures in 1900 was called 'National Life from the Standpoint of Science'.

(9)

The euphrasic exegete of it all was H. G. Wells. Looking forward to the year 802701 in his *Time Machine* (1895) he saw the end of the Darwinian struggle in the existence of two races —the Eloi—gentle, fair and communistic, and the Morlocks— demonic, dark and living underground. The real masters were the Morlocks, the Eloi were merely cattle.[41]

To Wells, Socialism languished in a state of 'exalted paralysis waiting for the world to come up to it while it marked time'.

He threw in his lot with the 'new men', for he was one himself.
Just such another was the electrician Holroyd, in the 'Land of
the Dynamos', who 'delivered a theological lecture on the text
of his big machine . . .' to an Afro-Asian assistant. 'Look at
that,' said Holroyd, 'where's your earthen idol to match 'im . . .
that's something like a Gord.'[42]

Wells visualized an *élite* of new men 'constricting and re-
stricting very greatly the . . . non-functional masses'.[43] Bernard
Shaw amplified his ideas in *Man and Superman* which offered,
as Shaw said, a 'contemporary embryo of Mr. H. G. Wells's
anticipation of the efficient engineering class which will . . .
finally sweep the jabberers out of the way of civilisation'.
Shaw's version of Holroyd in this play is Henry Straker:

> Here have we the literary and cultured persons,' says Straker's
> employer, 'for years setting up a cry of the New Woman whenever
> some unusually old fashioned female came along, and never notic-
> ing the advent of the New Man. Straker's the New Man.[44]

Straker tells one of his master's friends not to believe in the
dignity of labour:

> That's because you never done any, Mr. Robinson. My business is
> to do away with labour. You'll get more out of me and a machine
> than you will out of twenty labourers and not so much to drink
> either.

Shaw further supplemented Straker's Wellsian creed by a
Revolutionist's Handbook in which he stated that man must:

> change himself into the political providence which he formally con-
> ceived as God . . . The mere transfiguration of institutions as from
> military and priestly dominance to commercial and scientific
> dominance . . . are all but changes from Tweedledum to Tweedle-
> dee . . . But the changes from the crabapple to the pippen, from the
> wolf and the fox to the house dog, from the charger of Henry V to
> the brewer's draught horse and the race-horse are real; for here
> man has played the god, subduing Nature to his intention, and
> ennobling or debasing life for a set purpose.[45]

In other words Shaw suggested that the discarded formula
that man is the Temple of the Holy Ghost:

> happens to be precisely true, and that it is only through his own
> brain and hand that the Holy Ghost, formerly the most nebulous

person in the Trinity, and now become its sole survivor as it has always been its real unity, can help him in any way.

By flirting with the idea of a 'State Department of Evolution with a seat in the Cabinet for its chief and a revenue to defray the cost of direct State experiments' or even 'a joint stock human stud farm (piously disguised as a reformed Foundling Hospital . . .)[46] he shocked his hearers and readers into considering what he described as the 'only one problem' of Government: 'the discovery of a trustworthy anthropometric method'.[47]

Such a 'trustworthy anthropometric method' was now being devised, characteristically by a mathematician and engineer: Charles Spearman. Much attracted by the problem of identifying intelligence and intellective ability by mathematical means, Spearman fastened on Binet's attempt to differentiate between hypothetical general-intelligence and acquired ability. He devised tests, administered them to large representative samples of children and adolescents and from these he deduced that individuals possessed a general psycho-physical energy (g) and specific engines $(s_1, s_2, \text{etc.})$ through which it worked. Trustworthy psychometric methods rather than anthropometric methods now became a pressing social problem. Spearman's theory was refuted by L. L. Thurstone of Chicago working on factorial methods devised by Galton and Pearson, refined by Cyril Burt in England and amplified by massive employment of the Binet tests by the American forces during the First World War. By 1918 the possibility of sifting whole populations into grades was very real.

And, since the times demanded that merit be identified, this new selection mechanism was rapidly and purposefully improved.

(10)

Wells and Haldane were members of a group who first began to meet in December 1902. Known as the 'Co-efficients', it included the Fabian Sidney Webb, the great geographer of the heartland—H. J. MacKinder, the young Bertrand Russell, the economist W. A. S. Hewins and L. S. Amery, who remarked in his autobiography, that their meetings were much more concerned with putting into practice the ideas of the Welfare State than with any political party.

Their collective apprehensions that Britain needed a frontier

—German, American or Russian style—led them to imperialism. So other members brought into the group included Sir Clinton Dawkins the financier, Leopold Maxse the Germanophobe editor of *The National Review*, Carlyon Bellairs a naval officer and W. Pember Reeves, the Agent-General for New Zealand.

Obsessed with the superior efficiency of Germany, 'very keen on military organization, and 'disposed to spend money much more generously on education and research of all sorts than our formless host of Liberals seemed likely to do', they have been captured in Wells's book *The New Machiavelli* as 'The Pentagram Circle'.[48]

The industrial progress of Germany was attributed by Haldane and Webb to a partnership between the universities and industry. Since its hub was Charlottenburg, Webb and Haldane worked to establish an English counterpart. They secured an endowment of half a million pounds from two South African millionaires, Sir Julius Wernher and Sir Ernest Cassell, a four-acre site at South Kensington from the 1851 Commission, and against the opposition of John Burns and Ramsey MacDonald, an annual grant from the London County Council. So, by amalgamating the Royal College of Science and the Royal School of Mines into the Imperial College of Science and Technology, they got their way.

Seven years later, in 1914, confronted with the ingenuity of the country it had been overtly emulating for most of the previous century, Britain had to take yet further stock of its organization of science. Glass for Barr and Stroud's rangefinders, dyes for uniforms, magnetos for transport, tungsten for steel and zinc for smelting were all imported from Germany. Indeed up to 1915, the British Government were even paying royalties to Krupps for the fuses of the shells used against the Germans. The chemical glassware of British chemists was in such short supply that the Government made an inventory of those that existed as a prelude to commandeering them.[49]

Fitful shifts were adopted to remedy this state of affairs. First a committee was appointed under Haldane to survey the problem, then a 'Neglect of Science Committee'. The Royal Society and the British Science Guild began to agitate. In 1915 an Institute of Industry and Science was set up as a voluntary group and this urged the establishment of a Ministry of Industry. Meanwhile the Universities Branch of the Board of Education formulated a plan in conjunction with Sir William M'Cormick which would provide a wider solution. This was nothing less than the creation of new machinery to promote and organize scientific research, not only during, but after, the war; a small advisory council of scientists and industrialists and a Committee of the Privy Council responsible for expanding government grants. Both council and committee were to be under the Board of Education. From this the Department of Scientific and Industrial Research was born: endowed with a fund to encourage research in the universities and under the same chairman as the University Grants Committee.[50]

The Department of Scientific and Industrial Research was massive confirmation of a trend hitherto undetected: that scientists were already finding their way to advisory committees in government. The Colonial Office had set the precedent with its Tropical Diseases Research Fund in 1905 and, four years later, with its Advisory Medical and Sanitary Committee for Tropical Africa and its Entomological Research Committee. All three were committees of experts, to advise Colonial Office civil servants on their specialisms. All were concerned with scientific subjects, and with the development and use of scientific knowledge to improve the conditions of living in the territories with which they dealt.[51] An advisory medical research committee of nine experts was appointed after the National Insurance Act of 1911 and empowered to submit schemes to an advisory council but the latter proved so large—it had some forty-two members— that it was only consulted once. So eight years later this Medical Research Committee was transferred to the Privy Council and became an autonomous department, receiving a Royal Charter as the Medical Research Council in 1920.

(11)

Measurement—the activity of physicists—had long been a matter of international concern. In 1742 a yard measure and pound weight were constructed at the insistence of the Royal Society and dispatched to the French Academy in exchange for their measures. Similarly they had co-operated in 1787 in carrying out a triangulation between the observatories of Greenwich and Paris, repeating it thirty-three years later. In 1836 von Humboldt secured the Royal Society's support for the establishment of stations for the study of terrestrial magnetism in England and her overseas possessions.

International bodies, like the Bureau Internationale des Poids et Mesures (established in 1873 as a result of a metric measurement congress in 1869), and the International Mid-European Geodetic Association at Berlin (established in 1861), were both joined by Great Britain[52] in 1884, and it was an Englishman, Colonel R. E. B. Crompton, who proposed in 1904 the establishment of the International Electro-Technical Commission and became its first secretary in 1906.[53]

The need for the determination of electrical units in absolute measure was so urgent that Lord Rayleigh, on taking up the Cavendish chair in 1879 gathered round him a band of workers to do just this. He was subsequently one of the leaders of the movement which led to the establishment of the National Physical Laboratory and acted as chairman of the Treasury Committee which reported on the need for its foundation.[54]

Established to bring scientific knowledge 'to bear practically upon our everyday industrial and commercial life, to break down the barrier between theory and practice, to effect a union between Science and Commerce', the National Physical Laboratory was launched under a Cavendish man, R. T. Glazebrook. Helped by government support, experiments here made possible the superiority of British aircraft in the 1914–18 war. The director of its Chemical Research Laboratory was a Finsbury man, G. T. Morgan (1872–1942), who condensed phenol with formaldehyde leaving it to Baekeland in America to exploit this and make plastics.

But to Sir Norman Lockyer, the editor of *Nature* and veteran of the Devonshire Commission, it was not enough. Having unsuccessfully pleaded with the British Association in a brilliant address entitled 'The Influence of Brain Power on History' to serve as a pressure group for science, he founded the British Science Guild in 1905.

At its inaugural meeting, R. B. Haldane (Lord Moggeridge in H. G. Wells's *Bealby*) called for a permanent commission to advise the Government on the development and application of scientific knowledge.

As a Cabinet Minister, Haldane did what he could to promote the Guild's views. The Guild got under way in 1905, working through special committees, investigating and reporting upon matters of public importance like agriculture, industry, the conversion of national sources of energy, reform of the patent laws and the utilization of science in public departments.[55]

(12)

Indeed the physicists were busy drafting a new world picture. First holder of the pencil was William Thomson, architect of the Transatlantic Cable operation from 1857 to its successful conclusion in 1866. Thomson (or Lord Kelvin as he became) was seized with the principle that heat and energy are interchangeable (which he owed to Joule), and of the principle of Carnot that heat was not conserved, but energy was. He called the attention of the German physicist Clausius to this, and Clausius enumerated the principle of entropy, or the inavailability of the thermal energy of a system for mechanical work.

Like the law of evolution, the law of entropy gripped the Victorian mind. The apocalpytic spectacle of the ultimate death of heat (*warmetod*) when all the universe is of the same temperature and life ceases, had a strong appeal to a nation worried about its energy resources of coal.

Physicists, now acquiring an agelic personality as a profession (the Institution of Telegraphic Engineers was formed in 1871 and the Physical Society in 1874) fastened on the concept of energy and its conservation. Though in the hands of J. Clerk Maxwell, Boltzmann and Willard Gibbs, entropy became less deterministic, thanks to the application of theories of probability, yet Kelvin stuck to it as it explained the age of the earth.

His world was to be demolished by scientists from the Cavendish laboratory, the directorship of which he was three times offered and three times refused.[56] From ideas developed by him in Glasgow and by Clifton at Oxford, Lord Rayleigh inaugurated an apparatus fund at the Cavendish laboratory, securing two demonstrators, R. T. Glazebrook and W. N. Shaw, to help him in his work of redetermining electrical standards. On Rayleigh's resignation for a chair at the Royal Institution in 1884, J. J. Thomson succeeded him. Thomson's reign at the Cavendish from 1884 to 1919 marks the emergence of a new force in British scientific life—a new hatchery of scientists and a new seed-plot of ideas. Colloquia were instituted, the laboratory enlarged, graduates of other universities were allowed to register as research students and great use was made of the 1851 Exhibition Fund, which the Iron and Steel Institute had successfully argued should be used to encourage provincial talent.

One such provincial was a New Zealand scholar Ernest (later Lord Rutherford), who, at the British Association meeting of 1906, successfully argued against Kelvin's ideas of the conservation of energy. By utilizing Thomson's discovery that the atom had parts, he showed that the conversion of uranium to helium provided a measuring instrument which still farther backdated the age of the earth. 'It was Kelvin's death in 1907,' said Schneer, 'not the shot at Sarajevo in 1914 that brought to an end the comfortable world of the nineteenth century.'[57]

As A. J. Balfour, who as a politician and brother-in-law of Lord Rayleigh remarked, 'science was the great instrument of social change, all the greater because its object is not change but knowledge, and its silent appropriation of this dominant function, amid the din of political and religious strife, is the most vital of all the revolutions which have marked the development of modern civilisation'.[58]

PART III

Frontier Problems

9

<hr>

Improvised Europeans

<hr>

'YES, Sir,' wrote St. Simon to an American in 1817, 'the sole aim of our thoughts and our exertions must be the kind of organization most favourable to industry—industry understood in the widest sense, including every kind of useful activity, theoretical as well as practical, intellectual as well as manual.'[1]

Reporting to his government on the rapid development of the American industry state and its implications for Europe, one of St. Simon's disciples, Michel Chevalier, formerly editor of *The Globe*, prophesied that Europe would have to join hands with America, Russia and Asia for its own good. Nor was he the only Frenchman to supplement his fellow-countryman Tocqueville's neglect of American industrial expansion, for Guillaume Tell Poussin, with a sureness of vision that justified his name, predicted in his *De La Puissance Américaine* (1845) that America had initiated the industrial democratization of the world.[2] Such democratization owed much to the effective grafting of three distinct traditions: the English, French and German methods of organising science.

(1)

The virtuosi who formed the Royal Society of London, once (according to an eighteenth-century secretary), considered migrating to Connecticut, 'had not the Civil wars happily ended as they did'.[3] Whether true or not, the story indicates the attraction which America offered to some early Fellows. Robert Boyle sustained the interest, with the result that the College of William and Mary which opened in 1692, had a chair of mathematics and natural philosophy. Of its nine occupants up to the (American) Revolution, Dr. William Small,[4] who held it from 1758 to 1764, was the most influential. 'He fixed the destinies of my life', wrote Jefferson. He fixed the destinies of several others in England too, for he is generally credited with initiating the Lunar Society of Birmingham on his return to England, now recognized as a major industrial-research organization in eighteenth-century Britain. Small held that the doors of the university

> . . . are open to all, nor is even a knowledge in ye arts, Languages a previous Requisite for Entrance. The Students have ye Liberty of attending whom they please, and in one order they please, or all ye diffr. Lectures in a term if they think proper.[5]

The Boyle lectures, intended to confute atheism, did what St. Simon hoped he could do. For when fifteen-year-old Benjamin Franklin heard Cotton Mather, F.R.S. delivering them, he found they were virtually 'Newtonian discourses with religious improvements'.[6] Franklin acquired further insight into the works of Newton when he came to London three years later. At an age (18) when boys today are at a university, Franklin met Sir Hans Sloane and Henry Pemberton and from the latter acquired a zeal for physical science. Returning to Philadelphia he founded a library company for which Peter Collinson, F.R.S. agreed to purchase books. Franklin later lived in Philadelphia where the first botanical garden in America had been established by the Pietists in 1694. Here he formed a Friday club known as the Junto, which after 1736, began to throw off subsidiary clubs. Seeing how necessary then a larger society was, Franklin suggested on 13 May 1743 that an American Philosophical Society should be founded. It was, and twenty-three years later merged with the Junto into the American Philosophical Society, held at Philadelphia for Improving Useful Knowledge.

'All philosophic experiments that let light into the nature of things', wrote Franklin, 'tend to increase the power of man over matter.' His 'virtuosi', as he originally called them, corresponded with their counterparts in London and Dublin, met once a month or oftener at their own expense, and as far as possible emulated the older Royal Society of London. This society built an observatory where David Rittenhouse (1732–96) obtained the first accurate measurements of the earth from the sun—now called the astronomical unit. He was the first to build a collimating telescope and one of the earliest to use a spider's web. One of the first operations of the society was to observe the transit of Venus in 1769.

The 'religion of industry' exemplified in the Royal Society for the Encouragement of Arts, Manufactures and Commerce was also not without its effect, for societies of the same name and for the same purpose were founded in 1754 and in 1765, both in New York. A similar society began in Philadelphia in 1787, whilst a New York Society for the Promotion of American Manufactures was established in 1788. The institutional momentum imported by these was accelerated by the Lyceum movement, launched in 1826 by Josiah Holbrook, a variant of another popular English institution, the mechanics' institute. The likeness between them was emphasized by the way in which English popularizers of science exerted a widespread influence.[7]

Popularization of science was not confined to popularizers. The first professor of chemistry and natural history at Yale, Benjamin Silliman (1779–1864) covered all the important centres of population from New Orleans to St. Louis lecturing on geology; in addition he founded (in 1828) and edited *The American Journal of Science and the Arts*, as a 'deposit for original American communications'. It solicited and obtained contributions from scientists and 'from men versed in the practical arts'. Like the Jardin du Roi under the Jussieu family, it was a dynastic affair, for in the first hundred years of its foundation it was edited by himself, his son, his son-in-law and his grandson. As a pontiff of American science, Silliman's influence was exerted in many ways—not only in geology and chemistry, but in the organization of the Sheffield scientific school at Yale, in 1847.[8]

(2)

French help to the Americans in their War of Independence led to increased contacts.[9] The American commissioner in

France during the years 1778–9, John Adams, was so 'frequently entertained with inquiries . . . and with eulogiums' on papers in the transactions of the American Philosophical Society that on his return he suggested that Massachusetts should establish a similar society. So it did in 1780 when the American Academy of Arts and Sciences was established 'to cultivate every art and science which may tend to advance the interest, honour, dignity and happiness of a free, independent and virtuous people'. Not only French, but British scientists too were made honorary members. The British Navy went one better. Though it was blockading the coast it allowed the society to observe a solar eclipse in 1780.

Similar state academies were established by Connecticut and Maryland, and, as if Philadelphia had still to lead the way, the Chemical Society of Philadelphia (1792), the American Botanical Society (1806) and the American Academy of Natural Sciences (1812) were founded there. The last-named society essayed an experiment in a community living on the banks of the Wabash in Indiana, whose achievements 'command the admiration of everyone who has looked into the history of science in America'.[10]

More specifically French in origin was the scheme for L'Académie des États-Unis de l'Amérique. This was to be staffed by French professors, charged with the duty of communicating information on American natural resources to Europe.[11] Its Masonic overtones were evident at the dedication of the building in Richmond in 1786 and in a general programme for schools in Virginia. Its promoter, the Chevalier Quesnay de Beaurepaire went talent-hunting to Europe where he even secured Jean Rouelle. But three years later the French Revolution broke out and, since the impetus of the scheme was French, the scheme collapsed.[12]

Naturally enough, American chemists took up the new chemical nomenclature of Lavoisier. James Woodhouse did so and formed the first chemical society at Philadelphia in 1792. The battle was fought out in Dr. Samuel L. Mitchell's *Medical Repository* founded in 1798, the first really general scientific magazine in the country. The chemical renaissance spread through John Maclean to Princeton through Robert Hare and B. Rush to the College of Philadelphia and through Lyman

Spalding to Dartmouth. The New York Council bestirred itself to provide centres for the scientific education of the public during the first decade of the nineteenth century: John Griscom obtained the Old Alms House as a teaching centre. Museums like those of John Scudder in New York, of C. W. Peale in Philadelphia and Daniel Bowen in Boston also played a notable part.

But the grandest design of all was for a 'Polysophic Society', based on the Institut de France on which Joel Barlow (1754–1812) was seized during his seventeen years' residence there.[13] 'If you will put me at the head of the Institution,' he told a correspondent on 15 September 1800, 'and give it that support which you ought to do, you can't imagine what a garden it would make of the United States.' His scheme ripened with age, and by the time he issued a *Prospectus of a National Institution to be established in the United States* (1805), it had become a school of mines, of roads and bridges, a conservatory of useful arts and manufactures, a museum of fine arts, a national library, a mint, a military school, a school of general science, schools of medicine and veterinary science and an observatory. And, to show its French paternity, Barlow suggested that subsidiary colleges should be founded throughout the Union as necessity arose.

Circulated round the country, this very French prospectus secured such a favourable reception that a Bill was drafted in 1806 to incorporate the institution. Senator Logan of Pennsylvania introduced it into the Senate, but after a pleasant reception, it was lost. The reasons for its failure were twofold: the indifference of Congress and the opposition of existing colleges.

Other forward-looking citizens had been fumbling for much the same thing. A national university was mooted at the Federal Convention of 1787, and as scientists at the University of Pennsylvania were used by the Government at Philadelphia, the physician Benjamin Rush proposed an institution to rediffuse European knowledge. Libraries furnished with books of natural philosophy were advocated by Jeremy Belknap of Massachusetts, so that people 'might employ their leisure and their various opportunities in endeavouring to add to the stock of science and thus to enrich the world with their observations and improvements'. Belknap went on to say: 'I am so far an enthusiast in the cause of America as to wish she may shine Mistress of the Sciences, as well as the asylum of Liberty.'[14] The twin deities of Science and Freedom were invoked by Jezaniah Sumner in his *Ode on Science* (1798) to crown with laurels 'the young and rising states' which had spurned alike the 'British yoke' and 'Gallic chain'.

No more receptive or sympathetic listener could be found for such suggestions than Thomas Jefferson, who had chaired the committee that prepared the Declaration of Independence, presented it to Congress and eventually signed it. He had been the U.S. Minister to France from 1785 to 1789, and later President from 1801 to 1809. He listened sympathetically in 1794 to the proposal of a Swiss professor that the University of Geneva should be transplanted bodily to the United States. When Pierre Samuel Du Pont de Nemours emigrated to the United States, Jefferson persuaded him to write *Sur l'éducation nationale dans les États-Unis* (1800), which if it was not adopted in the U.S.A., undoubtedly influenced the French Code, as well as Jefferson's own project of a non-sectarian University of Virginia.[15] French influence can also be seen at work in the University of the State of New York (1784), the University of Orleans (1806) and the Catholepistemiad, or University of Michigania (1817). Du Pont's sons were pupils of the English expatriate chemist Thomas Cooper (1759–1839) at Dickenson College, Carlisle, Pennsylvania, who taught them that 'the history of an art or science is the proper introduction to it'. Cooper's passion for chemistry led to his resignation, for the trustees objected to his spending the Sabbath in the laboratory with some of his students. Joining the University of Pennsylvania (Franklin's foundation of 1749), Cooper then had a row with the medical school. But Jefferson valued him highly and sought his advice on the University of Virginia which when it opened in 1825, was the first real State university—public, secular and undenominational.

Though Jefferson aimed at making it 'the most eminent in the United States', by calling to it 'characters of the first order of science from Europe as well as our own country',[16] the University of Virginia recruited from a poor field. It was too new. The spirit of its founder animated others like the University of North Carolina, and the University of Tennessee at Nashville, as well as reformers in the older ones like George Ticknor of Harvard, and Francis Wayland of Brown. 'From our information of the character of the different universities,' Jefferson wrote, 'we expect we should go to Oxford for our classical professors, to Cambridge for those of mathematics, natural philosophy and natural history and to Edinburgh for a professor of anatomy and the elements or outlines only, of medicine.'

Haunted by the French concept of a central institution of arts and sciences, Americans launched the Columbian Institute for the promotion of arts and sciences in 1816. It established a botanical garden, but little else, and when its charter expired the National Institute was organized in 1840 also in Washington. This also deliquesced.[17] Paradoxically the illegitimate son of the first Duke of Northumberland, a chemist and mineralogist, provided for a third venture what the other two lacked— a substantial endowment: £100,000 in gold. Chartered in 1846, this took its name from him—James Smithson. His bequest charged it with 'the increase and diffusion of knowledge among men'; a charge taken seriously and successfully by the first secretary, Joseph Henry. In the Smithsonian, the first secular Romanesque building in the country, original research was undertaken that could not be done by any other body. Henry initiated a weather report system and inaugurated a system of international exchange of scientific periodicals. He was an apt choice, for earlier, as a professor of physics at Princeton he had, contemporaneously with Faraday, discovered a method of producing induced current. Hence the term *henry* to describe a unit of induction.[18] He also [published reports on explorations and issued *Contributions to Knowledge*.

Yet of all the French influences on American seed-beds of science, perhaps the greatest was that of the École Polytechnique. Jefferson was such an addict of science that he even set aside a room in the presidential mansion where he could work on fossil bones,[19] and had long been interested in the creation of an aristocracy of talent. To provide it he established West Point in 1802. The Swiss engineer F. R. Hassler, later to be Superintendent of the U.S. Coast Survey, spent three years teaching mathematics there. When a former pupil of the École Polytechnique, Sylvanus P. Thayer became director in 1817, he established traditions of teaching which persist today. As with the Polytechnique, West Point produced engineers to build railways and canals along which America was to grow, and surveyors to map its mineral deposits. Thayer subsequently established and endowed the school of engineering at Dartmouth which bears his name. Similar departments at Yale and Harvard were founded, whilst the Navy's own West Point was founded at Annapolis in 1845.[20] One of its graduates in 1873 was immediately made an instructor in physics and chemistry. This was A. A. Michelson, who there conducted the experiment that was to make him famous: he measured the velocity of light more accurately than ever before with apparatus costing a little over ten dollars.

Other graduates of the Polytechnique came over to America when Napoloeon was captured. His friend Simon Bernard (1779–1839), designer of the fortifications of Antwerp, spent fifteen years designing U.S. Coast Defences before returning to France where he soon became Minister of War. Another was Claude Crozet (1790–1864), taken prisoner during the Napoleonic retreat from Russia, who became Professor of Engineering at West Point in 1817, introducing the teaching of descriptive geometry there, and publishing four years later, the first textbook on the subject. He helped to create the Virginia Military Institute in 1839, built the aqueduct which supplies the city of Washington with water from the Potomac Falls and played a great part in the building of railways.[21]

As leader of the disastrous attack across the Niagara River on Queenstown during the Anglo-American war of 1812, Stephen van Rensselaer appreciated good engineers. Subsequent experience as a member of the commission to cut a canal between the Great Lakes and the Hudson River led him to found the Rensselaer Polytechnic Institute in 1826: this awarded the first degrees in civil engineering to be given in the United States. To its first principal, a botanist, Amos Eaton (1776–1842), 'a thirst for natural sciences' seemed already 'to pervade the United States like the progress of an epidemic'. One of Eaton's successors, B. Franklin Greene, after a visit to Europe, farther expanded its curriculum to include other types of engineering.[22] This epidemic infected older universities like Union College (in 1845), Harvard and Yale (in 1847), Dartmouth and Brown (in 1852) and the University of Pennsylvania (in 1855) all of which added laboratories and scientific schools. It is perhaps worth noticing that Joseph Henry, the first secretary of the Smithsonian, was a former tutor in van Rensselaer's family.

In assuming major responsibility for training technical experts and employing them in such governmental bodies as the Army and Navy, the Patent Office and Coast Survey, the American Government also showed it had French practice in mind.[23]

The École des Mines inspired Thomas Eaglestone (1832–1900) to approach the Smithsonian to establish something similar but 'they thought it out of their line'. He then approached Columbia University which appointed him and another classmate from the French École des Mines, F. L. Vinton (1835–97) to the chairs of minerology and metallurgy, and of mining respectively. As Dean of the new school and Professor of Chemistry, Charles F. Chandler (1836–1925), a pupil of Wohler's, was chosen. To teach inorganic chemistry, C. A. Joy, another pupil of Wohler's, was chosen.

From such a mating of French chemical and German mining traditions, the first successful American school of mines was born. It appeared just at the right time, when a vast storehouse in the deeper geological layers of the U.S.A. was being tapped. The Comstock Lode, Butte and Bingham Canyon all demanded mechanical competence and scientific training. The Columbia School of Mines provided both. Within two decades of its foundation it was said that 'one could not find a major mine anywhere in the world that did not number, or had not been aided by, a Columbia mining engineer.'[24]

(3)

German influence over the seed-beds of American science emanated first from Göttingen, one of whose graduates C. D. Ebeling edited the first German magazine devoted to American affairs: *Americanische Bibliothek*, published in 1777.[25] Eleven years earlier, Benjamin Franklin visited it, followed by others. When George Ticknor, a graduate of Dartmouth, went there in 1815 with Edward Everett, later to become President of Harvard, to obtain his Ph.D., he heralded a long line of academic migrants, whose quest led them to Berlin, Heidelberg and Leipzig as well. The travels of Rev. Henry E. Dwight, son of the President of Yale, made into a book, was much read. Over 10,000, students if existing accounts are to be believed, made the journey to Germany up to 1914.[26]

Of these early migrants, those who worked with Liebig at Giessen were instrumental in establishing two major American scientific schools. The laboratory of the Lawrence Scientific School at Harvard was established by E. N. Horsford (1818–93), where he had as a colleague Louis Agassiz, a Swiss geologist previously in the service of Prussia. The Sheffield Scientific School at Yale profited by Samuel Johnson (1830–1909), and John Addison Porter (1822–66), the son-in-law of its founder.

German influence, refracted via England, is also visible in the creation of the American Association for the Advancement of Science, founded in 1848 at Philadelphia. An expansion of the eight-year-old Association of American Geologists it was intended to 'give a stronger and more general impulse, and a more systematic direction to scientific research' in the U.S.A. Yet its name was taken from the British Association and so was its organization into specialist sections, its peripatetic character and its role. For it became a virtual parliament (congress would perhaps be an apter word) for American science.[27]

In the same year, 1848, a stream of political refugees from German polytechnics came to America. Astronomy gained C. H. F. Peters, and botany C. T. Mohr from Stuttgart, whose report on the forests of Alabama was famous. Nor should Joseph Zentmeyer, a Mannheim instrument-maker be forgotten, since from 1853 his microscopes were to become a model of how well scientific instruments could be made in Philadelphia.[28]

The great German universities, with their research schools, profoundly influenced the development of their American counterparts. The University of Michigania, originally proposed by a correspondent of Jefferson's as the Catholepistemiad in 1817, took shape twenty years later and became, in its turn, a beacon of influence in the West. Its charter influenced that of the University of Wisconsin (1848) and, even more, the University of Minnesota (1851). But whereas the Jeffersonian ideal had been basically French, the Michiganian, especially under H. P. Tappan (1805–81) was German. For as Tappan wrote, 'The system of public instruction adopted by the State of Michigan is copied from the Prussian, acknowledged to be the most perfect in the world.'

The first full-length plea for emulating the German university as a centre of *wissenschaft*, making provision for carrying forward all scientific investigation, was made by Tappan. In his *University Education* (1850), he envisaged a university like that of Berlin 'literally a Cyclopaedia where are collected on every subject of human knowledge, cabinets and apparatus of every description that can aid learned investigation and philosophical experiment, and amply qualified professors and teachers to assist the student in his studies'.[29]

So too Daniel Coit Gilman (1831–1908), returning from Europe, lamented the absence of opportunities in America where science could be pursued 'for its own sake' though there were plenty to accommodate postulant engineers, architects, farmers, miners and manufacturers. 'As a result, we are far behind European nations in many important branches of industry.'

The same sense of inadequacy oppressed A. D. Bache, Superintendent of the Coast Survey, who began to feel his way towards organizing an American group of scientists. This group, known as the Lazzaroni, included Charles H. Davis, the Chief of the Bureau of Navigation, Louis Agassiz and the astronomer Benjamin A. Gould.

Like their European counterparts they ate together first. Eating oysters and climbing mountains together kindled, as one of them said, a Florentine spirit. Sometimes their thoughts strayed from the sixteenth to the eighteenth century: in 1850 they discussed the possibility of establishing a polytechnic in New York where O. W. Gibbs, B. Gould, A. J. Hall and J. D. Whitney could teach and work. Later, acquiring historical perspectives even nearer to their own time, they talked of making Albany the site of a National University modelled on Berlin.

Berlin really struck their imagination, especially after they acquired a leader in H. P. Tappan. Tappan, father-in-law of an astronomer, turned his persuasive charm upon the wealthy New Yorker, Peter Cooper, hoping to extract from him the money for a University and Academy of Arts and Sciences. But though Cooper gave $100,000 for the cause, Tappan had to return to Michigan, and the scheme was unrealized.

The advent of the Civil War brought the schemes of the

Lazzaroni to fruition, when on 3 March 1863, the National Academy of Science was established to 'investigate, examine, experiment and to report upon any subject of science or art' referred to it by the Government. Aptly, A. D. Bache was chosen as its first president. Coincidental with its foundation, indeed, a month before, on 11 February 1863, Bache with Joseph Henry of the Smithsonian and C. H. Davis had been nominated as members of a Permanent Commission to advise the navy.[30]

(4)

All these efforts were focused and intensified by the needs of the frontier. As it moved westwards, it called for techniques, instruments and insight. The adjective 'yankee' was applied to the kind of hurried Archimedean fervour which, more than the gun, harnessed the frontier to the American economy. Growth was everywhere, and its possibilities outlined by the great expeditions like Sibley's (1803), Lewis and Clark's (1805), Pike's (1805), Long's (1819), Schoolcraft's (1831) and Frémont's (1845) blazed the trail for the government departments.[31]

The frontier offered land, and the practice of granting public lands for universities began in 1787 when the Rev. Manasseh Cutler secured the cession of two townships as a university endowment. This Ohio precedent stood firm; in the next fifty years or so fifteen states west of the Appalachians secured over four million acres for this purpose. Denominational battles raged over their control and local hostilities to their foundation often stimulated the growth of new colleges.[32] Nevertheless a steady increase in scientific teaching took place. West of the Mississippi a steady growth of chemical laboratories can be traced, beginning with St. Louis, where European textbooks were being used.[33]

Groups of inquiring and technology-hungry yankees sprang up in the wake of the westward-moving frontier organized not so much in colleges and schools as in Lyceums. To satisfy this hunger, Josiah Holbrook (1788–1854) established a factory in Boston to supply geometrical and astronomical apparatus to Lyceums, museums and libraries which he also helped to promote and organize. By 1837, with John Baldwin (1799–1884), a manufacturer, he organized a Lyceum Village and Seminary at Berea, Ohio. It lasted for over five years. Baldwin subsequently made a fortune from shaping grindstones from sandstone at Berea, and used it to endow two institutions both of which became universities in 1857 and 1859, whilst Holbrook returned to New York to manage a bureau for the dispatch of scientific material for schools. Indeed it was on a journey collecting minerals and plants for this bureau that he was drowned in a Virginian river.[34]

(5)

The most dramatic demonstration of the growth of American technology was at the Great Exhibition held in Hyde Park in 1851. Thanks, not to the American Government, but to the generosity of George Peabody, Colt revolvers, Hobbs's unbreakable locks, Goodyear rubber goods, McCormick reapers and other artifacts of yankee genius excited comment and emulation. The Chamberlain family acquired a screw machine that enabled them to start afresh in Birmingham—the citadel of British technology.

Americans saw this at the time. As Charles T. Rogers of Louisiana remarked in his *American Superiority at the World's Fair* (1852), America had shown how the power of machines could emancipate men from drudgery, multiply their capacities for producing, enhance their comforts and quicken their enjoyment. More recently another distinguished American historian has written:

> The significance of the American participation in this great technological show for shifting the emphasis in European images of American civilization and for challenging Americans to defend that civilization in positive and concrete ways has never been appreciated.[35]

The machine, reported Thomas Ewbank, the U.S. Commissioner of Patents from 1849, had given the entire body of mankind something like equal opportunities in the race for happiness and power. He described as 'a fond delusion' that 'the less wise men have to do with gross matter the nearer they resemble the Great Spirit; whereas God is the greatest of workers—the chief of artificers. So far from locking up his wisdom in abstractions' Ewbank wrote in his first report 'he is incessantly embodying it in tangible things, and in them it is that his intelligence, ingenuity and resources are made manifest. What is this world but one of workshops, and the universe but a collection of inventions?'

As the first socially engineered, secular, democratic, experimental society, America nourished the myth that was powerfully to influence Europe. During the Civil War, an English journalist described it as the 'Republic of Jones', a mythical neutral area between north and south.

'It may be', he wrote, 'that its President is a . . . modern St. Simon, a latter-day Père Enfantin; and that here are the aspirations that were dreamt of in the New Atlantis, and Sir Thomas More's "Utopia" and M. Cabet's "Icaria" and M. Fourier's "Phalanstère" are realized. Some of these days', he concluded, 'this shadow may surprise us all, by proving to belong to a substance of some magnitude.'[36]

10

◇◇

The Zapadniki

◇◇

(1)

THE contest over the cultural domination of Russia was very real. Perhaps it reflected the contest over the other colonies like America and India, for colony Russia surely was until the nineteenth century. French tutors in eighteenth-century Russia were described by an Englishman as 'parasites'. He remarked that lack of education was the chief obstacle to Russian progress, impeding its claim to be part of Europe, 'whereas', he added, 'it is more part of Persia or Babylon'.[1] An English peeress agreed with him and deplored French influence there.[2]

Even the great Tsar Peter recognized that his country needed nutriment in the form of foreign capital, methods, machines, technicians and ideas, since it could not create its own industrial techniques.[3] Round the doctors and savants he imported grew institutions for the training of native counterparts.

Of these, the greatest was the Academy of Sciences. Embodying features of the Royal Society (which he had visited in 1698), the Berlin Academy (with whose founder Leibnitz he had discussed plans in 1711 and 1712) and the French Academy (which had given him a royal reception in 1717), it began as an academy, a university and a secondary school.[4] Like other academies it had a journal, *Commentarii Academiae Scientiarum Petropolitanae,* and promoted expeditions and astronomical

145

measurements and produced the first atlas of the country.

As an index of Russian dependence on Europe, the academy at first admitted a few native Russians. The first, V. E. Adodurov, became an adjunct in mathematics in 1733, and the first native Russian, M. V. Lomonosov (1711–65), a professor in 1745. Lomonosov set up the first-known laboratory exercises in physical chemistry, began a mineralogical cabinet and helped found the University of Moscow in 1755, now called after him.[5]

Handicapped by theological dogmatism, discouraged for lack of an audience, tied to publishing its work in Latin for the sake of its imported cadre of Westerners, it was expected on State occasions to serve as an imperial poetic factory. It also had to inform the Government of its plans each year and serve it as a consultant body for scientific matters.

Not even its university role was taken seriously for most Russian students were sent abroad to study science. Lomonosov went to Germany from 1735 to 1741. Others who followed him had no easy time. Of these none were better able to appreciate the problems of unchecked arbitrary power than those chosen by Catherine the Great to study jurisprudence at Leipzig. Bullied by their insensitive Baltic German tutor, slapped and on occasions put under armed guard, these Russian students could not have been better conditioned to appreciate the Helvetian notion that morals should be experimental.

In spite of, or perhaps because of, Helvetius's book *De l'Esprit* being condemned by the Sorbonne and the Archbishop of Paris, ordered to be burnt by the public hangman and placed on the *Index*,[6] it was avidly read by Alexander Radischev (1749–1802), who returned and later published his *Journey from St. Petersburg to Moscow* (1790). This was as unpopular with Russian authorities as Helvetius's book had been with the French. For publishing it Radischev was stripped of his rank and exiled to Siberia. The opening words of Radischev's book— 'I looked about me—my heart was troubled by the sufferings of humanity'—are the overture to the main theme of the Russian intelligentsia.[7]

In the train of the technically minded Britons (and later of the French)[8] came Masonic ideas of rationality and the clockwork universe. The first provincial Grand Master appointed in

1731 was Captain John Philips. Forty years later the Russians had their own Grand Master. Masonic lodges incubated other groups like Masons, the Free Economic Society of St. Petersburg in 1765—a Russian analogue of the Royal Society of Arts. The leader of the Moscow Masons, Nikolai Novikov, published *On the Education of Children for the Diffusion of Useful Knowledge and General Welfare*, and founded a Friendly Learned Society in 1779 for the purpose, as well as the Blagorodny Pansion (or School for Nobles) and the Moscow Printing Company. For this last activity he was arrested in 1792 and imprisoned.[9]

The engineer Samual Bentham became Superintendent of the imperial favourite's dockyard,[10] the British doctor Sir James Wylie founded, and for thirty years presided over, the Medical Military Academy at St. Petersburg.[11] The British traveller, William Coxe (1747–1828), assessed Siberia and commented on the Russian progress: though 'proceeding towards civilization', he wrote, it was 'still far removed from that state'.[12]

The British rocket expert, Sir William Congreve helped Alexander Zasyadko establish the first artillery school (in 1818) and the first military rocket company in Russia (1826). Russian rockets were used against the Turks in the conquest of the Caucasus, where one of the captains of the engineering troops (I. I. Trelesky) suggested the use of rockets for engines.[13]

As a haven for Russian exiles, England was ideal. From 1832 A. I. Herzen lived here running his 'Free Russian Press', publishing his *Polar Star* and *The Bell* (*Kolokol*)—the latter the only source of information about reform. Herzen had no blind faith in the redemptive power of technology, which in Russia would produce 'Ghengis Khan with a telegraph'. Hence his wish that Russia would 'skip capitalism' and move directly to socialism.

The struggle for existence as interpreted by other Russians like Jacques Novicov was an intellectual conflict rather than a physical one. As it increased so would the spirit of justice and sympathy. This theme was also taken up by Kropotkin, another exile in England.[14]

Of all the English writers who appealed to the Russians by the middle of the nineteenth century, H. T. Buckle was perhaps the most widely read. Buckle's avowed intention in writing his

History of Civilisation in England (a powerful plea for intellectual struggle) was to get his book read. Buckle's wish for his book 'to get among the Mechanics' Institutes and the *people* . . . These are they whom I am now beginning to touch and whom I wish to move'[15] was certainly fulfilled in Russia. For when Donald Mackenzie Wallace went there, he found:

> During the first year of my residence in Russia, I rarely had a serious conversation without hearing Buckle's name mentioned; my friends almost always assumed that he had succeeded in creating a genuine science of history on the inductive method. In vain I pointed out that Buckle had merely thrown out some hints in an introductory chapter as to how such a science ought to be constructed and that he himself had made no serious attempt to use the method which he commenced. My objections had little, or no effect, the belief was too deep rooted to be so easily eradicated. In books, periodicals, newspapers and professional lectures, the name of Buckle was constantly cited—often violently dragged in without the slightest reason—and cheap translations of his work were sold in enormous quantities.[16]

Buckle reinforced the earlier cult of Comte and Saint Simon, which had made a great impact on the generation of Alexander Herzen, who reminisced:

> many people, superficial and otherwise, had a good laugh over Père Enfantin and his apostles . . . These rapturous young men with their terry cloth waistcoats and their sprouting beards, appeared triumphantly and poetically amid the world of philistinism. They proclaimed a new faith, they had something to say, and something in the name of which the old order of things could be brought before the judgement seat.[17]

For Russia had its polytechnic too. Known as the Institute of Engineers of Ways of Communications, established in 1809 at St. Petersburg, its curriculum was planned by Frenchmen like Augustin de Bétancourt, its first director, and G. Lamé and B. P. E. Clapeyron, both enthusiastic St. Simonians. The St. Simonian gospel of opening up the country through great engineering works was sedulously propagated. These men trained Russians to build the first suspension bridges on the continent of Europe; one, over the Neva, having a single span of 1,020 feet. From such practical experience, Lamé and Clapeyron wrote numerous papers on elasticity before returning to France in 1831 to become professors of physics at the École Polytechnique and the École des Ponts et Chaussées respectively. Their Russian successors included M. V. Ostrogradsky (1801–61), founder of the famous St. Petersburg mathematical tradition.[18]

(2)

St. Simonism found in Russia a most receptive audience. Enfantin, before he became high priest of the cult, spent the years 1821 to 1823 in Russia. Later, another St. Simonian won a prize in 1836 given by the French Academy of Moral and Political Sciences on the moral and material influence of the new industrialism, with a most comprehensive and detailed exposition of collectivism. His materialist approach, historical materialism, insight into the need for cartelizing industry and his prediction that it would increase, attracted the attention of Karl Marx, whom indeed he had anticipated in advocating the socialism of the means of production and distribution, as well as in the promulgation of the labour theory of value.[19] This St. Simonian, Constantine Pecquer by name, went farther. In 1850 he warned the readers of his newspaper *Le Salut du Peuple*:

> Take heed lest civilization plant her banner on the Summit of the Kremlin—lest she give her baptism of predilection to the countless race of the Slavs! Take Heed! Immortality is promised only to those nations which militate for progress, for liberty, equality and fraternity all over the world.[20]

Six universities on the French model were also provided for in 1804 by statute. Here the prime mover was a Polish-Lithuanian nobleman, Prince Czartoryski, who had been in France at the beginning of the Revolution. As in France, these six universities were to be responsible for inspecting all schools of their region, for training mathematicians, physical scientists and doctors, and for providing courses in moral and political science. Two were founded in the same year as the statute: Kazan and Kharkov. Three existed already: Moscow (1755), Vilna (1802) and Dorpat (1802). The remaining one was obtained by raising the Pedagogical Institute of St. Petersburg to university status fifteen years later (1819). Students were to be supported by State grants, kept at their studies by the threat of recruitment in the army and on graduating were to spend six years in government service.

In these universities, scientific endeavour began to stir. At Dorpat a great parallectic telescope, known as 'the giant refractor', was built by Joseph von Frauenhofer, the pioneer of spectrum analysis. Also at Dorpat, G. F. Parrot, an early expositor of the chemical theory of the voltaic pile, devised various schemes for projecting bombs into the air.

But Parrot's bombs at Dorpat were harmless activities compared to what went on at the University of Kazan, where riots broke out. The Tsar dispatched a commissioner to inspect the university, who recommended that it should be closed. Though this severe recommendation was not actually endorsed, the Tsar ordered the professors to conform to Biblical views in their teaching of physics and medicine, whilst professors of mathematics were required to show geometrical proofs of the Trinity. This was especially ironic in view of the fact that Lobachevsky, who taught there, announced on 24 February 1826 the discovery of non-Euclidean geometry.

The University of St. Petersburg, founded ten years later, received an enormous accession of strength from its acquisition of the Military Medical Academy (originally founded in 1799) in 1835. Here N. I. Pirogov (1810–81) taught anatomy after leaving the University of Dorpat, moving on when the Crimean War broke out to pioneer the administration of ether on the battlefield. His successor S. P. Botkin (1832–89), originally a mathematician, employed quantitative criteria to the human body, as did his friend and colleague I. M. Sechenov (1829–1905), a former military engineer. Both were to increase the trend towards materialism in philosophy. So did Darwin's *Origin of Species*, which was seized upon by S. S. Kutorga at the University of Moscow in 1860. His pupil, K. A. Timiryazev (1843–1920), was to become the Russian Huxley.[21]

(3)

German influence had long emanated from the University of Dorpat (now Tartu in Esthonia) which became an imperial University of Russia in 1802. This was Russia's real 'window on the West', and was dear to the heart of the Baltic German gentry. Here N. I. Pirogov was a student, and after studying in

Germany, became a professor in 1836. At Dorpat, instruction was given in German, and its statutes were modelled on those of Berlin. Here, within the Russian Empire, was an enclave of German science. So was the Academy of Science, sometimes called the *Dreifussige Akademie*, because the three mathematicians called Fuss were so prominent in it: Nicholas (d. 1824) and his two sons, P. H. and G. A. Fuss.

Sechenov had worked under Helmholtz, Du Bois Reymond and K. F. W. Ludwig in Germany and his book *The Reflexes of the Brain* (1863) greatly influenced Pavlov, who regarded him as 'the father of Russian Physiology'. He was, like many of his own and preceding generations, profoundly influenced by the German emphasis on measurement.

Another German family, the Gmelins, virtually opened up the Urals. One of them, Johann Georg (1709–55), had explored Siberia as far as the Lena, another, his nephew Samuel Gottlieb (1744–74), had explored south-eastern Russia, and yet another nephew Johann Friedrich (1748–1804) was Professor of Mineralogy and Chemistry at Tübingen.

This, and other German institutions like Marburg and Freiburg had taken young Russian scientists. Lomonosov was sent from 1730 to 1741 to the two latterly mentioned towns. A Russian Freiburg was established in 1773 at St. Petersburg, and a mineralogical society was organized.

Other German academicians in Russia like Peter Pallas (1741–1811) and G. F. Muller (1705–83) helped survey Siberia. The Tsar Alexander I even imported a German to make a flying machine which would deter the French from burning Moscow. Though unsuccessful, it was a landmark in Russia's drive for the air.[22]

By the middle of the nineteenth century, German chemistry was flourishing at the University of Kazan on the Middle Volga. Here Liebig's pupil, N. N. Zinin (1812–80), taught, amongst others, Alfred Nobel that the industrial application of nitroglycerine would be an interesting field to exploit. Nobel responded by building up the great industry that once bore his name.[23] Another of Zinin's pupils, Vasilii Petrushevksii (1829–91), also profited from this advice to organize the mass production of nitroglycerine. So well did he do this that he was invited to teach chemistry to the future emperor Alexander III. Yet a third pupil of Zinin's was Borodin. who devised a method of measuring urea, and also wrote the famous Russian opera, *Prince Igor*.

Zinin's laboratory, a miserable affair mounted in a single room with two Dutch tables, a large stove, a sand bath and several furnaces, was refurbished by a fourth pupil, A. M. Butlerov (1828–86)[24] who in the course of three trips abroad (in 1857, 1861 and 1867) brought even more German techniques and skills to Russia. V. V. Markovnikov (1838–1904), one of Butlerov's pupils, studied the position of the various halogen and hydrogenations in a haloginard: an example of early activity in the field of electron structure in organic reactions. German domination of Russian science continued up to Lenin's death when German physicians, Foerster, von Strumfell, Vogt and others, were in attendance at his bedside.

With German science came German materialist philosophy, notably that of Karl Marx whose economic theory secured its first serious Russian convert in Nikolay Ivanovich Sieber, the Professor of Economy and Statistics at Kiev, who, following the publication of the German edition of Volume I of *Capital*, began to publish articles on 'scientific' socialism, as opposed to the *narodnik* socialism based on the guilt feelings (or sense of duty) of the nobility. Sieber saw the great obstacle presented by sentimentalization of the peasant (*muzhik*) commune, and remarked, 'We shall have no sense in this country until the Russian *muzhik* is cooked up in the factory boiler.'[25]

Symbolically enough it was the grandson and nephew of a German professor at Dorpat University who was to be the central figure of the 'Legal Marxists'. And, like his fellow Legal Marxists, Peter Struve was to enter the natural science faculty of the University of St. Petersburg.[26]

(4)

The universities became incubators of the kind of secret societies by now traditional in Russia. Masonic models influenced the officers from the campaign against Napoleon. Their voice was Pushkin, the Russian Byron (whom he studied), who founded *Sovremennik*, a paper of importance in history. These various unions, like Pavel Pestel's Union of Salvation at St. Petersburg in 1818 or Murav'ëv's Union of the Public Good,

The Northern Society, the Southern Society and the Society of United Slavs, all testify to the leavening effect of outside ideas during the 1820s.

'The first visible object to emerge from the universal fog' was, according to Alexander Herzen, the University of Moscow.[27] To him it was an island of light, for its doors were opened to all who could pass the entrance examinations. Here the sons of great nobles competed on a footing of equality with children of village priests, small gentry and merchants. These talented students were no respecters of incompetence: they drove the Professor of Law into the street with little ceremony and threw his books after him.[28]

Not unnaturally the Government placed restrictions on the universities in 1835, limiting their intake to the sons of gentry and bureaucrats. More restrictions were imposed during the 1848 revolution, the revolution of the intellectuals. So not unnaturally the universities remained small. Only one new one—in Kiev in 1834—had been founded since the first six, whilst Vilna had been closed in 1832. St. Petersburg, the last of the six to be founded, had only 84 students in 1828 and 241 in 1838. The total number of university students in all Russia was 3,758 by 1852. Even musical compositions were examined for secret ciphers.[29]

In this oppressive climate, groups like the circle that gravitated round Petrashevsky in 1845–8 were all infected by St. Simonian and Fourierist ideas. He built up a St. Simon-Fourier type group which set up a phalanstery on his estate for the peasants. But the peasants burnt it, just as they rejected the Socialist intelligentsia some thirty years later. Petrashevsky's group was arrested and twenty-one were sentenced to penal servitude—one of them being Dostoevsky.

From now on the Russians, especially the intelligentsia, began to look still farther west for inspiration. Their gaze was directed to America—where western European science blended with a democratic form of government. The smuggled writings of Alexander Herzen, freely circulating in Russia from 1853 to 1863, advised all who could slough off the old Adam of Europe to migrate to Wisconsin or Kansas. 'Though the standard of their civilization is lower than that of Europe,' he wrote, 'they have but one standard and they all reach it. There lies their tremendous strength.'

Particularly did Herzen praise the boundless theatre of operations open on the frontier. This he said in January 1863 he had developed 'a new nation out of old people'. Here Russia and America were alike. Both countries were poor in a past, both stretched out over unending valleys, both were searching for boundaries to the Pacific—in his phrase 'the Mediterranean of the Future.' In the *Bell* (*Kolokol*), his aptly named paper, his friend and fellow-exile Nicolai Ogarev (to whom he dedicated his *Autobiography*) described America on 15 September 1864 as the only country where religious freedom and the development of science were 'the sole path for the liberation of the masses from intellectual stagnation'.[30]

(5)

For, like their American counterparts, Russian scientists were becoming increasingly self-concious and self-confident. Whereas in the eighteenth century only 34 of the 107 members of the Academy of Sciences were Russians, during the nineteenth century (to 1908) the native Russians increased to 139 out of a total of 189 members.[31]

This self-consciousness was nurtured by the same factor—an increasing awareness of Russia's vast resources, especially in Asia. This was kindled by explorers like F. I. Soymonov, S. P. Krasheninnikov, P. S. Pallas, I. L. Lepëkhin and V. F. Zuyev. The publication of V. M. Severgin's *Mineralogical Land Description of the Russian Empire* (1809) followed the mapping of the Nerchinsk mining district in the last decade of the previous century and was itself followed by the mapping of the Donets Ridge in 1829, and of the Urals in 1846, this last by an Englishman, R. Murchison.

As early as 1810 Count Ugarov presented a project for an Asian academy to the Ministry of Education. Later Michael Pogodin urged his countrymen to turn their attention to Asia, 'where our enemies, following some blind instinct want to hurt us'.[32] Now, with Herzen directing Russian eyes to America as an exemplar, the striking parallels between the two countries became apparent.

Rostov-on-Don was founded in the same decade as the two Kentucky towns of Harrodsburg and Boonesborough, Ekaterinoslav within two years of Marietta in Ohio, whilst Nikolaev and

Cincinnati were founded in the same year. Indeed, in the year in which Ohio entered the Union, Odessa, the capital of New Russia, was founded.[33] America and Russia also began as colonial powers, and in their early stages were colonized by many races. We know of the many nationalities that colonized America, but what is not so appreciated is the variety of races that moved into southern Russia from the time of Catherine the Great. America herself could scarcely show a more motley list in her statistics of population: for in 1870 one-fifth (12 million) of her 61 million population were of foreign origin. A Scottish colony even existed between the Sea of Azov and the Caspian— at Pyatigorsk. An Englishman, reporting this, remarked that in the North 'often I encountered boys who recalled young America rather than young Russia'.[34]

This moving frontier was to be the historical determinant of the future history of both countries: Russia's in Siberia, America's in the West. In both cases, this found its own inimitable interpreter who looked at it from the edge: Schopav (who came from Siberia), F. J. Turner (who taught at Wisconsin). But whereas the American frontier was romanticized, Siberia was ostracized. One was the land of opportunity and agrarian democracy, the other a prison house. Both views are exaggerated.[35]

For exile in Siberia was often inflicted for trivial matters like card playing, tobacco smoking, for letting one's house get on fire and mistakes in drill, as well as for political reasons.[36] We hear so much of it because many of those sent there were gifted and articulate. They had no prisons, many certainly were not chained, and, if any died by the roadside in transit, they piously erected little mounds of stones to commemorate them. (That is why we know more about them than the myriad emigrants who were buried at sea.) The real terror was the climate, which was agony. Then again, many of the political offenders had a high code of ethics, and were indignant at being removed from the centres of power. Yet we should also not forget that in Siberia they escaped the gentry and serfdom, and in the case of runaways, were often hidden by the officials.[37] Indeed, it has been said that 'among the peasants west of the Urals, Siberia was regarded as a kind of Utopia', whilst as for the punishments meted out there, an Englishman called Harry de Windt remarked that the birch used to punish convicts was 'precisely similar to those used at Eton'.[38] As a matter of fact another Englishman remarked that a third of the 298,574 convicts in Siberia 'escaped all control of any kind. We observed that half of them were banished by the Russian communes'.[39] When, between 1858 and 1911, the population of Siberia increased from 5,760,169 to 9,366,355, the native component only increased from 638,000 to 972,866—all the rest being Russians and foreigners.[40]

(6)

Official Russia (as opposed to the various wings of the intelligentsia) was now drawn closer to the United States of America by suspicions of the British activities in Asia. The Governor-General of Siberia and founder of Nikolaevsk-on-Amur, Nikolay Murav'ëv, wrote in a memorandum to the Tsar in 1853:

> We allowed the intrusion of this part of Asia by the English who very naturally to the detriment and reproach of all Europe, disturbing the peace and well being of the nations, prescribe from their little island their own laws in all parts of the world, excluding America, laws not the least aimed at the benefit of mankind, but only at the satisfaction of the commercial interests of Great Britain —but the matter *can still be mended by a close tie* on our part with the North American States.[41]

Having helped John Rogers of the U.S. Navy with facilities when exploring the Aleutians, Murav'ëv much impressed a Californian merchant called P. McD. Collins, who was anxious to promote the idea of a round-the-world telegraph between America and Russia via the Behring Straits. Collins went to Washington in 1856 and was made a commercial agent to the Amur River, whence he submitted a series of reports to the U.S. Government. He was so impressed by his visit that he wrote a book, which he dedicated to Murav'ëv. It was published just before the Civil War and reissued in 1864.[42]

As a result of Collins's scheme a corps of scientists, explorers, technicians and telegraphists were gathered together to make preparations for laying the line from California to British Columbia, then north through Russian America, across the Behring Straits to the mouth of the Amur. The Smithsonian

Institute was involved in it, a sure indication that it was no wild-cat scheme. Unfortunately for Collins, the British outflanked him in 1866 by laying, with the help of Cyprus Field, the Atlantic Cable. Though the Russo-American Cable was abandoned, it had two tangible results. The first was that in the following year Secretary of State William H. Seward, one of Collins's staunchest supporters, bought Russian America—now called Alaska—for 7 million dollars.

Incidentally, the American Ambassador tried to claim the credit for the purchase of Alaska. He was a swash-buckling character who bore the name of Cassius Marcellus Clay, who, as his name might indicate, was a relation of the great Henry Clay, a relationship that saved him from many embarrassments. For Cassius Marcellus Clay used to carry a bowie knife around with him to fight duels provoked by his amorous nature, and used it to such effect that at least one person was killed. He was that curious paradox, a Southern abolitionist, whose support of Lincoln led to his being appointed Ambassador to Russia in 1861. After Lincoln's death he was asked to resign but he clung to his post. Clay was a Russophile, and thought that 'the Russians of the higher class are more like Southerners than the Southerners are like the Northerners'. He told the Tsar's Foreign Minister that eastern Asia comprised 'vast countries yet to be opened up in a land where, for ages, the wealth of the world has accumulated'. He was also anti-British. 'If England', he wrote, 'could move all her wealth to India, and there establish her central power, assimilating Indians and Chinese under one great consolidated empire, giving up her island to Ireland and her insatiate European rivals, she might survive indefinitely. Otherwise, it is but a question of time when she must go.'[43]

The second result of the Russo-American Cable project was that one of the young telegraph engineers, a 19-year-old George Kennan, set out on 1 July 1865, for the Behring Sea and Niko-laevsk-on-Amur. After returning to New York he published an account of his travels in *Tent Life in Siberia* (1870). In the same year he was back in Russia, exploring the Caucasus. In the then current vogue of sponsoring explorers, Kennan was financed to cross Siberia, and publish an account of his journey in the *Century* magazine during the years 1888 and 1889. When Kennan's book *Siberia and the Exile System* appeared in 1891 it showed Siberia as one vast prison cage. And the irony of it was that though Kennan was no revolutionary and certainly no Marxist, his book became a kind of bible for the early Revolutionists and Bolsheviks. As Kennan's most recent editor and illustrious namesake remarked:

> Even the Russian Communist instrument of the Stalin era was not wholly unaffected in its views towards the United States by the recollection that it had been, after all, an American who had once achieved so perceptive and informed an understanding of the Russian revolutionary movement and had carried its cause to the world public with such striking effectiveness.[44]

The kind of horror that Kennan kindled was, if anything, magnified by that most American of writers, Samuel Clemens, otherwise known as Mark Twain, who in his autobiography, remarked:

> We are accustomed to speak of Russia as medieval and as standing still in the Middle Ages, but that is flattery, Russia is way back of the Middle Ages; the Middle Ages are a long way in front of her, and she is not likely to catch up with them so long as the Czardom continues to exist.[45]

Yet Mark Twain had once, much earlier, in 1867 been to Russia himself. And what is more, he had at Yalta, as chairman of a committee of American fellow-travellers (if I may call them so without punning), written an address to the Tsar on the 25th August of that year (the day before they went to his palace), expressing their appreciation that he had 'loosed the bonds of 20 million serfs'. In this address Twain and his fellow-travellers stated that 'America owes much to Russia—is indebted to her in many ways—and chiefly to her unwavering friendship in seasons of greatest need'.[46]

In the great wave of indignation that any nation can generate for wrongs far from home, no American was more emotional than Mark Twain. In 1890 when a lecturer described the penal mines in Siberia, Twain stood up in a Boston audience and cried under great emotion, 'If such a government cannot be overthrown otherwise than by dynamite, then thank God for dynamite.' He went further, and told the editor of *Free Russia*, the anti-Tsarist exiles' periodical, 'Necessarily I am with you, it goes without saying.' Indeed he advised one group to 'keep the throne (of Russia) vacant by dynamite until a day when candidates should decline with thanks'.[47]

Mark Twain was shrewdly aware of the enormous importance of Siberia and those who have read his novel the *American Claimant* will perhaps remember the map which Colonel Mulberry Sellers kept on his wall. It had once borne the name SIBERIA, but now the word *future* had been written in front of that word. There were other additions in red ink—many cities, with great populations set down; scattered over the vast country at points where neither cities nor populations exist today. One of these cities, with population placed at 1,500,000 bore the name 'Liberty-or-Loffskoizalinski', and there was a still more populous one, centrally located and marked 'Capital' which bore the name 'Freedomolovnaivanovich'.[48]

Similar thoughts crossed the mind of Henry Adams, that shrewd American speculator on world affairs. He was convinced that America had no future in the Pacific. 'Her best chance', he wrote on 4 August 1891, 'is Siberia. Russia will probably go to pieces; she is rotten and decrepit to the core, and must pass through a bankruptcy, moral and political. If it can be delayed another twenty-five years, we could Americanise Siberia, and this is the only possible work that I can see open on a scale equal to American means.'[49]

(7)

That an American telegraph engineer should write the most influential book on Siberia by a non-Russian and that Lincoln should write his emancipation proclamation in a telegraph office emphasizes the importance of this medium to these two land mammoths. This, together with energy resource development and control, or in simple language, physics, chemistry and mathematics, were fields in which Russian scientists were not behind any in the world. The electromagnetic telegraph was successfully demonstrated at St. Petersburg by P. L. Schilling in 1832, and four years later an experimental telegraph line was laid round the Admiralty Building. A recording telegraph was also built in St. Petersburg in 1839, followed two years later by an experimental line from the Winter Palace to the headquarters of the General Staff and a second in 1842 between the Summer Palace and St. Petersburg.[50]

In the same year (1842) an American engineer, George Washington Whistler went to Russia to build the famous railway between Moscow and St. Petersburg for that most peripatetic of emperors, Nicholas I. Moreover, the engine works at Alexandrovsky which, with the Winans brothers, Colonel Whistler built, became the virtual 'railway university' of Russia. Indeed, it played a role in Russian industry not unlike that of Peter the Great's naval academy in the history of Russian education.[51]

During the Crimean War another American, Samuel Colt (who had patented the revolver eighteen years before) was shown round a Russian mechanical museum by a young attaché at the American Embassy, A. D. White (later to be President of Cornell and Ambassador to Russia). There they saw 'machines which had only been reinvented in Europe and were worth a fortune'.[52] As a result of the Crimean War (1854–6), freer access to the universities was granted and a mission was sent abroad to study university administration. One of the leaders was the distinguished surgeon N. I. Pirogov, whom we have met twice before, teaching at Dorpat, and later in the Crimean War. At Kiev he inaugurated a liberal *régime* giving students powers of self-government.

The sons of merchants and priests who had been to the universities, known as the *raznochintsy* (or commoners), now emerged, whose spokesman, Vissarion G. Belinsky, was a student of the University of Moscow. He dilated on the importance of science and a middle class in Russia. A 'proletariat of thought', began to appear, many of whom thought science was the only subject worth studying, deploying materialist ideas from Buchner's *Force and Matter* to support their arguments. They attempted to gather together the scientific knowledge of the time and organize it into an explanation of all events by analogy with the natural sciences, and not by any irreligious or metaphysical way.

Comtism now came into its own. From 1858 to 1863 his message, 'the end is progress', gripped groups of itinerant missionaries, bent on winning the workers and peasants to his religion of humanity, holding before them the vision of a sociocratic State. This was indeed ironic. For Comte himself had written to the Tsar suggesting that Russia's very insulation enabled it to by-pass the fragmented state of Europe and adapt an integratory religion of humanity, dating his letters, according to his Positivist calendar 19 Bichat 64 and 20 Archimedes 65.[53] That his theology should fall on the ears of the intelligentsia instead of the Tsar was to incline them even more to the Americans, themselves now infected by Comteian ideas, for fourteen years later (in 1868) the American Ambassador to Russia, Cassius Marcellus Clay, told the Secretary of State, W. H. Seward:

> no people are making more advances, comparatively, in the fine and useful arts, in science, letters and general intelligence. A great destiny lies before her and let us be careful for our own sakes and the cause of humanity to reciprocate her friendly sentiments towards us.[54]

After the Crimean War in 1857, P. H. Sobky (1819–70) went to the U.S.A. to study bridgebuilding. He was a professor at the Institute of Ways and Communications. The Russians Colonel Gortov and Captain Hunius were sent there to study ordnance and, with Colonel Burdon's co-operation, produced a new rifle, the Berdanka, which was adopted in 1868. Nobel obtained the contract to make it and in searching for walnut for the stocks, Robert Nobel stumbled on oil in the Caucasus. The Caucasian aromatics stimulated German-trained N. A. Menshutkin (1842–1907) at St. Petersburg, to found the Russian Chemical Society in 1868: the first scientific society in Russia to be founded by private initiative. He edited its journal, and published a book on qualitative analysis which was translated into German and English. The potential of their native larder was now apparent, and to open it up, more scientific training was needed.

Menshutkin's son Boris (1874–1938) carried on his work. In 1877 Letny pyrolysed oil in the presence of a catalyst to increase its aromatic contents: work continued by Rudnev, Nikiforov and Telinsky. Oil hydrocarbons also engaged V. V. Markovnikov at Moscow and F. K. Beilstein (1838–1908), another German-trained chemist, at the St. Petersburg Technical Institute. Indeed the Russian chemist Shukov actually preceded the American Burton in the 'cracking' of oils.[55]

11

◇◇

Science and the American Frontier
1862-1918

◇◇

(1)

I tell you these are great times. Man has mounted science and is
now run away with. I firmly believe that before many centuries
more, science will be the master of man. The engines he will have
invented will be beyond his strength to control. Some day science
may have the existence of mankind in its power, and the human
race commit suicide by blowing up the world. Not only shall we
be able to cruize in space, but I see no reason why some future
generation shouldn't walk off like a beetle, with the world on its
back, or give it another rotary motion so that every zone should
receive in turn its due portion of heat and light.[1]

I⊤ was April 1862 when Henry Adams wrote this to his
brother. He was then in England where he had become 'a
Comteist within the limits of evolution'. Ironically enough, he
was later to replace a teacher at Harvard who was 'turned out'
for similar beliefs. Attracted by the Comteian theme of an enlightened aristocracy working towards a vast unselfish end,
Henry Adams continued:

We want a national set of young men like ourselves or better to
start new influences not only in politics, but in literature, in law,
in society, and throughout the whole social organism of the
country—a national school of our own generation. In England the
universities centralize ability and London gives a field. So in

France, Paris encourages and combines these influences. But with us, we should need at least six perfect geniuses . . . whereas our generation has not produced one or the promise of one. It's all random, insulated work, for special and temporary and personal purposes, and we have no means, power or hope of combined action for any unselfish end.

This was now to happen.

Such 'combined action' of scientists for infusing into the nation 'that vital and animating spirit that shall win this gigantic civil war'—to quote from the sponsoring speech delivered by Senator Henry Wilson of Massachusetts—was effected by the creation of a National Academy of Science. Chartered to investigate, examine, experiment and report upon any subject of science or art whenever called upon by any department of government, it was the first institutional expression of the professionals' desire that the government should have adequate scientific advice. As a recent commentator on its genesis remarked, 'In 1863 the professionals only needed the politicians to put a legal rubber stamp on their arrangements. In his long career Henry Wilson showed little interest in or understanding of Science'.[2]

Another collegiate Comteist, Andrew Dickson White, whose anxiety to use his father's wealth to found 'A new *University*, worthy of our land and time' which should afford 'an asylum for *Science*—where truth shall be sought out for truth's sake'—not accommodated 'to fit "Revealed Religion" ', was held up by the American Civil War. But when, to provide personnel for the North in the same way as the Polytechnique had provided them for France seventy years earlier, grants of land were given for colleges, A. D. White became guardian of the large grant earmarked for New York. For, like other states, New York obtained 30,000 acres of public land for each of its representatives and senators. All income accruing from this was to be used to establish and maintain at least one college:

> where the leading object shall be . . . to teach such branches of learning as are related to agriculture and the mechanic arts, in such a manner as the legislatures of the states may respectively prescribe, in order to promote the liberal and practical education of the industrial classes in the several pursuits and professions of life.[3]

Such federal grants-in-aid for technical training, first made possible by this Morrill Act of 1862, were to be further extended when the Hatch Act of 1887 established agricultural experimental stations attached to the land-grant colleges, and by the second Morrill Act of 1890 providing annual federal grants to the colleges on certain provisos like no racial discrimination, certain standards of work and more vocational courses.

(2)

To the near-million acres obtained by New York under the first Morrill Act, the telegraph magnate, Ezra Cornell, added an endowment for a university at Ithaca: White, as its first president, set its non-denominational tone so effectively that he was accused of 'infidelity' and 'atheism', which he had to rebut. One of his rebuttals, slowly inflated from a report in the *New York Herald Tribune*, to a booklet—*The Warfare of Science*— was to be supplemented with various of his articles in *The Popular Science Monthly*, to become *The Warfare of Science with Theology* (1896).

Aptly, this was finished in his study overlooking the River Neva, in Moscow, when he was the American Ambassador. Watching a crowd of Russian peasants at work he likened his labour to theirs. Both were icebreaking. In White's case, the ice was 'vast masses of myth, legend, marvel and dogmatic assertion' built up 'round the atmosphere of thought', which he now professed to see 'dissolving away like icebergs drifted into the Gulf Stream'.[4]

His majestic survey concluded with the implication that, as a result of the establishment of land-grant colleges, 'the physical and natural sciences are henceforth likely to be developed normally, and without fear of being sterilised by theology or oppressed by ecclesiasticism'.[5]

Of the sixty-nine land-grant colleges, established over the years, some had experimental stations established in conjunction with them, where fundamental discoveries were made. Hybrid corn increased yields by 30 per cent and gave America the equivalent of one year's extra crop during the Second World War. Streptomycin, discovered in 1943 by Dr. Selman A. Waksman, stemmed from early experimental work at the New Jersey Experimental Station in the 1890s by Dr. Jacob Lipman.

They were based on a completely instrumental theory of education. 'What Knowledge is of most worth?' was the searching question of Herbert Spencer and it is no coincidence that he became a myth-maker of the age. For even when his ideas were vitiated by the process they described, his terms—'Science', 'Progress' and 'Education'—became quasi-holy.

Hitting bookstalls in 1866, his *Social Statics* sold 368,755 copies in authorized editions alone up to 1903. By analogies from biology and mechanics he argued that non-interference by the State was essential for progress. American Protestants relished him:

> this positive philosophy (exulted the *Christian Spectator*) comes with a veil over its face, that its too divine radiance may be hidden for a time. This is Science that has been conversing with God, and brings in her hand His law written on tablets of stone.

Justification by science was a synthesis of justification by faith and by works. All the elements of the old religion were present in the new; God (Evolution) versus the Devil (the State), the Good Book (the operations of nature) with its necessary testaments, the Old (Biology) and the New (Engineering) both needing study if the Kingdom of Heaven was to be brought about.[6]

Free choice and self-directed study had a Spencerian flavour as wafted by Charles W. Eliot, the chemist-president of Harvard from 1869 onwards: 'The university recognises no real antagonism between literature and science, and consents to no such narrow alternatives as mathematics or classics, science or metaphysics.' They also indicated how closely universities could work with a developing community. In the next generation, the geologist-president of the land-grant University of Wisconsin, Charles R. Van Hise, developed its service facilities: off-campus correspondence courses, centres of extension teaching, a 'Bureau of General Welfare'. University teachers served on the non-political commissions of the State. In 'applied' research, university scientists, by devising the Babcock fat test, saved State dairymen hundreds of millions of dollars.[7]

Wisconsin's 'militant conception of the university as an organ of reasonable and voluntary guidance amid the labyrinthine mazes of community life' caught the imagination of the English banker-sociologist Victor Branford and of his friend, Patrick Geddes.[8] Geddes especially wanted, as he said, 'to avoid the separation of the school of industry from the school of science, which produces pedants in the university and philistines in the workshop'. Geddes was to carry the Wisconsin idea to Scotland and India, and to inspire the expository genius of Lewis Mumford, just as he was inspired by Charles Ferguson, whose *University Militant* (1911) and concept of the Technarchy (the age of the engineers), he did so much to humanize.[9]

(3)

Given presidential approval a day after the Bill for construction of the Union Pacific Railway, and a month or so after the Homestead Act, the Morrill Act was to be one of a battery of operations for opening up the frontier. The railway pioneered for the farmer, and the farmer, given a homestead, would subdue the virgin soil.[10]

But the assumption that a farm of 160 acres would provide an adequate homestead for immigrants was a cruel underestimation of the problems posed in the high plains and the sub-humid regions. These had been overlooked by the legislators of the Homestead Act, and when exposed by the Director of the Federal Survey of the Rocky Mountain, had collectivist implications which were far from welcome.

This director, J. W. Powell described the homestead unit as needing to be increased by a factor of at least 17, and pleaded for a scientific survey of the public domain to ascertain the potentialities of yet unsettled areas. For all the country west of the 100th meridian (except a little in California, Oregon and Washington), needed irrigation. Irrigation implied communal effort, and communal effort needed priming by the State.

Sneering at the 'new-fledged collegiates' and 'scientific lobbyists' who wanted to 'shut up the West' and 'create federal jobs for themselves', the land speculators accused Powell of wishing to destroy the yeoman farmer and foster 'baronial estates'. All poor Powell could salvage from his proposals was one small concession: the consolidation of all the surveys into the U.S. Geological Survey[11] with Clarence King as its first and (soon after) Powell himself as director. In the Geological Survey Powell used professors from the land-grant colleges, and by inventorizing America's mineral wealth, built up one of the most formidable scientific bureaux ever known. Appropriations for his department leapt from $165,000 to half a million dollars. A gigantic geological map of the U.S.A. was projected. So rapid was its growth that a commission was set up in 1884 to examine it (together with that of other bureaux), 'with a view to secure greater efficiency and economy of administration in the public service'. Challenged by Agassiz to defend such massive 'centralization' of science, Powell replied that 'a hundred millionaires could not do the work in scientific research now done by the General Government', and asked: 'shall the work of scientific research and the progress of American Civilization wait until the contagion of Agassiz' example shall inspire a hundred millionaires to engage in like good work?'

Powell did much to awaken Americans to the importance of conserving their natural resources. He wanted dams built in arid regions and launched an irrigation survey in 1888, only to have it torpedoed, together with the Geological Survey two years later, by short-sighted Western politicians. So he resigned. He left those he had trained to press for conservation: F. H. Newell, A. P. Davis, C. D. Walcott and W. J. McGhee.

Science was now obviously impinging on government, so it is no surprise to find that his survey nourished, amongst others, Lester Ward—officially a palaeobotanist but actually a sociologist. Service in the survey from 1883 to 1892 led Ward to enunciate his concept of 'sociocracy'; the best way of accelerating the Spencerian processes of nature. As he saw it, sociocracy implied 'the laying aside of irrelevant issues. The important objects upon which all but a few are agreed will receive their proper degree of attention, and measures will be considered in a non-partisan spirit with the sole purpose of securing those objects.' Putting it another way, Ward wrote: 'The individual has reigned long enough. The day has come for society to take its own affairs into its own hands and shape its own destiny.'[12] He concluded that energy must be controlled by planning if evolution were to result. This he called 'social telesis' or the adjustment of means to ends. He showed that evolution was animal and planless, whereas mind, being 'telic', can plan. Mind could, and should, according to Ward, preserve the dynamic and prevent the statical condition of the social forces (and) prevent the restoration of equilibrium between the social forces and the natural forces operating outside of them.[13]

This is why Ward followed Comte in stressing that only after the widest diffusion of scientific knowledge amongst the people could such telic forces begin to operate. With characteristically mechanistic analogues he described this diffusion as 'the piston of civilisation' and 'the mainspring of progress', and insisted that only the State could secure it.

Ward's influence on his colleague in the Geological Survey, Charles Van Hise, was considerable. After Van Hise became President of the University of Wisconsin in 1903, he did his best to secure this wide diffusion of knowledge, transforming it into the leading community-service university in the U.S.A.[14] Indeed, the University of Wisconsin was so much concerned in 'social planning' that it was to be known in the 1930's as 'Little Moscow'.[15]

(4)

Lester Ward's writing found one outlet in a journal called *The Open Court*. This was specifically devoted to 'the Religion of Science' and was subsidized by E. C. Hegeler, a German-trained engineer, who had set up a zinc-smelting works, aptly enough near South Bethlehem, in Pennsylvania. Moving to La Salle, Illinois, in 1860, Hegeler made a fortune when his zinc was adopted for cartridges during the Civil War.

The Open Court had an unbroken run from its first issue in 1886 until 1936. In addition to Ward's, it carried articles by Alfred Binet (the pioneer of intelligence tests), Pierre Janet (a pioneer psychiatrist) and Henri Poincaré (the astronomer). Poincaré contributed his thoughts on the philosophy of science, and was joined by Ernst Mach (the physicist). These went down so well that the editor, Paul Carus, started an 'Open Court Library'.[16]

Carus, Hegeler's son-in-law, was a pupil and popularizer of Hermann Grassman, whose creation of the calculus of extension (or general science of forms), was so brilliantly reworked by Alfred North Whitehead, in his first book *Universal Algebra*. To Carus, God was the sum total of such forms, and man's comprehension of things was his 'spirituality'. Exegesis of this mathematical religion was provided by stuffing *The Open Court* with articles on the basis of mathematics by Hilbert, Dedekind, Bertrand Russell, Poincaré and Jourdain: evangelism by a second journal called *The Monist*. Monism explained the universe by the one materialist principle—energy. As we have seen, it stemmed from German materialists and had already made its impact on American thinkers. Henry Carey had dedicated his book on *The Unity of Law* to Eugen Dühring.[17]

The St. Paul of the Monists was Ostwald, the famous physical chemist. Having virtually completed the intellectual seduction of some of the Russian Marxists, Ostwald now began to strike vibrant and responsive chords in the United States. Reading Ostwald's *Vorlesung über Naturphilosophie* in 1902, William James found it 'a most delectable book', and confessed, 'I don't think I have ever envied a man's mind as much as I have envied Ostwald's—unless it were Mach's.'

James wrote the term 'pragmatism' in the margin opposite Ostwald's interpretation of scientific concepts in terms of their experimental consequences. During the same year he received letters from Ostwald urging him to formulate this in philosophical terms.[18] James's English friend Schiller added:

pragmatism . . . is much too obscure and technical and not a theory one can ever stampede mankind into. Besides the word has misleading associations, and we want something bigger and more extensive (inclusive). It does not express the whole meaning of what we are saying, and I feel that I'm constantly stretching the term. But why should we not call it HUMANISM? 'Humanism' as opposed to 'scholasticism'; 'humane' as opposed to barbarous.[19]

On 9 June Schiller appended a new Pythagorean 'table of contraries':

1.	The Good and Finite	vs	The Evil and Infinite
2.	Humanism		Scholasticism
3.	Pragamatism		Verbalism
4.	Personal Idealism		Naturalism
5.	Pluralism		Absolutism
6.	Radical Empiricism		Apriorism
7.	Voluntarism		Intellectualism
8.	Anthropomorphism		Amorphism
9.	Briticism		Germanism
10.	Witticism		Barbarism

James replied, in a revealing metaphor:

> Humanism doesn't make a very electrical connection with my nature, but in appellations the individual proposes and the herd adopts or drops . . . we shall see if the name sticks. All *other* names are bad, most certainly—especially pragmatism.[20]

Even more revealingly, he remarked that he felt it

> queer to be assisting at the eclosion of a great new mental epoch, life, religion and philosophy in one,

and wrote from California to Schiller where he had joined John Dewey: 'What a triumvirate we shall be, and how humanism will hum—drowning the roar of Russo-Japanese artillery across the Pacific.'[21]

The new mental epoch, at whose 'eclosion' James felt himself assisting, was a vaster one than he imagined. If, as he wrote, *all* knowledge was to be judged by its application, and if application was to be construed in terms of control of environment, it only needed the additive idea that both knowledge and its application should be socialized to make it the purest Communism—or Fascism, perhaps.[22]

(5)

To the pragmatist John Dewey, the largest selling book, and the most influential since *Uncle Tom's Cabin*, was Edward Bellamy's *Looking Backwards 2000–1887* (1888): the first completely technological Utopia. Many of the devices he forecast were indeed to become part of the everyday life of the Americans—

> If, [said the narrator] we could have devised an arrangement for providing everybody with music in their homes, perfect in quality, unlimited in quantity, suited to every mood, and beginning and ceasing at will, we should have considered the limit of human felicity already attained, and ceased to strive for further improvements.

To achieve this state of felicity Bellamy wanted conformity to his doctrines. Well might a Swiss critic comment 'Technocracy is at work in Bellamy's state'.[23]

Belief in a press-button world was satirized by Anna Bowman Dodd. In *The Republic of the Future* (1887) she described it as leading to a state of universal *ennui*. But the dreams of the engineers persisted. One of them, Chauncey Thomas, envisaged the great glass city Tone, electrically lit by wind generators, serviced by tubes and governed by a technocracy. Thanks to the organization of a crystal button society by John Coster, 'the age of science supplanted the age of guesswork'. Having absorbed public utilities, transport, land and insurance, a 'Government of Settled Forms' is established, which takes steps to conserve the soil (by regulating agriculture) and the people (by sterilizing the unfit). Chauncey Thomas' book, *The Crystal Button* (1891), was but one of numerous technological fantasies, some of which like John Bachelder's *A.D. 2000, Electrical Development at Atlantis* (1890), and Colonel Edward House's *Philip Dru: Administrator, A Story of Tomorrow 1920–1935* (1912) adumbrated policies to be followed in the 1930-ties.

Industrialists caught the mood. After publishing *The Human Drift* (1894), King Camp Gillette established the safety razor corporation that bore his name and expanded his theme that the competitive system wasted nearly ninety per cent of human productive efforts, causing industrial and international strife. He proposed to create concentrate population and production near the Niagara Falls. His variant of Bellamy's 'industrial army' was to have mobile battalions of agricultural labour. His solution of housing problems was the huge apartment block with central kitchens. In 1910 the 'World Corporation' was incorporated in Arizona and Gillette offered a million dollars to Theodore Rosevelt to act as its president for four years.

(6)

The churches of the Bellamy faith were American universities, where the religion of the infinite improvability of man through the redemptive potential of science was nourished. For these universities were the nineteenth-century counterparts of medieval churches and cathedrals.[24] An archetype was the New York College for the Training of Teachers (now Columbia Teachers College) virtually founded by the Industrial Education Association.

The analogy of the religious test (imposed until 1871 on English university teachers) was the Ph.D. Before the Civil War, this was sought abroad, especially in Germany; after the

Civil War post-graduate schools mushroomed to meet the demand. Only a year before the Morrill Act, one of the earliest doctorates, was conferred upon W. Willard Gibbs, perhaps the greatest theoretical physicist since the time of Newton. By 1900 there were 5,668 graduate students, by 1930 47,255 and by 1950 223,786. The number of Ph.D.s awarded annually grew from 44 in 1876 to 562 in 1918, 1,064 in 1924, 3,088 in 1940 and 6,633 in 1950.[25]

Well might F. P. Barnard predict:

Our universities will not be new creations, they will be formed by the expansion of the system of post-graduate instruction.

The numbers of undergraduates and technical students per million of the American population doubled between 1872 (573) and 1900 (1,233). Even more impressive was the increase in the population of scientists and engineers to the rest of the U.S. population. In 1880 there was 1 to every 30,900; by 1900, 1 to 8,900; by 1920, 1 to every 2,210 and by 1949, 1 to 910. Looked at in yet another way the figures tell an even more impressive story. In 1900 there was one scientist or engineer to every 250 people employed; by 1950 the ratio was 1 to 60. The number of engineers per thousand workers in the labour force of the U.S.A. increased from 0·4 in 1880 to 2·4 in 1930 and 7·0 in 1950. Both a reason and a result of this was the increasing use being made of physics in the American electrical industry, and of chemistry in the petroleum industry. So hungry was American industry for new knowledge that they began to develop research units and departments of their own.[26]

The redemptive potential of technology in liberating man from servile labour can be best illustrated by the growth of inanimate energy slaves. In 1880 these were producing only 53·5 per cent of the total horse-power hours (as opposed to 9·4 by humans and 37·1 by animals). By 1950 they were producing 98·5 per cent (as opposed to 0·9 by humans and 0·6 by animals). In the same period the total number of horse-power hours increased from 29·9 billions in 1880 to 674·9 billions in 1950.[27]

The impressive arithmetic of this technological apocalypse inadequately metered the intensity of the work being done in the most characteristic of all American institutions, the graduate schools.

Scholars have and will contest primacies and prides of place but most agree that, prestigiously, the exemplar of the graduate school was Johns Hopkins, whose first principal, Daniel Coit Gilman had travelled abroad with A. D. White as a fellow-student.

Intended to be to the U.S.A. what Berlin University had been to Germany, and with an initial endowment of $3\frac{1}{4}$ million dollars, nearly all its 53 professors and lecturers in 1884 had studied in German universities, and 13 of them held German doctorates. Their researches, as in the Polytechnique, were disseminated by journals of mathematics, chemistry and physiology. The intention was matched by achievements.

Hopkins graduates, according to Gilman, were to be 'wise, thoughtful, progressive guides in whatever department of work or thought they may be engaged'. Other industrial patrons shared this view: Leland Stanford, who built his university on the family farm in California and endowed it with 24 million dollars was a persistent correspondent of Francis Amasa Walker, the second president of the Massachusetts Institute of Technology.[28]

Thrilled with enthusiasm at the dawn of a new era, William H. Welch returned from Germany (where he had been a fellow-student with Pavlov) 'to use the master key forged by pathology and bacteriology . . . to transform the face of modern medicine.'[29] Opening the first physiological laboratory in the United States, he trained, amongst others, Walter Reed, then a young army recruiting officer in Baltimore, who in turn became Professor of Bacteriology at the newly established Army Medical School in Washington, and a leader in the campaign against typhoid, yellow fever and malaria then claiming more than six times the number of battle casualties in the Spanish-American War.

Another 'first' at Johns Hopkins was the psychological laboratory established by G. Stanley Hall (the first in America and the second in the world). This produced, amongst others, John Dewey, Joseph Jastrow, J. McKeen Cattell and G. T. W. Patrick, contributors all to Hall's other creation, the *American Journal of Psychology*. Unfortunately, Hall responded to the overtures of a wealthy business man, J. G. Clark, to launch a Johns Hopkins-type graduate school specializing only in science, mathematics, physics, chemistry, biology and psychology. By

1889 a small but select group of specialists like the physicists A. A. Michelson and A. G. Webster, the chemists Arthur Michael and J. V. Nef and the anthropologist Franz Boas were assembled, but the founder's habit of demanding the printed doctoral theses to display in his front parlour, together with the miserable endowment, weakened their enthusiasm. They became easy victims of the persuasive tongue of William Rainey Harper, then transforming an old Baptist college into the University of Chicago with 34 million dollars provided by the oil magnate John D. Rockefeller.

The lure of Chicago with its Ryerson laboratory (dedicated in 1894) was strong. Not only did Michelson win a Nobel prize, but so did Robert Millikan (in 1923) and A. H. Compton (in 1927). Only one other American won a Nobel prize in the same period. Further money, given by Charles Tyson Yerkes (engineer of the London Underground Railway), enabled George Ellery Hale to build his world-famous observatory, parent of an even greater one at Mount Wilson in California.[30]

Just as William Rainey Harper built a 'multiversity' out of a Baptist college, so Hale built up the Throop Institute in Pasadena into the California Institute of Technology, with the Nobel prizewinner Robert A. Millikan from Chicago as its principal and his own old teacher A. A. Noyes (1866–1936) from Massachusetts Institute of Technology as Director of its Gates Chemical Laboratory. Here the pace of research accelerated. For Noyes's pupils at M.I.T. or Cal. Tech. included Willis R. Whitney (later of General Electric), G. G. Abbot the astrophysicist, R. C. Tolman, W. D. Haskins, E. W. Washburn, R. B. Sosman, John Johnston, F. G. Keyes and Linus Pauling. Of these Linus Pauling, elucidator of the structure of complicated organic molecules, is still a bright star. T. H. Morgan the geneticist and Lee du Bridge have carried the tradition into other fields.

The nearby University of California caught the fever. E. O. Lawrence built a linear accelerator or cyclotron, to produce concentrated streams of elementary particles. His first was made of a window pane, scrap brass and sealing wax. Paced by the work of Harold Urey of Columbia, the Curies in France and Carl Anderson and Robert Oppenheimer of his own university, Lawrence began to make substances radio-active by bombarding them with protons. This demanded high voltages and led to the establishment of the radiation laboratory at the University of California in 1926; a precedent for the 'big' laboratory where a team of researchers worked on a growing scale. For Lawrence's cyclotron was to physics what Galileo's telescope had been to astronomy. With it such valuable tools as carbon 14, iodine 131, tritium and uranium 238 were built up.

This set the stage for the largest of all experiments in science: the Manhattan project which created the Hiroshima bomb.

(7)

In the shadows of these schools grew the scientific societies: no longer, as in eighteenth-century Europe, gentlemanly affairs with noble presidents and 'star' members, but *entrepôts* of ideas and personalities. One feature of the slave-markets the professional activities of their predecessors had helped to eliminate was embodied in these societies: the flexing of intellectual sinews in public. To go 'on show' in front of one's peers in one of these societies was practically the only reliable path to a university chair.

Three times as many general scientific societies (48) were founded in America after the Civil War as in all the decades before it (15); nearly five times as many biological and natural history societies (44 as opposed to 9), and more than twice as many professional associations. Many of them stimulated or swallowed subsequent formations. The American Chemical Society, for instance, was founded in 1876, and by 1941 had nearly a hundred local societies affiliated to it, becoming the largest scientific society in the world. The American Physical Society from 1902 issued the *Physical Review*, now one of the most eagerly-awaited journals in the world.

As the great sub-continent was dug, drained, dammed, electrified, fed and clothed, engineers associated in powerful groups: Mining (1871), Mechanical (1880), Electrical (1884) and Chemical (1908). The young took cues from their elders, forming special scientific fraternities like Sigma XI: founded in 1886 at Cornell by a group of geologists. Journals like the *Popular Science Monthly* (founded by E. L. Youmans in 1872) attracted great scientific editors like James McKeen Cattell and Waldemar Kaempffer, and fanned his enthusiasm. To satisfy it David Van Nostrand (1811–86) the largest specialist publisher in America, encouraged American scientists like Squire Whipple to publish their work, and also issued biographies of the great engineers.[31]

Publication demanded scientific methods of classification. Even Melvil Dewey took his duties of classification so seriously that in recruiting students for his school of library economy at Columbia he asked them to state their height and weight and give colour of their hair and eyes. For this he was suspended. So he promptly resigned, migrated to Albany and built up the New York State Library, devising the decimal system of classification by which he is still remembered.

Dewey was a figure in the new world of information retrieval, a subject dear to the heart of John Shaw Billings. Impressed by the difficulties of 12,343 medical officers and contract surgeons of the Union and 3,000 surgeons and assistant surgeons of the Confederacy, he used a surplus of $50,000 of the Civil War Hospital Funds to build up the Army Medical Library. For this he began compiling the index (59 volumes of which were issued up to 1950), and with the help of Herman Hollerith, devised the punched-card system of filing.[32]

Other case-histories of new sciences evolving from social needs can be seen in the work of Charles F. Chandler, Director of the Columbia School of Mines, who was active in improving the manufacture of sulphuric acid, the refining of petroleum and the distillation of coal gas, and from his fees as an industrial chemist often helped students financially. He helped the College of Physicians and Surgeons and the New York College of Pharmacy to grow.

Similarly a course in electrical engineering originally proposed by T. A. Edison in 1882, was established in 1888 at postgraduate level and under a former graduate, M. I. Pupin, became a model of what could be achieved by a close alliance of scientists and engineers. From this school came Millikan and Irving Langmuir. It was indicative of the growth of the Pupin Laboratory that John Denning should first demonstrate nuclear fission there in January 1939.

The American Chemical Society (1876) owed much to Chandler; the American Mathematical Society even more to Pupin and C. P. Steinmetz; the American Physical Society, thanks to Pupin with A. A. Michelson, W. F. Magee and E. L. Nichols, held its first meeting at Columbia on 30 May 1899.

(8)

That the amateur benevolent plantocrats with their botanic gardens and societies had ceased to dominate science was made abundantly plain in 1862 when the Board of Agriculture was established in the same year as the Morrill Act received presidential approval. It had, as its first commissioner, the presidential milkman. True, he bore a name venerated by scientists— Isaac Newton—but he was peculiarly ill-fitted '. . . to acquire and diffuse . . . useful information on subjects connected with agriculture in the most general and comprehensive sense of that word, and to procure, propagate and distribute among the people new and valuable seeds and plants'. Not only did the milkman do little to live up to his name, he even quarrelled with its only professional scientist, who might have done so, C. M. Weatherill, a chemist who had studied with Pelouse at the Collège de France and with Leibig at Giessen.

The bureau's horticulturalist, William Saunders, was much better. He encouraged the cultivation of eucalyptus and navel orange trees and helped found the Grange: a farmers' movement which stimulated the formation of State boards of agriculture and experimental stations.[33]

Locusts in the wheatfields, Australian lady-birds in citrus trees, moths in Massachusetts, boll weevils in the cotton belt and mosquitos in southern areas stimulated the development of a department of entomology in 1881. Animal diseases, pleuropneumonia, Texas fever, hog cholera and trichinosis led to the Bureau of Animal Industry in 1884. New crops posed such problems for the Botanical Division that a section of Vegetable Pathology was established in 1888 under Beverley T. Galloway, with Erwin Frank Smith helping fundamental research. The need for better grasses led to the establishment of a division of Agrostology in 1895. Other divisions like Pomology, Gardens and Grounds, and Seeds were merged with these in 1900 to form a Bureau of Plant Industry. This introduced durum wheat, Sudan grass, Smyrna figs and soya beans.

Federal help was given to the agricultural experimental

stations of the land-grant colleges, and within sixteen years twenty-eight states were carrying on research. Pressure by professors secured the passing of the Hatch Act in 1887, which gave the experimental stations a semi-autonomous relationship with the Department of Agriculture. There were sixty-four such stations by 1914.

After the Commissioner for Agriculture had been raised to cabinet rank as Secretary for Agriculture in 1889, Charles W. Dabney (assistant secretary and second to hold the post) was determined that the Department had to become 'more and more a training ground for scientific experts'.

These experts pressed relentlessly for State action to control pests, disease and fraud. A case in point is that of Harvey W. Wiley. Appointed to the chemistry division of the Board in 1883, he experimented with sorghum and beets as sugar producers, and campaigned vigorously, if at times unfortunately, for pure and healthy food-preservation techniques. These new techniques and discoveries were disseminated by the extension services established by the Smith-Levers Act of 1914.[34]

As an example of science in government, the Department was outstanding. With its 1,323 demonstrators, 1,812 researchers and 6,021 'regulators', served by 687 administrative personnel and 4,635 clerks and others, it could boast about having a greater research establishment for the application of science than any other economic interest.[35]

(9)

Neither inside nor outside government, but rather in those unexplored corridors in between, science had no more persuasive expositor than Henry Adams.[36] Accumulating evidence from the past in a series of studies, most notably his nine-volume *History of the United States* (1889–91)—covering the administrations of Jefferson and Madison—to discover the origins of a Comteian aristocracy, he had also, after returning to America, visited the geologists who, in the late sixties under his friend Clarence King's supervision, were surveying the mineral resources of the western United States by analysing a strip of territory centering on the 40th parallel. 'They held', he wrote, 'under their hammers a thousand miles of mineral country with all its riddles to solve, and its stores of possible wealth to make.

They felt the future in their hands.'[37] For they found, not sermons in stones, but prophecies.

Something more personal held Adams to the Geological Survey. King, who became its first director in 1879, was 'the ideal American they all wanted to be',[38] whilst there is a theory that Adam's wife (who later committed suicide) was secretly in love with him.[39]

For the Adams were a strange family. Meeting one of them, said William James, was 'like meeting the augurs behind the altar—and *none* of them were smiling'. 'Powerful race these Adamses,' he added, 'to remain plebians after so many generations of Culture.' Mr. Justice Holmes, to whom we are indebted for this story, added, 'though capable of queer things, they had an inward delicacy that was far from plebian'.[40]

This inward delicacy led Adams to circulate in 1907 a privately printed acknowledgement that 'the whole mechanical consolidations of force (had) ruthlessly stamped out the life of the class into which (he) Adams had been born'. Thirteen years later (in 1920) this was given to the world by the Massachusetts Historical Society, as *The Education of Henry Adams*.

The symbol of the displacer was the dynamo: 'a moral force, much as the early Christians felt the cross'. He went on: 'The planet itself seemed less impressive, in its old-fashioned, deliberate annual or daily revolution, than this wheel. . . .' Watching it at the Great Exposition in Paris in 1900 he confessed that 'before the end, one began to pray to it; inherited instinct fought the natural expression of man before silent and infinite force. Among the thousand symbols of ultimate energy, the dynamo was not so human as some, but it was the most expressive.' Adams came to believe that the dynamo abolished all distinctions hitherto kept separate by history or metaphysics, and suggested that history itself had become dynamic in the sense that progress itself had become 'the development and economy of Forces'. Thus he argued that man was merely the sum of the forces which attracted him: 'his body and thought are alike their product; the movement of the forces controls the product of his mind, since he can know nothing but the motions which impinge on his senses, whose sum makes education'.[41]

Looking at the Paris Exhibition of 1900 he mused:

There are things in it which run close to the day of judgement. It is a new century and what we used to call electricity is its God. . . . I go down to the Champs de Mars and sit by the hour over the great dynamos, watching them run as noiselessly and smoothly as the planets, and asking them—with infinite courtesy—where in Hell are they going.[42]

And again: 'Every afternoon I went to the Exposition and prayed to the dynamos.'[43]

But perhaps most significant of all was that Adams looked to the universities rather than the churches, and to the historians rather than the clergy to provide the interpreting principles. To 'suggest a reform of the whole University system, grouping all Knowledge as an historical stream, to be treated by historical methods and drawing the line between the University and technology',[44] he wrote the *Rule of Phase applied to History* in 1904. The university he defined as

a system of education grouped about History; a main current of thought branching out like a tree, into endless forms of activity, in regular development, according to the laws of physics; and to be studied as a single stream, not as now by a multiversal, but by a universal law; not as a scientific but as a historical unity; not as a practise of technical handling, but as a process of mental evolution in history, controlled, like the evolution of any series of chemical or electric equilibria, by one general formula.[45]

His estimation of the new technocrats was low:

The work of domestic progress is done by masses of mechanical power-steam, electric, furnace, or others—which have to be controlled by a score or two of individuals who have shown capacity to manage it. The work of internal government has become the task of controlling these men, who are socially as remote as heathen gods, alone worth knowing, but never known, and who could tell nothing of political value if one skinned them alive. Most of them have nothing to tell, but are forces as drunk as their dynamos, absorbed in the development or economy of power. They are trustees for the public, and whenever society assumes the property, it must confer on them that title; but the power will remain as before, whoever manages it, and will then control society without appeal, as it contents its stokers and pitmen. Modern politics is, at bottom, a struggle—not of men but of forces. The men become every year more and more creatures of force, massed about central power houses. The conflict is not between the men, but the motors that drive the men, and the men bend to succumb to their own motive forces.[46]

Henry Adams cried out in defiance of the forces surging into the twentieth century:

> Seize, then, the Atom! rack his joints!
> Tear out of him his secret spring.
> Grind him to nothing!—though he points
> To us, and his life-blood annoints
> Me—the dead Atom King.[47]

This interpretation of life in terms of force or energy he put into syllogistic form:

All Civilization is Centralization
All Centralization is Economy
Therefore all Civilization is the survival of the most Economical.

Under economic centralization, Asia is cheaper than Europe.
The world tends to economic centralization
Therefore Asia tends to survive, and Europe to perish.

He also drew the necessary implications of this:

Progress is Economy! Socialism is merely a new application of Economy which must go on until competition puts an end to further economies, as the whole world becomes one socialistic society and rots out. One need not love Socialism in order to point out the logical necessity for Society to march that way; and the wisdom of doing it intelligently if it is to do it at all.[48]

The interpretation was held even more intensely by his brother, Brooks.[49] Brooks Adams was a scientific determinist. To him civilization was based upon centralization, centralization upon administrative capacity; a quality singularly lacking in the capitalists of a complex industrial State, since Democracy had proved itself 'incapable of continuous collective thought except at long intervals under the severest tension'. When printing some of his brother Henry's essays under the title *The Degradation of the Democratic Dogma*, Brooks Adams stated that as a form of collective energy, Democracy tended to lose intensity as it expanded.

(10)

A more optimistic view of the Comteian *élite* was held by others like Herbert Croly, the first child to be baptized in the 'Religion of Humanity' in the United States of America. Croly was taught by his father from his earlier years' to understand and believe in the religion of Auguste Comte'.[50] No Christian lived up to his baptismal promises with greater intensity than Herbert Croly did. In an aptly named book, *The Promise of American Life* (1909), he outlined the tradition of technological competence underlying its optimistic title. To him 'the perfect type of authoritative technical methods are those which prevail among scientific men in respect to scientific work',[51] and he urged that 'the appropriate moral and intellectual standards should be applied as incorruptibly as those born of specific technical practices'.[52]

As a journalist on the *Architectural Record*, Croly was professionally oriented towards system-building. He looked to a State which could integrate the oligopolies of industry and the factionalism of unions: a nationalized rather than a nationalist America. 'Organic units' were his aim, a *corps d'élite* of dedicated men his agents. Their dedication was to be achieved through the elimination of the profit motive, which he detested so much that he insisted that the only way in which work could be made entirely disinterested was to 'adjust its compensation to the needs of a normal and wholesome life. Descanting on this, a recent commentator has remarked:

> he wanted for an 'ultimate end' something close to the Communist ideal of 'from each according to his ability, to each according to his need'.[53]

Croly's friend Walter Lippman wrote in 1914, 'the scientific spirit . . . is . . . the discipline of democracy'. Only this could evoke the 'same loyalty and courage to which religions of old could point as their finest flower'.[54]

(11)

The finest flower was ironically enough to bloom in the twentieth century in war and the threat of war. For just as the Civil War initiated one series of bureaux to cope with the exploitation of the frontier, the First World War initiated others to cope with its defence. With only 123 planes to France's 1,400, the United States had to move quickly, so a National Advisory Committee for Aeronautics was formed in 1915 under C. D. Walcott. His appointment was symbolic: the Smithsonian had been involved in the experimenting of S. P. Langley, whilst he was a personal example of the mutual stimulus afforded by the Geological Survey's forestry conservation and mining research. Walcott saw too, that these bureaux were hungry for the graduate students being produced from the universities and were not getting enough of them. Most of them employed both staff and students on research projects. He still further entangled American universities with State research, so much so that one foreign observer remarked that 'research was the nervous system' of the American university, as opposed to the 'profound anaemia' of the French universities, and especially of the École Polytechnique.[55]

But even more significant was the evolution, from the National Academy of Sciences (itself a product of the Civil War), of a committee under G. E. Hale, with Simon Flexner and R. A. Millikan as members, to help the president in the emergency. This committee became the National Research Council, the first co-ordinator of all the scientific research in the U.S.A., with branch offices in Paris and London, to help discharge its function of 'securing, classifying and disseminating scientific, technical and industrial research information, especially relating to war problems'. It did this so well that on 11 May 1918 it was put on a permanent basis, to promote scientific knowledge and apply and disseminate it, 'for the benefit of national strength and well being'.

12

◇◇

The Rise of the Russian Technical Intelligentsia

◇◇

(1)

A DAY before Abraham Lincoln took office as sixteenth President of the United States, assuring the South that he would take no provocative step against slavery where it already existed, the Tsar Alexander of Russia freed more than 23 million serfs. A subsequent proclamation of Lincoln's freed only 4 million negroes, and Lincoln, after the Civil War broke out, suggested to the secretary of the Moscow Embassy then in Washington, that 'a good lecture or two on serfs, serfdom and emancipation in Russia would be both interesting and valuable. Could you not get up such a thing?'[1]

Lincoln's desire to use Russian precedent as propaganda in the United States was sharpened in September 1863 when two Russian battlefleets dropped anchor: one in New York, the other in San Francisco.[2] 'God bless the Russians',[3] wrote the Secretary of the U.S. Navy. For their presence, after the bloody battle of Chicamauga, was a reassurance that France and England would not interfere on behalf of the South.

The two images of Alexander the Liberator and Lincoln the Emancipator were vigorously defaced by the *Richmond Examiner*, the Southern paper:

> The Czar emancipates the serfs from their bondage of centuries and puts forth the whole strength of his empire to enslave the Poles.

184

Lincoln proclaims freedom to the African, and strives at the same time to subdue freeborn Americans.[4]

Russia's 'South'—the Poles—had also recently rebelled and declared their independence, but had asked for and obtained support from England and France. England and France thereupon demanded, under threat of force, that the rebels be allowed to form a duchy. The threat led to the dispatch of the two fleets to America: The Black Sea Fleet (based on Sevastopol) to New York and Boston, the Far Eastern Fleet (based on Vladivostok) to San Francisco.[5]

Sailors of the Black Sea Fleet heard John Quincy Adams[6] say at a reception for them in Boston that, 'The Yankee farmer and the Russian peasant are the only rustic people on earth who are capable of holding town meetings, and do so instinctively and practically.'[7] His comparison of the American town meeting with the Russian *Mir* was another timely comment on the freeing of the serfs. For the Russian serfs had been liberated to preserve the rural commune and prevent the mushrooming of a rootless proletariat: a truly conservative measure since it put the serfs on the road to becoming communal proprietors, so preserving and developing the old communal institutions.[8]

(2)

The operation of these communes was supplemented in 1864 by the establishment of *Zemstvos*, or regional committees to take cognizance of higher public wants like rural credit, mutual insurance, fire insurance, hospitals, schools and roads (though it must be confessed that the last two never seemed to be quite as pressing as the rest). The commune resembled a democratic committee of a collective farm.[9]

Through the *Zemstvos*, a type of communal medicine was now introduced, and a greater interest liberated in education. The two went together and Pirogov, the Russian physician who had done so much during the Crimean War, had insisted that 'the *Zemstvo* must combat the ignorance of the masses.' In his honour Pirogov congresses were established in 1881. Similarly, Sechenov, the great physiologist, a pioneer in disseminating a knowledge of sciences to the working classes, advocated an eight-hour day on physiological grounds. For a time he taught at Odessa where his friend I. I. Mechnikov (1845–1916) worked as a *Zemstvo* entomologist. Mechnikov left Odessa in 1882 as a protest against the reactionary attitude of the authorities towards Jews and foreigners. Before he went, however, he discovered 'phagocytes': those mysterious devourers of organisms which invade the human body.

The *Zemstvos* absorbed and neutralized arbitrary action from above. By employing an increasing number of teachers, doctors, agronomists and veterinarians, they became voluntary leaders of the liberal movement for a national *Zemstvo* or *Duma*. Indeed it was an illegal *Zemstvo* conference that founded the Union of Liberation in 1903. In this movement, statisticians like N. F. Annenskey and economists like S. N. Prokopovich were leaders.

The *Zemstvos* played two other historic roles. Their very existence undoubtedly helped lower the death-rate in Russia. For whereas in 1800 there were 37 million people in Russia with only 274 doctors (of whom only 38 were Russian) to cope with them, by 1900 there were 129 million people in Russia and the number of doctors had risen to 18,000.[10]

For the *Zemstvos* encouraged the growth of household, as opposed to heavy, industry in the villages, and the formation of co-operative groups of artisans called *Artels*. Though Plekhanov and Axelrod, Marx's disciples in Russia, argued that the communes would not protect them against capitalism, their arguments were not so much directed at the *artels* as at the romanticism of the agrarian Socialists.

Secondly, they evoked much selfless service. Students especially liked to serve as agronomists, technicians, teachers, doctors and statisticians. Indeed, Mikhailovsky's doctor commented that they worked 'not as bureau employees putting in a specified working day, but as individuals for whom their work had idealistic and social value and who gave to it their minds and hearts'.[11]

Visiting Russia at the close of the century, Lincoln's biographer, Albert J. Beveridge, compared the emancipation of the serfs to what Lincoln's might have been, if Lincoln had given to American negroes the lands of their former owners, under provisions for repayment.[12] But then, said Beveridge, the Russians could take liberties with the law of property which 'would not be tolerated for an instant by an American in the same situation'.[13] Being an American, he noted that American reaping machines were widely employed in Russia, and he called attention to the way in which they were bought by communal effort. These communes, he remarked, were 'forming all over the Empire', and he compared them to 'the granger store with which the American public became familiar in the great farmer movement of the seventies. Their bottom idea is similar to that of those American Socialistic enterprises which with us flourished for a few brief months and then died.'

Then came his most percipient observation on the commune:

> It has back of it the racial tendency of the Russians to do business on the communistic principle. The influence of the government is always favourable to every form of communistic industry. Indeed the Russian state may be said to be at the bottom communistic. The government's policy in this particular is not so much the plan of cunning statecraft as it is obedience to the landowners, conditions and natural aptitudes of the Russian people.[14]

Beveridge published these words in 1904, indicating the real sinews of what he called 'The Russian Advance'.

(3)

Almost simultaneously with the passage of the Morrill Act in America—on 30 June 1863, to be exact—many of the restrictions which had been endured almost since their foundation were lifted from the Russian universities.

Yet another American, Eugene Schuyler (who had met his first Russian when the Black Sea Fleet put in at New York in 1863), remarked at the same time that 'whatever failings there may be in providing education for the lower classes in Russia, no pains have been spared for the higher education and there is an abundance to meet the demand of students in every art and science'.

Ominously enough, Schuyler added 'in Russia as elsewhere, the Government is afraid of the students . . . yet', he also observed, 'it is the poor students who give the tone, they are in the majority. . . . He (the poor student) swears by Büchner and Moleschott, Darwin, Buckle and Draper, the most of whom he has probably read in the original. Wild theories of all sorts, of crime, of life, of communism, are the mode of the day.'[15]

That a poor Russian student should swear by J. W. Draper is not surprising, for Draper saw in history a logical fact, a scientific explanation of man's progress. His *History of the Intellectual Development of Europe*,[16] appearing in 1861, reinforced the already considerable impact of Comte and of H. T. Buckle that 'in the *long run* (or on the great average of affairs) individuals count for nothing'.[17] Buckle was so widely discussed in Russia that its author's name and ideas are mentioned in *The Cherry Orchard*. Yet neither Draper nor Buckle was the first to preach this doctrine. Earlier, H. C. Carey, an American economist, stressed the dynamic improvements effected by man's power over nature, whereby the Malthusian bugbear was laid to rest. In *The Past, The Present, and the Future* (1843) Carey had stressed that wealth consisted of the power to command the services of nature. Later, as virtual editor of the *New York Tribune* (from 1849 to 1857) Carey sided with Russia against England and France and indicated the tendency of Russian policy towards the emancipation of 20 million serfs and her onward march to civilization. Carey did not agree with Lincoln's notion of giving the negro political without economic freedom, considering it better to hasten the industrialization of the South, enabling it to be less cotton-centred and more a manufacturer of goods. Like a good St. Simonian, Carey urged Lincoln to build a great highway across the South to link it more closely with the North.[18]

It is unbelievable that Marx, who considered Carey to be 'the only American economist of importance', should have failed to understand what Carey was talking about. For though America confirmed Marx's doctrines of the concentration and centralization of capital, it was at the same time refuting his counterpart law of impoverishment and pauperization. Though Marx displayed some inkling of this in 1865 at the General Council of the International Working Men's Association, when, to refute a suggestion that the working class could not improve its condition through increased wages, he admitted that the labour theory of value might be modified by two additional factors— price, and the historico-moral increment of dynamic character that Carey presented—he explored the matter no further in *Capital*.[19] As a distinguished American Marxist has recently remarked, 'if he had recognised these elements in America . . .

he would have been forced to recast his entire theoretical system. Unfortunately for the realistic development of ideology he thought of America as still, economically speaking, only a colony of Europe.'[20] America had already replaced England as the classic ground of capitalism, higher hopes were already attracting the new inventions, whether of machinery or new applications of science in general.

Now one of Carey's most influential Russian disciples was N. G. Chernyshevsky, in whom the Russian intelligentsia found its most effective spokesman to date. While his country's fleets were in American ports, he was imprisoned in the fortress of St. Petersburg, where he wrote a Utopian novel—*What is to be Done?* (1863). This became the set-book of the revolutionary intelligentsia. Its very title indicated Chernyshevsky's rejection of the impractical idealism of the previous generation, typified by Pushkin's *Eugen Onegin*, Lermontov's Pechorin (in *A Hero of our Times* (1830)), and Turgenev's *Rudin* (1855). We can recognize the type from one of Turgenev's stories which is called *The Diary of a Superfluous Man*. In Russia the type is known as *Oblomov*, from a novel of that name published by Goncharov in 1857. Sloth and ineffectiveness in face of impending doom are the hall-marks. But, to Chernyshevsky's way of thinking, something could be done, and with the passionate puritanism of an arch-priest's son he propounded it in the dream of Vera Pavlovna: co-operative workshops.

What is to be Done? struck far and deep. Its purified (or rather puritanized) materialism became known as nihilism, after the name given by Turgenev to the medical student Basarov in his novel, *Fathers and Sons* (1861). It penetrated the sinful luxuries of art and metaphysics, superstition and prejudice with its powerful 'red' message: a man could be redeemed from his suffering by the power of natural science. The cult of science in Russia found its St. Paul in Chernyshevsky. As Nicholas Berdyaev remarked,

> The attitude of the Russian nihilists to science was idolatrous. Science, by which was to be understood principally the natural sciences, which at that time were presented in materialist colours, became an object of faith, it was turned into an idol.[21]

Karl Marx studied Russian to read Chernyshevsky. Plekhanov, Marx's first and chief Russian disciple, wrote a study of him. Lenin, who read him as a young man, was converted to Communism by so doing.

(4)

In the opinion of Ludwig Feuerbach, scientists were the most dangerous of intellectuals because of their contact with the orderly rational world of nature, and he scoffed at the policy of reactionary governments in exempting them from censorship.[22] Proof of this was shown at Kazan University in 1858 when seventy students requested the Professor of Physiology to resign: 'Please forgive us, Professor,' they said, 'if we have been the first to speak of this. Love of science and the desire to be useful to our Fatherland have made us precipitate.'[23] Resign he did, and so did two others at Moscow. Now further restrictions, followed by open demonstrations at St. Petersburg, then by arrests, drove the corporate life of students underground. There they became the 'seed bed of the revolutionary movement'.[24]

Count Dmitry Tolstoy, who controlled Russian universities from 1866 onwards, adopted subtle British precedents, and in 1871 closed the universities to all but students from the classical secondary schools from which history and geography had been excluded. New universities like those at Odessa (founded 1865) and Warsaw (founded in 1869) were subjected to a strict police inspection. Special reformatory institutions for the 'politically infected' were actually considered,[25] as groups were formed like the Society of Communists, founded in 1861 by P. G. Zatchenevsky (1842–96). At the St. Petersburg Technological Institute, A. D. Mikhailov led a student protest and was sent back home. Six years later he died on the scaffold. When N. I. Kibalchich was imprisoned for making bombs for an assault on the Tsar, he whiled away his time by designing a rocket aeroplane which he asked his attorney to forward to a committee of technical experts.[26]

Tolstoy's promotion to the Ministry of the Interior sharpened his scrutiny. Universities were again deprived of their autonomy in 1884, student clubs were banned and students from the lower classes again excluded. At the beginning of 1885, 640 students had to leave St. Petersburg University because their grants were stopped. Students' protests increased with each bunch of arrests until by 1887 five universities had to be closed. This was the time that one student at Kazan, N. I. Lenin, received his baptism of governmental autocracy. Professors were asked to help the Government in its campaign but, to their great credit, thirty-nine professors from Moscow refused. One hundred and eighty-three students were expelled from Moscow, Kazan and St. Petersburg. By 1890 Kazan, Dorpat and Novorossiisk had 16, 10 and 13 chairs vacant. In seven universities by 1889 there were 11,431 students. The numbers of these receiving scholarship grants in that year were small: 249 out of 1,799 at St. Petersburg, 450 out of 3,257 at Moscow and 63 out of 1,632 at Dorpat. After all, universities had been on strike for three months, and in 1889 Cossacks with whips had been sent into one town to drive the students back. Where whips failed, strikers were conscripted into the army. So the students organized secret committees (*Zemlyachestva*) to fight back. Between 1894 and 1904 nearly 10,000 of them were expelled. Others were confined to their local universities. It is little wonder that they remained active cells of unrest until the revolution.

(5)

Since the Tsar would not allow individual prospecting for oil before 1873, Russian industry leaned heavily on the lucky concessionaires, like the Nobels, who moved in to work it.[27] The Nobels needed D. I. Mendeleev, and sent him to visit the Pennsylvania oil fields in 1876. He returned with a plan for exploiting the naphtha springs in South Russia and the coal of the Donets Basin, the latter by setting it on fire underground and pumping water into it to generate gas for power. Mendeleev's ability (he is famous for his classification of the elements in order of increasing atomic weights, starting with hydrogen and ending with uranium) was accompanied by a troublesome social conscience. This led the Government to send him abroad on technical commissions to get him out of the way. When he was put up for membership of the Academy of Sciences on the death of Zinin, Dmitry Tolstoy, the then president, opposed him, so much so that when dying he said, 'Only remember, Mendeleev must not be recognised by the Academy in any way.'

Like Mendeleev, other Russian scientists preached the Baconian gospel that by organized research man could conquer nature. Mendeleev rejected the 'semi-childish' doctrines of

Rousseau and Leo Tolstoy and stressed the importance of the commercial and industrial development of the Urals and the Caucasus:

> After the industrial epoch [he wrote] there will probably follow in the future a more complex epoch which, according to my view, will denote a facilitation or an extreme simplification of the methods of obtaining food, clothing and shelter. Established science should aim at this extreme simplification towards which it has already been partly directed in recent decades.[28]

As Trotsky was later to acknowledge, Mendeleev 'outlined the technico-scientific perspectives of communism', even though he was a monarchist. His optimism, anti-malthusianism and practicality were to be of far greater use to the new régime than the despair of the intelligentsia. For as Trotsky remarked, 'In the transition from socialism to Communism no revolution will be necessary since the transition wholly depends upon the technical progress of society.'[29]

When Mendeleev first published his periodic table of the elements, arguing that they would be found, when ranged according to their atomic weights, to display a certain regularity (so that, for example, each eighth element revealed somewhat similar properties) it won attention as a further proof that nature was intelligible to those who accepted her pronouncements.

One of Mendeleev's close friends, an engineer turned doctor, carried this idea further, and startled the intellectual world of Moscow in 1863 by announcing that

> all psychical acts without exception, if they are complicated by an emotional element, take place by means of a reflex. Consequently all conscious movements arising out of these acts, i.e. movements that are usually called voluntary are, strictly speaking, reflex movements.[30]

This was I. M. Sechenov. His attempts to prove that all acts of conscious or unconscious life are reflexes had political implications for they negated free will, and destroyed the concept of a soul. Not unnaturally Sechenov was charged with expounding a materialist viewpoint, his case was put into the hands of the Attorney-General who recommended that Sechenov's book be destroyed. Seven years later, Sechenov resigned from St. Petersburg Medical Academy over the treatment of a colleague and went to the University at Odessa. As the confirmation of his appointment was delayed he did research in Mendeleev's laboratory.

Inspired by a Russian translation of G. H. Lewes's *Practical Physiology*, Sechenov's pupil, I. P. Pavlov (1849–1936), won a travelling fellowship established by the Englishman Wylie which took him to Leipzig, where he met a young American, W. H. Welch, also a passionate researcher. Both men on their return were destined to reorganize the scientific work in their respective countries: Pavlov by constructing the first surgical department in a physiological laboratory at the Institute of Experimental Medicine founded by Prince Oldenburgsky in 1891, Welch to organize the Johns Hopkins Medical School in Baltimore. Pavlov had discovered the presence of psychic gastric secretion before the institute was founded. After he had received the Nobel Prize in 1904, he began his work on conditioned reflexes, which carried the techniques of quantitative measurement into psychic functions.

With Pavlov, Russian science began to flow outwards and influence other countries. Two of his pupils, L. A. Orbely and P. S. Kupalov, worked for a time in England and two others, B. P. Babkin and L. A. Andreev in McGill University, Montreal, the former becoming an authority on digestion; whilst laboratories on the Pavlov model have been established by Liddell at Cornell University, U.S.A., and in the Phipps Clinic at Johns Hopkins.[31]

(6)

To provide more scientific manpower for the developing industrial areas, a scheme was devised in 1888 for a hierarchy of institutions for training engineers, technicians, craftsmen and workers. The exploitation of Siberia was facilitated by the establishment of a university at Tomsk (in west-central Siberia) in 1888, followed by a technological institute twelve years later. The gold, platinum, iron, copper and bauxite of the Urals were increasingly tapped by the Trans-Siberian Railway, which began at Ekaterinoslav (now Sverdlovsk), where in 1899 another polytechnic was founded.

Tomsk, the first university to be founded in Siberia, was given

170,000 roubles by that remarkable merchant-adventurer Alexander Sibiryakov, himself an engineer trained at the polytechnic at Zürich. Sibiryakov's great-grandfather had smelted silver at Nerchinsk, his grandfather had controlled the salt trade of East Siberia, his brother Innokenty financed a survey of Mongolia and China. Like a good polytechnician, Sibiryakov himself was a firm believer in the need of a good traffic artery through Siberia: the road through the Urals not only bore his name but also carried his wheat from the River Ob to the River Perchora, whilst he explored another much farther east, from Yakutsk to Okhotsk. His apparently boundless purse financed non-Russian explorers of the northern coastline, like the Englishman, Henry Wiggins and the Swedish geologist, N. A. E. Nordenskiold. Nordenskiold in fact solved the problem of the North-East Passage by sailing from Tromsö to pass through the Bering Strait on 18 July 1879.[32]

The application of American engineering techniques to the construction of the Trans-Siberian Railway was in the hands of Prince Khilkov. In his method of acquiring his knowledge he emulated Peter the Great, for he went to work on the American railroads as a young man, acquiring on the footplate a knowledge of railways that enabled him, on returning to Russia, to become Minister of Transport in the last decade of the century. He mobilized engineers and agronomists to build the Trans-Siberian Railway, and open up Siberia in the same way as the Union Pacific opened up America a generation before.[33]

Even more obsessed with the need of a transport artery was his chief, Count Witte, a graduate in mathematics and physics of the University of Odessa, and such an exponent of planning that the pamphleteer Tsion accused him of promoting Communism. Becoming Minister of Ways and Communications in 1892 and of Finance in 1893, Witte exhibited the true spirit of a polytechnician, throwing his whole weight behind the Trans-Siberian Railway. Like his cousin, the notorious Madame Blavatsky, Witte had big ideas. As his friend and adviser, E. J. Dillon, later of the London *Daily Telegraph*, remarked, 'He would have educated the entire people and endeavoured to qualify the State or a department of it to discharge the function of social direction.' He used a corps of scientific professors to supply him with data for his policy, organized Russian participation in the Great World Fairs at Chicago (1894), Paris (1900) and Glasgow (1901) (issuing sumptuous volumes on Russian trade for them), and maintained agents to canvass investors in Russian industry. The three polytechnics he established—at Kiev, Warsaw and St. Petersburg—were outstanding institutions, the last named being the most magnificent institution of its kind on the European continent. Witte saw clearly that a union of European states was long overdue, and remarked: 'the time is near when Europe will be regarded with the respect which well-bred people show former beauties who have grown so decrepit they can scarcely move about'.[34]

(7)

As opposed to the university intellectuals, the technical intelligentsia were very well provided for. In 1867 an American report described Russia as 'one of the European countries where the greatest efforts for the foundation of schools of this technical class have been made in the last half century', whilst another, three years later, described Russian schools of science and the arts as 'liberally endowed', adding that 'many of them have attained a high degree of development'.[35]

Mikhailovsky, a nobleman who had followed courses in mathematics, physics and natural science at the St. Petersburg Mining Institute, acquired a reverence for science, but he soon saw what he considered its inadequacy as a philosophy for the redemption of labour—'that mass who in the last analysis, directly or indirectly, feed, dress and protect us, while at the same time they remain in poverty, filth and ignorance'.[36] So he adopted a modified Comteian positivism in place of Büchner's materialism, or to put it in another way, he found that biology and social science would restore the balance which scientism had disturbed. Here his mentors, the German Haeckel and the Russian N. D. Nozhin, provided him with arguments for cooperation. He wished science to accommodate the consciences of the intellectuals and devoted his life to what he called the *Pravda* system. In other words 'truth' and 'justice', both meanings of *Pravda*, would be his goals.

The only institution in Russia offering an education in general engineering was the St. Petersburg Technological Institute. Students came there from Poland and the Ukraine as well as other parts of the Russian Empire. Unlike the literary Marxists at the University of St. Petersburg, its technologists were brought, by their work, into greater contact with the workers. They were therefore able to educate and organize them along lines already laid down in Poland and elsewhere. The fusion between these two groups of technologists and workers began under the dynamic leadership of Leonard B. Krasin, later to be a Siemens-Schuckert representative in Moscow, his brother Herman (1871–1947), Stephen I. Radchenko (1869–1911), and Gleb Maksimilianovich Krzhizhanovsky (1872–1959). These were later joined by Lenin, whose first printed work appeared under their sponsorship in 1895.[37] All were later to take part in the revolution.

By nature of their work, students in the higher technological institutes were more organized than other students. They had, for instance, their own dining-hall, where they could collect funds, meet for discussions or meet the workers, and distribute literature, usually illegal. Looking at the activities of these students, an American historian remarked that one of the original centres from which the illegal factions developed seems to have been the higher technological institutes.[38]

(8)

The technological humanism of the groups at the St. Petersburg Technological Institute appears in the novels of Aleksy Nikolaevich Tolstoy (1883–1945), Russia's H. G. Wells: *Seven Days in which the World was Plundered, Aelita, The Hyperboloid of Engineer Garin, Eccentrics* and *The Lame Master*.

An even more startling horizon was scanned by Konstantin Eduardovich Tsiolkovsky (1857–1935), a deaf self-educated mathematical physicist, whose paper *Investigating Space with Rocket Devices* (1903) envisaged the use of reaction motors for inter-planetary flights. He was the first to investigate the problem of rocket flight in a gravitational field and to explore the possibility of life and work in a manned space capsule. 'His ideas', wrote a recent commentator, 'fertilised a whole generation of Soviet scientists and science-fiction writers.'[39]

Criticism by scientists like Mendeleev led Zenger, the Minister of Education, to set up a special commission in 1902 to consider the universities' claim for increased grants, post-graduate scholarships and a higher standard of qualification for chairs. The revolution of 1905–7 unfortunately led to another reaction.

With the apparently laudable motive of promoting a conference on technical education on 3 to 5 January 1904, the *Zemstvos* drafted a programme for a constitutional monarchy. At the request of the Union of Liberation (formed in 1895 by Martov and Lenin to train the workers), the Union of Unions was formed, consisting of intellectuals, radicals, engineers, teachers and lawyers. The *Zemstvo* constitutionalists and the peasants' union joined this in the following year but it faded away when the *Duma* was convened in 1906. Upon the failure of the *Duma* another series of expulsions from universities and of banning scientific societies ensued.

P. N. Lebedev (1866–1911), the physics professor at Moscow, wrote in 1905:

> All of my activity as a propagator of science in our dear old country appears to me to be an insipid long-drawn-out affair and I feel that I am irretrievably perishing as a scientist: the environment is a kind of continuous stupefying nightmare, a hopeless despair.[40]

Trotsky, the Odessan student in exile, went to work in an Austrian chemical works. Lenin, as always, was writing: 'Russia is the only European country left which is so uncivilized and where the masses are robbed so much of opportunities for education, enlightenment and knowledge.'[41]

(9)

Lenin's troubles were not all of the Government's making. On the contrary, he had to contend with heresy amongst his followers. Heresy is the operative term, for by now analogies from physics were deeply embedded in the revolutionary creed. Especially was this true of Ostwald's 'energetics', which to Lenin was at variance with J. J. Thomson's theory of the atom. Most unmaterialistic, it proved as congenial to Russian Social Democrats as it had been to American pragmatists.[42]

A particularly penetrating thorn was the physician, A. A. Bogdanov,[43] who joined Lenin in 1904. He had a scheme for a proletarian encyclopaedia (on the model of Diderot's in the previous century), and for workers' universities which were

197

ultimately to supersede existing ones. Both were to promote a new creed—'techtology'—a new *scientia scientiarum*. According to Bogdanov, history was a process whereby a constant struggle with nature resulted in various technical and scientific advances with various organizing adjustments being made to ensure further progress. This process moved from authoritarianism to exchange, and was developing into a collective self-sufficient economy wherein all ideological forms were being phased, merged or fused. The philosophic foundations of this collectivist society were Bogdanov's special concern, and to further them he and A. Lunacharsky,[44] a Social Democrat, issued a collection of essays, embodying these Ostwaldian ideas, entitled *Studies in the Philosophy of Marxism* (St. Petersburg, 1908). This provoked Lenin to ransack the British Museum and the *Bibliothèque Nationale* for material not in the Geneva Library, in search of the latest ideas of atomic structure to reinforce the theory of materialism. From his researches he wrote *Materialism and Empirio-Criticism* (1909): the second major work in the Marxist-Leninist canon. In it he denounced the 'Machists':

> It is the misfortune of the Russian Machists, who undertook to 'reconcile' machism and Marxism, that they trusted the reactionary professors of philosophy and as a result slipped down an inclined plane. The methods of operation employed in the various attempts to develop and supplement Marx were very naïve. They read Ostwald, believe Ostwald, paraphrase Ostwald and call it Marxism. They read Mach, believe Mach, paraphrase Mach and call it Marxism. They read Poincaré, believe Poincaré, paraphrase Poincaré and call it Marxism! *Not a single one* of these Professors, who are capable of making very valuable contributions in the special fields of chemistry, history or physics, *can be trusted* one iota when it comes to philosophy . . . why? the professors of philosophy are the learned salesmen of the theologians.[45]

(10)

If materialist American professors like H. C. Carey and J. W. Draper infected Russians, the materialist Russian professors like Victor Della Vos were affecting Americans. As Director of the Moscow Imperial Technical School, an institution founded in 1868, he fortified, or supplemented, the teaching of mathematics, physics and chemistry by training in construction workshops built for teaching purposes.

The point of Della Vos's innovation was that these workshops supplemented those used for *in*struction by giving opportunities for *con*struction. In constructing, students worked out their difficulties by analysing each trade into its component skills and grading them into orders of pedagogical difficulty.[46]

Exhibited at the Philadelphia Centennial Exhibition in 1876, Della Vos's method much impressed the President of the Massachusetts Institute of Technology, John D. Runkle, who on returning to Cambridge, Mass., recommended the building of similar workshops for a new school of Mechanic Arts. The Massachusetts Institute of Technology was not the only institution to copy the Della Vos trend, nor was Runkle its only apostle. Dr. Calvin M. Woodward also commended it to Washington University, where a school was founded in 1879 based on Vos's method of tool and job analysis. Woodward's school provided a three-year course divided equally between the workshop and theory. As apostles of manual training, Woodward and Runkle were accused of subversion and of undermining standards. In fact, they were doing the very reverse: they were refining standards, helping along the movement which became known as Taylorism.

For job analysis was the very basis of the system whereby Frederick Winslow Taylor systematized shop management and reduced manufacturing costs. Entering the Midvale Steel Company in 1878 he became its chief engineer in twelve years, and after a period applying his system at the Bethlehem Steel Works he set up as a consultant in 1901.[47] One of Taylor's most valuable associates, Carl G. Barth (who devised a slide rule for his theories),[48] taught manual training and mathematics at the Ethical Culture School in New York.[49]

After visiting Taylor in 1908, Dean Wallace E. Sabine of the Harvard Graduate School of Applied Science wrote:

> While listening to you, and even more in thinking it over since I left you, I am persuaded that you are on the track of the only reasonable solution of a great sociological problem. The systematization and standardization of work has a bearing far beyond the organization of a particular business or industry. I do not believe that you are a socialist any more than I am, but you are preparing data for the solution of a problem on which socialistic and cooperative movements have time after time been wrecked.[50]

The Taylor system was adopted as central feature in the Harvard School of Business Administration, opened in 1918.

Over the years, Taylor made such a great impression that a society was formed to disseminate his ideas. His *Principles of Scientific Management* (1911) was translated into French, German, Dutch, Swedish, Lettish, Italian, Spanish, Japanese, Chinese, Hindi—and Russian. By 1918, Lenin could write in *Pravda*:

> The last word of capitalism (in learning how to work), the Taylor System, as well as all progressive measures of capitalism, combined the refined cruelty of bourgeois exploitation and a number of most valuable scientific attainments in the analysis of mechanical motions during work, in dismissing superfluous and useless motions, in determining the most correct methods of work, the best systems of accounting and control, etc. The Soviet Republic must adopt valuable and scientific technical advance in this field. The possibility of Socialism will be determined by our success in combining the Soviet rule and the Soviet organisation of management with the latest progressive measures of capitalism. We must introduce in Russia the study and teaching of the new Taylor System and its systematic trial and adaptation.[51]

Taylor's almost messianic belief in his new gospel was noted by a fellow-American, who commented:

> Fred Taylor may be God Almighty all right, but the only resemblance I can see is that he has in your fellows such damn poor representatives on earth.[52]

(11)

The godlike power of science, even to resurrect the dead, was, to the Russian polymath N. F. Fyodorov, predestined. 'Put the engine together, and consciousness will return to it' he wrote. His desire to resurrect and reconstitute the ever-dispersing forms of nature took more practical shape in ideas for regulating the weather to ensure good harvests, utilizing solar energy and travelling between the planets.

Though he died in 1903, his ideas found expression by the creation in 1915 of a Commission for the Study of the Natural Productive Forces of Russia. Here the moving spirit was V. I. Vernadsky of the Academy of Sciences whom we shall meet again in Chapter 14. This Commission retained its quasi-autonomic status till 1929. Like many others, it marked a new stage in the emergence of the technocracy.

'A new impulse, the highest which has yet arisen' was identified by I. P. Pavlov as 'coursing through the whole cultured world—the interest in experimental science and its applications'. In 1910 he told the Ledenzov Society for the Advancement of the Experimental Sciences and their Practical Application:

> The vast territory of Russia with its incalculable resources and natural strength cries out for an enthusiastic and well-supported experimental study of nature, and the application of the results of this experimental activity to the advancement of human welfare.[53]

This new stage was hastened by the First World War, when other special councils and committees for the control of economic life brought in specialists and gave them wide powers, powers which the holders envisaged as becoming even wider after the war. Especially was this true of the Moscow War Industries Committee, amongst whose members was the director of the Moscow Technical High School, V. I. Grinevetsky whose *Post War Prospects of Russian Engineering* served, as S. V. Utechin has said, 'as the basis for all post war economic planning'.

It only needed the failure of the 'revolutionary democracy' of 1917 to enable these aspiring technocrats to surface. To quote Dr. Utechin again, it 'must have made even those who had tended towards it doubt the validity of the democratic premises, and strengthened the élite-ist tendencies in their thinking'.[54]

13

✦✦✦

The New Political Arithmetic

✦✦✦

(1)

'In America there is no mistake about what is considered to be the duty of the government in regard to scientific research—we wish we could say the same for England.'[1] The lament of *Nature*, a newly established British scientific journal in 1869, was endorsed by another new British journal, *The Engineer*, founded and edited by an American: 'In the engineering and engineering practice of the United States we can find a much closer parallel than is afforded in France and Germany.'[2] That practice was described by the young and gifted Sir Charles Dilke as 'cheap, large and practical', and he commended the way in which 'each of these young states has established a university of the highest order and placed in every township not only schools, but public libraries, supported by the rates, and managed by the people'.[3]

Such tributes grew over the years. The first British scientific peer, Lord Playfair, who had been campaigning for more State aid to British science for thirty-four years, told the British Association in 1885, that 'a young nation like the United States by reserving large tracts of its national lands for the promotion of scientific education is in advance of all European nations in adding science to its administrative offices'.

He went on:

Its scientific publications are an example to other Governments
. . . in the United Kingdom we are just beginning to understand
the wisdom of George Washington's farewell address to his
countrymen, when he said 'Promote as an object of primary importance, institutions for the general diffusion of knowledge.'[4]

The way in which land-grant and other colleges 'set learning
in a visible form, plain, indeed, and humble, but dignified even
in her humility before the eyes of a rustic people in whom the
love of knowledge, naturally strong, might never break from
the bud into the flower but for the care of some zealous gardener',[5] also drew from Lord Bryce the opinion that they were
'the mind of the State or at least the organ which the State may
employ to think out the problems which the State has to deal
with'.[6] Of these problems, agriculture was, to the Director of
Statistical Intelligence and Educational Department of the
British Board of Agriculture, Major P. G. Craigie, paramount.
He went over to see the colleges and experimental stations,
envied their 'co-operation'. and concluded: 'the American
government seems willing to face any cost to the community
that promises the better to equip the farmer with a knowledge
of his business'.[7]

(2)

Behind the gospel of social efficiency a new arithmetic of
apocalypse was laboriously calculated by a new type of academic
—the economic historian. The first chair ever to be created in
the subject—at Harvard—was occupied by an Englishman, Sir
William Ashley, who returned to the University of Birmingham
to supply arguments for Joseph Chamberlain's campaign for
tariff reform. A more sanctified version of this new gospel was
presented by Archdeacon Cunningham, who, like Ashley, owed
much to the United States: he was actually introduced to the
Anglican Prayer Book by two American students at the University
of Tübingen in 1869.[8]

A strong tendency to disparage the American land-grant
college and what it stood for was exhibited by Matthew
Arnold, Professor of Poetry at Oxford and one of Her Majesty's
inspectors of schools. To him Cornell—where the Professor of
Modern History at Oxford had migrated—was founded 'on a
miscalculation of what culture truly is, and was calculated to

produce miners, or engineers, or architects, not sweetness and light'.[9]

This led him almost wilfully to misunderstand the arguments of John Bright for increased 'Assistance by Government to Technical Education'. In a speech at Birmingham on 5 February 1868, Bright argued that 'the people of the United States have offered to the world more valuable inventions during the past forty years than all Europe put together'.[10] Arnold substituted the word *information* for inventions and used it to prove a point about America's lack of religious establishments. Unfair? But it made his point about America, which he described a little later in the book as 'up to the present time . . . hardly more than a province of England, and even now would not herself claim to be more than abreast of England'.[11]

The spirit of Bright and the needs of Birmingham evoked answering chords in at least one American patron who told Bright's political successor, Joseph Chamberlain, a generation later: 'I fear none of Mason College buildings and not much of its apparatus would be of the slightest use as part of a modern scientific university school.' So Chamberlain sent a deputation over to the U.S.A. in 1899, consisting of G. H. Kenrick, and Professors Poynting and Burstall. 'Not until after this visit to America', say the official historians of the University of Birmingham, 'did the committee arrive at some conception of what was required of them.'[12]

What was required of them was to purchase a new site at Edgbaston. As Chamberlain publicly confessed on receiving the charter,

> The report of the Committee which visited Canada and the United States opened my eyes and I think it must have opened the eyes of all who have read it. The Committee found great institutions and connected with a general university, real colleges of Science occupying large spaces, in which the area was counted by many acres, fully equipped with proper buildings with the most modern and complete machinery, with the latest scientific appliances, with laboratories for every conceivable scientific purpose. And in these great colleges a training was given such as we desire to see imitated in this country, a training based, as all education ought to be, upon a foundation of general culture, but specialized according to the work which each student intends to take in life. And as a result of this

we begin to see how it is that in America the great commercial and industrial undertakings . . . found no difficulty whatever in obtaining the services of as many young men as they may require to manage and complete and develop the undertakings.[13]

Even more influenced by the land-grant colleges was Reading: its deputation to the U.S.A. in 1910 described a transatlantic university as 'a lever to be used in numerous ways to advance the interests of civilization'. 'Because its work ministers so directly to public needs,' they wrote, 'there is far less hesitation about the propriety of liberal state aid.'[14]

By 1917 as a result of a broad hint from the Foreign Office, Oxford established a D.Phil. in 1917 to attract foreign students, particularly Americans. Other universities followed suit. Oxford was so anxious to attract representative students from the U.S.A. that it abolished the examination in Greek from the requirements of the Rhodes Scholarship—only 1 per cent of American college students were studying Greek.[15]

(3)

The twentieth century opened in Britain with a newspaper scare. *The Times* published between April and June 1900 fifteen articles on American engineering competition: the *Daily Express* followed with a series entitled 'Wake up England', and was in turn followed by an even more startling series in the *Daily Mail* for June 1901 on 'The American Invaders, their plans, tactics and progress'.

In the very war which Britain was fighting in South Africa with such indifferent success, American engineering skill was called upon in the persons of Gardner Williams, the famous Californian mining engineer who did so much for De Beers, and Louis Seymour, who so successfully built bridges for the British Army during the Boer War. This generated in Alfred Mosely, who had himself made a fortune in the diamond fields, the impulse to return to England and organize two groups of experts, one from trade unions, the other from universities and schools, to visit America. Their missions, scheduled for 1901, were delayed until details of the 1902 Education Act were made known. Both groups left for America in late 1903 and each produced a report that had a considerable influence in the years before the First World War. The Board of Trade bought 3,000 copies and one M.P. wanted it issued as a parliamentary paper.[16] The Labour Commission gave it as their opinion that one of the principal reasons why the American workman was better than his British counterpart was that 'he has received a senior and better education, whereby he has been more thoroughly fitted for the struggles of after life'. Service on the Education Commission converted, amongst others, Professor Henry E. Armstrong, who was

> satisfied that, in the years to come, in competing with American commerce we shall be called upon to face trained men, gifted with both enterprise and knowledge. We desire to impress on the British public the absolute need of immediate preparation on our part to meet such competition.[17]

Eleven representatives of the new Local Education Authorities created in 1902 were on the education section of the Mosely Commission. The districts they represented were important ones: London, the West Riding, Newcastle, Sheffield, Liverpool, Manchester and Rochdale. Other authorities, which had not been represented on it, soon took steps to remedy their deficiencies by sending fact-finding deputations of their own. Leicester sent one which reported in 1907. Permanent officials of the Local Authorities (whom we would now refer to as their chief education officers) sent a deputation on their own in 1911 to examine technical schools, and their report, compiled by the secretaries of the Barnsley, Ealing, West Bromwich and St. Helens authorities, were warm in their praise of American vocational schools as compared to English ones.[18] In short, the Local Authorities were so primed with information about technical schools and colleges in America that when, in 1918, they were empowered to levy more than a twopenny rate to finance such colleges, they went ahead, prodded by the various professional associations, to emulate what they had seen.

(4)

Other industrialists who had profited from the Yankee Archimedianism were equally active. As early as 1889, county councils were endowed with the power to levy a rate for technical education, largely due to Sir William Mather, who owned the English rights for manufacturing the Edison dynamo. In

England Mather pioneered the first tube railway in London and his works in Manchester were one of the earliest to provide adequate technical training.[19]

The American firm of Westinghouse opened an electrical works at Old Trafford in 1899 and to provide English employees with an adequate technical training, sent forty of them to Pittsburgh for two years. Known as the 'Holy Forty', these technological pilgrims included Miles Walker (who became a professor of electrical engineering) and A. P. M. Fleming (who became Director of Research and Education at British Westinghouse). Fleming never lost his admiration for American scientific skills and when the First World War broke out, returned to America to report for the British Government on the research departments of American industrial firms like Du Pont, Kodak and G.E.C. He drew attention to the

> growing tendency in many of the research laboratories to devote more and more attention to investigations in pure science having no immediate commercial object in view,

and noted that

> almost invariably such investigations result in industrial application, sometimes bringing about the development of entirely new industries. Prominent examples of this kind are represented by the work of the General Electric Company's laboratory at Schenectady.[20]

Indeed it was partially as a result of Fleming's report that the British Government established an Advisory Council for Scientific Research in 1915. Fleming had suggested that a large central institution for co-operative research was needed and the formation of the new Department of Scientific and Industrial Research owed much to his suggestion. For, embodying both the Advisory Council and the Committee of Council for Scientific and Industrial Research in December 1916, it was followed six months later by a plan for assisting co-operative research associations in industry on a pound for pound basis out of a fund of a million pounds voted by Parliament in 1917–18. These research associations were to serve during the subsequent forty years the seven major groups of the British industry.

Twenty-one of them were formed in three years, three being based on co-operative industrial laboratories already existing.[21]

(5)

Industrial science itself owed much to American stimulus. As early as 1880 two Americans founded the firm of Burroughs, Wellcome and Company, manufacturers of fine chemicals in Britain. One of them, H. S. Wellcome (1853–1936) used the great wealth he amassed thereby to become a generous patron of science, founding the Wellcome Physiological Research Laboratories (1894), the Wellcome Chemical Research Laboratories (1896), the Wellcome Historical Medical Museum (1913) and the Wellcome Bureau of Scientific Research into Tropical Diseases. He also financed the establishment of research laboratories in the Gordon Memorial College at Khartoum. All these were subsequently integrated into the Wellcome Research Institution as part of the Wellcome Foundation in 1924.

Another spur to private industrial laboratories was the adoption of oil firing by the British Navy just before the First World War. The opening up of the great Persian oil refinery at Abadan by Anglo-Persian (now Anglo-Iranian) necessitated a research station at Sunbury in England. In thirty years its director, A. E. Dunstan, created an establishment covering 38 acres and employing 1,200 people. Here, in the quest for an odourless gas for Great Western Railway restaurant cars, S. F. Birch discovered the alkylation process.[22]

Professor Soddy of Oxford also pleaded for more industrial laboratories in Britain. 'Some of the finest research in pure physical science that is being produced in America today,' he wrote, 'emanates from the General Electric Company's Research Laboratories at Schenectady, N.Y.'[23]

The growth of research laboratories was facilitated by the tendency of industry to become oligopolic. C. J. T. Cronshaw of Levinstein's research department went to America to exchange information with Du Ponts in 1917. His firm was in 1926 to become, with Nobel and Brunner Monds, a constituent member of Imperial Chemical Industries.[24] This built up sixteen laboratories in its eleven divisions employing 2,500 scientists, together with Jealotts Hill, Berkshire (for agricultural research) and Akers Laboratories, Welwyn, Herts (for long-term researches). These industrial research laboratories excited much envy which turned in some cases to apprehension when they began to operate laboratories in Europe. The Batelle Institute, for instance, opened branches in Geneva and Frankfurt, whilst Bell Telephone dangled tempting offers to British personnel. True, attempts were made to establish British counterparts to the Batelle Institute. Non-ferrous metallurgical interests promoted the Fulmer Research Institute at Stoke Poges in 1947, and a private consulting chemical laboratory, originally established in 1936, blossomed into the Sondes Place Laboratories at Dorking in Surrey. But these were isolated gestures, gallant, but relatively impotent to stem the tide. American research contracts, whether from civilian or service sources began to be sought by universities, traditionally free from such influences.

The real impact of the American research laboratory in England can be seen in the steady increase of American investment in Britain during this century. By 1900 seventy-five American subsidiaries or Anglo-American enterprises were in operation in the United Kingdom, mainly in engineering and chemical products, with combined capital holdings of nearly 100 million dollars. By 1940 there were 233 concerns with a value of 306 million dollars. By 1955 the amount invested had reached the total of 941 million dollars, and by 1959, 1,607 million. The spurt came after each World War, accelerated by shortages in the United Kingdom and the American desire to breach tariff walls.

In this way the American research laboratory became a familiar feature in England, especially after the Second World War. By 1958 it was estimated that almost a quarter of the 5,600 million dollars which American industry spent on private research and development was made directly available to the United Kingdom; more than the whole of the British industry and the Co-operative Research Associations spent annually on research.

Too much reliance on the research and development department of the American concern (warned Dr. J. H. Dunning) could well mean that the British Company refrains from independent research, which in the long run might have proved more profitable. Alternatively, the withdrawal of U.S. capital may deprive the U.K. of research facilities, which, left to itself it might otherwise have built up. Then finally, too much dependency on U.S. research and development knowledge may result in the demand for pure scientists and technologists being restrained, and hence in the stifling of initiative and development of this country's industry in its own right.[25]

A similar warning was given by the Advisory Council on Scientific Policy:

Whilst we warmly welcome this substantial financial support for research in this country, we recognise that research grants, and particularly specific contracts of this magnitude (one and a quarter millions annually) must have a considerable influence on the general pattern of research undertaken. We, therefore, consider it desirable that the various bodies concerned with the financing of research in our universities and other institutions should be aware both of the extent and purpose of these numerous United States research grants and contracts.[26]

(6)

'One of the religions that Americans believed in', remarked Sir Michael Sadler in 1921, 'was education. It has its orthodoxy, its pontiffs, its noble buildings. Education is the Established Church of the United States.'[27] Its creed was perhaps most succinctly penned by Carnegie's grandfather Thomas Morrison, in an article to *Cobbett's Register* on 21 December 1833 on 'Heddekashun' and 'Handication'. These ideas, dominant in the philosophy of the land-grant colleges, so possessed Carnegie that, having made a fortune from industry, he devoted it to priming the pumps which refreshed industry.

Ideologue and practitioner of this new religion was Andrew Carnegie, a great friend of Andrew D. White, the first president of Cornell, and, incidentally, Matthew Arnold's host when Arnold visited America in 1883. Passionately fond of Britain, he drew out the technocratic implications of industrialization:

The ablest and best citizens of every country are inspired to favour the development of its resources. They cannot consider it right to hide the talents given them, and are now enabled to see clearly that the evident law of Nature is that there shall be given to many nations the blessings of diversified industries in the pursuit of which the various aptitudes and talents of the people shall find scope.[28]

Carnegie cushioned the British from having to provide education for themselves in the early years of this century. His liberal doles made possible many individual town libraries in Britain, whilst The United Kingdom Trust which he founded in 1913 was responsible for inaugurating the county library service. Indeed, until Parliament passed the necessary legislation in 1919 enabling local authorities to spend more than a penny rate on library services, the Carnegie Trust sustained it. It housed the National Central Library and encouraged the construction of playing fields, the Cambridge village colleges and museums.[29]

Carnegie's generosity was emulated and surpassed by Rockefeller, who made possible the rebuilding of University College Hospital Medical School after the First World War at a cost of 4 million dollars. A further half-million dollars was given to the University of Edinburgh to improve teaching and research facilities in medicine. As an overall stimulus, a system of fellowships was instituted to bring the leaders of medical education to the United States or Germany, indeed to anywhere where new ideas were germinating.

When one places beside these grants the falling of U.G.C. non-recurrent grants from £393,000 (for 1919–20) to £272,750 (for 1921–2) then to £48,285 (for 1922–3) and finally to £19,000 (1923–4), their value is enhanced.

The Rockefeller Foundation also provided London University with an administrative headquarters. The remainder (some £212,500) needed a parliamentary supplementary estimate. The functional crag that was subsequently built in Bloomsbury now serves both as a headquarters for the University of London and as a central meeting place for a large number of bodies concerned with the university policy in Great Britain.

The secretary of the General Education Board and the driving force behind the programme of cultivating the humanities in the universities, Abraham Flexner, pointed out in 1930 that investment in higher education would actually reduce the National Debt:

From the standpoint of ability to finance universities and research, it is, however, well to remember that as a matter of fact the British Debt at the close of the Napoleonic Wars bore the same relation to the national wealth as is now borne by the present debt. The previous debt was not extinguished, but it was virtually reduced to insignificance by the expansion of English industry, by steam, coal, iron. Is it not conceivable that if England similarly developed physics and chemistry, a comparable phenomenon would occur.[30]

In the same year, 1930, Rockefeller money also enabled both Oxford and Cambridge to reorganize their long-obsolete library systems. Nearly forty years before this Gladstone had appealed to Carnegie in a letter written with his own trembling non-agenarian hand for money with which to save the Bodleian. Now more practical and, as it transpired, more successful methods of reorganizing these libraries were undertaken.

Cambridge, helped by a legacy of £65,000 from the Rev. J. H. Ellis enabled the Senate to provide a quarter of a million pounds, and a matching sum came from the Rockefeller Education Board. The Board did more: they invited a commission to visit some of the chief American libraries in the autumn of 1930. The main reading room in the South Pavilion of the new library was named the Anderson Room, in honour of Sir Hugh Kerr Anderson, the Master of Caius, to whom 'more than any other man' was due the securing of the Rockefeller grant.

If anything in a worse plight, Oxford obtained three-fifths of the £944,300 needed for a new library from the Rockefeller trustees on condition that the university found the remaining two-fifths within a given period of four and a half years. That condition was satisfied in one.

Rockefeller research grants to the civic universities enabled many new lines of research to grow. Thus at Leeds from 1933 onwards, they supported X-ray studies of the biomolecular structure of wool, keratin and other proteins by W. T. Astbury. Astbury's X-ray work, which had already established the skeleton structure of the wool molecule, was the foundation of all later knowledge of wool textile processes, of all present-day methods of cold permanent waving in the hairdressing industry and of the work on the production of Ardil from the protein of ground-nuts by Imperial Chemical Industries. The £45,000 which the Rockefeller gave to these researches was well spent. A similar story could be told at Sheffield of their help to Professor H. A. Krebs, the Nobel Prize biochemist.

Other divisions of the Rockefeller Foundation awarded regular training fellowships. For thirty years it enabled the British Medical Research Council (established in 1919) to dispatch a picked nucleus of research workers to study overseas. Half a million dollars has been expended in this way, and the names of the Fellows include Sir Howard Florey, Sir John Conybeare, Professor A. A. Moncrieff and Professor C. H. Waddington. Then again, during the Second World War, when British facilities for medical training were stretched to breaking point, the Foundation, working through the Committee of Vice-Chancellors and Principals, enabled many promising young medical trainees to spend two-year periods at twenty-three medical schools in the United States and Canada. Promising individuals have also been helped in their own institutions to obtain vital apparatus at a time when the calls on university finances have been unusually heavy. The projects so assisted include the scientific research units as well as the restocking of the National Central Library at London (itself owing much to Carnegie generosity). Up to 1956 no less than 28,761,453 dollars was spent in Britain by Rockefeller trustees.[31]

(7)

What made America one of the decisive determinants in the genesis of new English scientific institutions was that it was the first nation to face the problem of educating everybody. No American college, whatever its material drawbacks, could afford to confess itself a third-class waiting room for adult life. To cope with the thousands that funnelled out into the west, new types of institutions had to be built and new techniques of teaching in them improvised. Many of these techniques have, with modifications, been found stimulating in Britain.

America helped the English to adjust their many-tiered, deeply embedded, educational system to the conditions of modern life. The American frontier, moving westwards, pulled at the class layers of English society. But as the frontier moved westwards, prairie corn destroyed the amateur English farmer, and American inventions rapidly supplanted the expensive English handicraft worker. And the very pace of American technological change precipitated the solution of social problems long shelved (or at best tentatively handled) in English industrial areas.[32]

Starting in a new country, with no tangible, visible or potent past to enfold and conservatize them, American universities and colleges planned for an indefinitely expanding future. The British civic universities caught some of this spirit.

Britain also woke up to the idea that it too had a frontier. In 1893, the year of the Chicago World Fair, there opened in South Kensington the Imperial Institute, ostensibly 'to promote the utilization of the commercial and industrial resources of the Empire by the chemical and technical investigation of raw materials'; this purpose and another, 'the supply of information relating to such materials', were overshadowed by a third: 'the maintenance of comprehensive exhibits illustrating the economic resources of all the countries of the Empire'. This is what the gigantic building in Prince Consort Road became, a museum, and hopes for it soon faded.

(8)

Glass for rangefinders, dyes for uniforms, magnetos for transport, tungsten for steel and zinc for melting were all imported from Germany. Even the chemical glassware of British chemists was in such short supply that the Government made an inventory of all that existed as a prelude to commandeering it.[33]

War with Germany in 1914 exposed this state of affairs. First a committee was appointed under Haldane to survey the problem, driven by the 'Neglect of Science Committee' of the Royal Society and British Science Guild. In 1915 an Institute of Industry and Science was set up as a voluntary group to promote research and this urged the establishment of a Ministry of Industry.

Meanwhile the universities branch of the Board of Education formulated a plan in conjunction with Sir William M'Cormick of the Carnegie Trust which has been described on page 207 *ante*. This was nothing less than the creation of new machinery to promote and organize scientific research, not only during, but after the war: a small advisory council of scientists and industrialists and a committee of the privy council responsible for expending Government grants. Both council and committee were to be under the Board of Education.

Just before, during and after the First World War, three other State pipes to help research were laid down. The first was the Development Commission to help rural industries and fisheries. To link these industries with universities, research institutes were built up round groups of chemists, biologists, mycologists and entomologists. These research institutes were to expand in numbers and scope as the century wore on. This set a pattern for State-subsidized research.

The second took shape following a committee appointed to administer a fund raised from a levy imposed by the National Insurance Act of 1911: the Medical Research Council. This extended its helping hands to research units and groups in universities, hospitals and public health authorities. By 1960 it was sustaining 49 research units, 22 research groups, 9 reference libraries for special subjects and 5 special laboratories. In addition 59 constituent public health laboratories were in relationship with it. It also controlled the public health laboratory service, the Clinical Research Board and the National Institute of Medical Research.

The third governmental agency to be established was the Agricultural Research Council on 23 July 1931. Like D.S.I.R. its powers were redefined in 1956 by the Agricultural Research Act, which empowered it to establish or develop institutions or departments in institutions and make grants. It has 22 research institutions and units under its wing and aids 23 more.[34]

(9)

Perhaps the most symbolic case history of an American trained electrical engineer was that of D. N. Dunlop (1868–1935). Born in Scotland, he joined the American Westinghouse Company at Pittsburgh in 1894. Returning to England in 1899 at the time of the construction of Old Trafford, he served as assistant to, and then as, the publicity manager of Westinghouse in Europe.

Dunlop was convinced of the need for leading electrical manufacturers to associate to discuss and deal with matters of common interest. In 1911 he got his way and the British Electrical Appliance Manufacturers Association (B.E.A.M.A.) was formed with Dunlop as its organizing secretary. In 1917 he became its director, a post he held till 1935.

Any movement concerned with electrical progress, like the Electrical Research Association, or the Electrical Development Association, found in him a fervent supporter. His enthusiasm transcended the purely national, and in 1926 he brought together the representatives of some forty nations in the first World Power Conference: an ecumenical body which, has, as yet, had an unbroken history of interchanging ideas. Dunlop was a superb promoter of such parliaments of experts: his obituarist in the *Electrical Review* of 7 June 1935 described him as believing in committees 'heart and soul'. 'He was never more resourceful' wrote M. J. Railing of B.E.A.M.A. 'than when pointing the way by which men of strong conviction might tread a common path together to attain a common purpose'.

PART IV

The Politics of Science

14

<hr>

Amerikanski Tempo

<hr>

(1)

There is only one road for Russia to follow, and that is the road that the United States has pursued. We must study America's experiment, and at the same time try to bring over her enormous capital and her mighty technical means.[1]

So wrote N. A. Borodin, and his opinions were shared by Vladimir Ivanovich Vernadsky, a leading Russian geologist. Born in 1863 (when the Russian fleets were visiting New York and Boston), Vernadsky had, as a professor of mineralogy and crystallography at Moscow, located radium and uranium deposits in Russia and at the beginning of the war had organized a mineralogical museum in Russia. He too wrote in January 1917 'our work of investigation, especially as it concerns the productive forces of our country, must be carried out on the same scale as America developed it after the Civil War'. He recognized that 'the world centre of scientific organization is being transported to the United States'.[2]

The most potentous technocrat of them all, however, was Gleb Maksimilianovich Krzhizhanovsky. We have already seen that it was in his room in St. Petersburg that Lenin had, as a young lawyer, joined the secret group of 'intelligentsia' known as the Social Democratic circle in 1893. Though Krzhizhanovsky regarded Lenin as temperamentally too red and insufficiently

219

reliable, they nevertheless shared the exile subsequently imposed upon them, and at the East Siberian town of Shushkenskoe,
Krzhizhanovsky and his wife would visit the Lenins on Siberian
ponies. Characteristically, Lenin would shut his ears when
Krzhizhanovsky tried to read him the current news. For exercise
they used to skate and wrestle. It was there, too, that Lenin took
his name—from the River Lena, for up to now he had been
known as Vladimir Ul'yanov.[3]

Released from exile, Krzhizhanovsky went to work on the
Samara–Zlatoust Railway, and in 1905 became chairman of a
strike committee. Afterwards he worked as an electrical
engineer, supervising the Moscow Cable Network, and in 1911
helped build and operate the first peat-fuel electric power
station.[4]

When Lenin came to power in 1917, it was to Krzhizhanovsky
that he turned as his procurer of energy slaves, as chairman of
the State Planning Commission (GOSPLAN) and of the
electrification programme (GOELRO).[5]

The dazzling future opened up by the possibility of in-
numerable kilowatt-hour energy slaves was appreciated and
exploited by Lenin, who asked Krzhizhanovsky in 1920,
'Couldn't you produce a plan (not a technical but a political
scheme) which would be understood by the proletariat? For
instance, in 10 years (or 5?) we shall build 20 (or 30 or 50?)
power stations covering the country with a network of such
stations, each with a radius of operation of say 400 *versts* (or
200 if we are unable to achieve more) . . . we need such a plan
at once to give the masses a shining unimpeded prospect to
work for: and in 10 (or 20?) years we shall electrify Russia,
the whole of it, both industrial and agricultural. We shall work
up to God knows how many kilowatts or units of horse power.'[6]

Another companion of those early St. Petersburg days had
become the Siemens-Schuckert representative in Russia: L. B.
Krasin. He now resigned to join the highest echelon of power
around Lenin after the revolution, becoming not so much a
technocrat as a diplomat. He came to London on Lenin's behalf
in 1920. Having heard him address the Fabian Summer School
in August 1920 Beatrice Webb wrote in her diary 'remarkable
. . . admirably conceived and delivered with a cold intensity of
conviction which made it extraordinarily impressive. . . . Every

expedient of modern industrialism designed to increase the output of the individual worker, whether new mechanical inventions,
new forms of power, new methods of remuneration, piece work,
premium bonus, the concentration of business in the best
equipped factories, were to be introduced to work out this
plan.'[7] She wrote in her diary:

> Krassin, with his tall lithe figure, his head perfectly set on his
> shoulders, with his finely chiselled features, simple manner and
> keen direct glance, looks, every inch of him, the highly bred and
> highly trained human being, a veritable aristocrat of intellect and
> bearing. So far as one can gather from listening to him he is a
> curious combination of the practical expert and the convinced ad-
> herent of a dogmatic creed. But one is tempted to wonder whether
> this creed does not consist almost entirely in an insistent demand
> for the subordination of each individual to the working plan of the
> scientifically trained mind; though, of course, the plan is assumed
> to be devised in the interests of the community as a whole. Whether,
> for instance, he altogether believes in the Communist ideal of
> equality among men, in culture, personal freedom and the means of
> livelihood.[8]

(2)

Just such a 'curious combination of the practical expert and the
convinced adherent of a dogmatic creed' was Henry Ford, idol of
many of those who chose to stay and build the New Russia. Most
explicit (he had to be) was Krzhizhanovsky, who observed:
'In reality, our age is an age of energy. Behind the machine
there is energy, particularly hydraulic energy.' He went on:
'Mr. Ford in this instance hits the nail on the head . . . the production of energy is the base which guarantees the maximum
possibility of possessing the earth.'[9] This showed great insight,
for Henry Ford would have fitted Beatrice Webb's description
of Krassin very well, except that he wasn't tall. He had also
been the chief engineer of the Edison Illumination Company of
Detroit, before building his great motor works. He was also
'the convinced adherent of a dogmatic creed', and the first
chapter of *My Philosophy of Industry* (1921) was called
'Machinery, the New Messiah'. In the Henry Carey tradition
Ford saw machinery as the great emancipator and his seven
principles—power, accuracy, economy, continuity, system, speed
and repetition—as applied at the Highland Park Plant in 1914,

enabled one motor car to be assembled in 93 minutes—whereas the year before it took 14 hours.[10] As Coolidge remarked, 'the man who builds a factory builds a temple, the man who works there, worships there'. For behind this Ford had a real philosophy of industry—an 8-hour, 5-dollar day, in the days when 9-hour, $2\frac{1}{2}$-dollar days were the rule—thereby doing much to demolish Ricardo's 'iron law' of wages which allegedly provided capitalism with its spinal cord. His fusion of mechanics and morality (Ford once said: 'Rightness in mechanics and rightness in morals are basically the same thing and cannot rest apart') led to an industrial autocracy, with its party members, its police, its purges and indeed its terror.[11]

Henry Ford was born in the very year in which the Russian fleets had sheltered in American ports—and incidentally in the year in which Lenin's parents were married. His co-pioneer in mass production was Albert Kahn, whose technique of factory building was 'all on one floor, all under one roof'. Kahn not only built the River Rouge Plant, but some 200 million dollars' worth of buildings for the U.S. Army during the First World War, as well as motor plants for Packard, Ford, Chrysler and General Motors. Now, in 1928, Kahn went to Russia, where he built 521 factories and trained 4,000 engineers.[12]

Another engineer Ford recommended to the Soviet Government was John Knight Calder (1882–1946), who built tractor works at Stalingrad and Chelyabinsk, together with the second-largest blast furnace in the world at Magnitogorsk and a large copper refinery at Lake Balkhash. In fact, Calder became the chief engineer of the Soviet Steel Trust—a singular honour for a non-citizen and a non-Communist, since it made him the virtual director of ninety of the most important plants in Russia. So important was he that the Russian playwright, Nikolay Fedorovich Pogodin (Stukalov) came to live for several months with him before writing his famous play Tempo.

Tempo dealt with the construction of a Stalingrad tractor factory and is itself an interesting social document. 'If only we could master Americanism and suffuse it with communist principles,' exclaims a Komsomol worker in Tempo, whilst the non-political American engineer confesses, 'I am far from political, but I am sure that such a record is outside the reach of any country with a different political organization from yours here.'[13]

This political difference lay in engineering with vision: the permeation of the masses by the doctrine of electrification. Socialist Russia, according to Krzhizhanovsky, could use technology which capitalism could not handle: 'the real *Kingdom of Machines* which are not enemies but friends of mankind is not behind us but *in front of us*'. Commenting on this Dr. Davis observes 'He was rehearsing along somewhat crude lines present-day arguments about the nature of the social processes and the appropriate structure of investment in the industrialization of underdeveloped countries like China and India'.[14]

Both Lenin and Stalin wooed the technical intelligentsia, hitherto neglected. 'We need,' Lenin said, 'more and more engineers, agronomists, technicians, scientific experts of every kind',[15] whilst Stalin said, in 1924, that unless Russian revolutionary scope was united with American practicality, it would degenerate into 'empty revolutionary phrase-mongering' and 'flights of revolutionary fancy'.[16] Indeed whatever abuse Stalin subsequently showered on American politicians, he always remembered what American engineers had done, and twenty years later admitted that two-thirds of all the industrial enterprises in the Soviet Union had been built with American aid or technical assistance.[17]

(3)

Two-thirds is a pretty large share. Americans participated for a variety of reasons, philanthropic, business, and, of course, the enormous technical challenge presented by having to do a job almost regardless of cost.

Apart from the relief Americans afforded to the famine-stricken Russians in 1921–2 and again in 1928, which saved millions of lives,[18] Americans helped the provisional Government of 1917 to put the railways into order. John F. Stevens helped especially, going on to rebuild Vladivostok.[19] This should be contrasted with the more inept behaviour of other Allied powers who invaded Russia on behalf of the White Russians. American help continued during the first and second Five Year Plans, when the President of the Great Northern Railroad, Ralph Budd, became the transportation adviser to Soviet engineers.[20]

The Soviets frankly wanted American technological help after

1918, and courted it through a purchasing organization called Amtorg. Westinghouse, General Electric and International Harvester had been working in Tsarist Russia, and Amtorg continued to deal with them, but brought other firms in as well. Over thirty other companies' products were brought in by A. H. Hammer of the Allied American Company. Other American firms undertook specific tasks: Averill Harriman to exploit their manganese; Stuart, James and Cooke to examine the productivity of the Donets Coal Trust, and Du Ponts to build fertilizer plants.[21]

Though the leading organization in the trade, Amtorg was not the only one. Other governmental trusts were established which studied American methods: the All-Russia Textile Syndicate, the Tsentrosoyuz-American Inc. for studying U.S. office methods, the Sel'skosoyuz-American Inc. for Farming Products, Amkino for Films and the Soviet Naphtha Syndicate, which worked with Standard Oil and Vacuum Oil. Saul G. Bron, the former chairman of the Amtorg Trading Corporation, observed in 1930 that the economic development of the Soviet Union was proceeding along the lines laid down by the United States, namely, the generation of power, the exploitation of natural resources and large-scale farming. Bron argued that the U.S.S.R. was by far the greatest potential market of the U.S.A., as it was already one of the most important existing markets. Bron noted that 'research' in the Soviet Union had 'outstripped' the growth of industry and commented on the increased subventions it received: 65 million roubles in 1929, 210 millions in 1930. Its co-ordination under the Scientific Technical Administration of the Supreme Economic Council led to State trusts—analogous to the large industrial combines built up in the U.S.A.—being established for industry, like Gipromez (for designing metal works), Giproschakht (for designing coal mines), Khemstroy (for chemical engineering works) or Avtostroy (for motor car factories), made it possible to reduplicate large-scale American plant in Russia.[22]

This technical assistance flowed through many channels. There were technical contracts with firms like Ford, G.E.C., Du Ponts, R.C.A., Sperry and others.[23] Individual engineers were engaged. Thirdly there was the training of Soviet workers and technicians in the U.S.A., or visits of Soviet engineers to

American works. Lastly there was the American-Russian Chamber of Commerce, which sent business men's delegations of nearly 100 persons representing nearly 150 firms.

There was sound logic in looking at America rather than Britain, for American industrial development was only half a century old, and moreover it was unhampered by conditions which supplied the basis for the industrial expansion of western Europe. Also, whereas western European labour was linked to craft traditions like apprenticeship, American labour was recruited from agrarian immigrants by what the Russians called Fordian ideas. And since the Soviet labour force was largely agrarian they made the factory school their trump card. As Stalin himself rephrased the classic Communist slogan in June 1931, 'From each according to his special ability, to each according to his special achievements.'

Perhaps the best example of American expertise in Russia was provided by Hugh L. Cooper. He had been responsible in 1918 for building the nitrate plant at Muscle Shoals, Alabama, the nucleus of the Tennessee Valley Authority. Eight years later he was asked to consider the possibility of a power plant below the Kitchkas Rapids on the River Dnepr. His report, based on the experience of taming Niagara, the Mississippi and the Nile, secured him the contract to build Dneprostroy—the largest hydro-electric plant up to that time. Its 850,000 h.p. and 2,500 million kWh. capacity increased Russian power output fivefold and put her into third place in that particular league table: previously she had been tenth. The area served by Dneprostroy was some 70,000 square miles—about the size of New England, whilst the navigability of the Dnepr was vastly improved. In 1932 he obtained the Order of the Red Star—the first foreigner to receive the decoration—and in 1933 the Order of the Red Banner.[24] He also enjoyed with J. K. Calder the privilege of personal conferences with Stalin,[25] and advocated that the Soviet Union should be recognized by America:

> For the time being we have their confidence, and unless this confidence is abused, and if it is encouraged in a practical way, we can do more to advance peace and create happiness in Russia than any other nation or group of nations.[26]

Cooper's brother Dexter, incidentally, dreamed of harnessing the Bay of Fundy and conceived of the Passamaquoddy Tidal Project, the plan of which he laid before the Federal Power Commission in 1924.[27] This would have been the first power plant in the world to harness the tides, and the U.S. Government is still (1965) debating whether or not to go forward with it. Cooper himself thought of harnessing the St. Lawrence at the same time and complained in 1923 that the equivalent of 54 million tons of coal was being dumped into the river annually 'and would continue to do so', he was reported as saying, 'until constructive statesmanship joins with our best economic and engineering abilities and corrects the present situation'.[28]

In the year before he obtained the Dneprostroy contract, Cooper advocated the creation in America of a permanent group of expert investigators, numbering about 100, who would substitute facts for guesswork and organize a new science of government.[29] He later returned from Russia to address the American Academy of Political and Social Science on the theme that the development of natural resources and their conversion to domestic use were the foundations of all true prosperity the world over.[30] Was this not *l'esprit polytechnique* at work?

(4)

'No dark power', said Lenin in 1920, 'can withstand the union of the representatives of science, the proletariat and technique.'[31] He determined to unite them. Three years later he was affirming: 'We must set as our objective: first to study; second, to study; third to learn and then verify this learning in order that science should not remain with us a dead letter or a stylish phrase, but should really penetrate the skin and blood.'[32]

So that science might 'penetrate the skin and blood' Lenin opened the Soviet universities to all citizens over the age of 16 on the production of an identity card and birth certificate. The immediate increase in the student body was startling. From 100,000 in 1917–18 it grew to 170,000 in 1919–20, 190,000 in 1920–1 and 217,000 in 1923. To cope with this swollen flood of students new universities were created by local soviets.

Of the 200-odd institutions of higher learning that sprang up, five call for special mention, straddling as they did the central and southern regions of the U.S.S.R. These were the National

University of Georgia at Tbilisi; the Azerbaidzhan State University at Baku on the Caspian (an early centre of petroleum production), the Ural State University at Sverdlovsk, the Turkestan Central State University (now the Central Asian University) at Tashkent, and the Irkutsk State University (for south-eastern Siberia near Mongolia). Of these that at Tashkent bore the appealing title of the University of the Toilers of the East—a fine propagandist stroke. Another with the same role was the Kazakhstan State University at Alma-Ata, founded in 1934, also in central Asia.

As 'free socialist universities' these and others roused the animosity of the conservative professors and some pre-revolutionary foundations. This drew from Lenin the tart remark that the first defect of the revolution was an 'excess of bourgeois intellectualism', so he put appointments to the professoriate under the Commissariat for Education (NARKOMPROS). But to lessen the load, tests of admission were imposed in 1924 and time limits for the courses were set. These courses were also reorganized. Moral science was to include philosophy and Marxist ideology while technical science embraced pedagogy, sociology and medicine.

Existing universities were reconstructed, especially those in the Ukraine, where Kiev and Kharkov were broken up into medical, agricultural and technological institutes. At Kharkov these were called the Institute of People's Education. A palace of industry was planned there too, focusing the mining and industrial interests of the Donbas. Amongst the important institutions was the University at Dnepropetrovsk in the Ukraine, founded in 1918 by Lev Pisarzhevsky, who earlier had organized the first plant for the extraction of iodine from algae (1915–17). He later founded the Institute of Chemistry and Technology in 1930.

To feed these universities and high-powered specialist institutions with talent, and to provide others to exploit Russia's vast resources, the whole country became a school. Youths were brigaded to transform society. Since technical manpower was urgently needed, the Commissariat of Education ordered in 1921 that 15 should be the age at which general-polytechnic education should pass into professional-polytechnic. The bases of a polytechnic education Lenin defined as a basic understanding of electricity; the application to mechanical industry; to chemical industry . . . one to three visits to an electrical station, factory, or *sovkhoz*; basic knowledge of agronomy and similar matters.[33]

Polytechnization, as at first interpreted, meant linking the school with some productive enterprise, even though it meant, in one case, a barber's shop.

To provide phalanges for these technical enterprises, a decree in 1926 set up what were to be the most typical and important nurseries of Soviet talent: the technicums. In these the rapid professional preparation of engineers, administrators, teachers and doctors was undertaken; students being recruited at 15 after seven years schooling.

Not even politics was to interfere with their study of science. As the Young Communist League were told by M. I. Kalinin on 11 March 1926,

I think that if the fulfilment of Komsomol duties in our schools were to hinder the study of mathematics—I deliberately say mathematics, since it is a subject that most sharply differs from the rudiments of political knowledge, then we should be doing the wrong thing;

and again,

the Komsomol organization has to impress on each of its members that his chief task is to acquire a perfect knowledge of the trade he is learning, to work as well as his teacher does.[34]

By the side of the universities (VUZ), beginning in 1929, superior technical institutes (VTUZ) were set up under the special commissariats for industry. Thirty-nine such institutes were attached to the University of Moscow, and forty-four to the University of Leningrad. And a general, S. A. Boubnov, took over the Commissariat of Education from Lunacharsky.[35]

As scientific manpower became more important the Commissariat of Education ordered in 1931 better preparation in the sciences for those going on to technicums and higher institutions. In other words they called for a training in basic science rather than 'integration with productive labour'. This change was further underlined in 1937 when workshop and 'labour equipment' was ordered to be transferred to the physics laboratories. Rooms hitherto devoted to these activities were converted into laboratories, and 'teachers of labour' were ordered to 'requalify' as teachers of physics and mathematics. Money hitherto spent on workshops was to be reallotted to equip laboratories in physics, chemistry and biology. The new definition of 'Polytechnization' was given final substance when the Scientific Research Institute on Polytechnic Education was converted into a Scientific Research Institute for the Secondary School.

(5)

'When the real history of the Russian revolution is written,' remarked J. B. S. Haldane, 'it may prove that Karpov's reorganisation of the chemical industry was as vital a factor in its success as the more showy activities of Trotsky.'[36]

L. Y. Karpov's Institute of the Chemical Industry was one of many such specialist institutes on the German model that were now rapidly built up. As Lenin wrote, 'What the *junker* state has carried out in Germany, that is what will be fully carried out in Russia for the Soviets, for the dictatorship of the proletariat'.[37] To the pre-revolutionary institutes like the Institute of Applied Mineralogy[38] (under V. V. Arshinov), of Fertilizers (under Y. V. Samoilov)[39] and Karpov's own, were now added more, like the Central Institute of Aero-Hydrodynamics (founded in 1918 by N. Y. Zhukovsky and S. A. Chaplygin) whose work on high-speed aircraft was lavishly encouraged. Schools of 'aspirants' were also organized in each research institute. In fifteen years there were 99 of them concerned with heavy industry, with 27 subordinate institutes. In them, 33,380 people were employed, of whom 11,189 (33·5 per cent) were scientists, 9,358 (28·1 per cent) were technicians, engineers or laboratory assistants, and 12,833 (34·4 per cent) were service personnel.[40]

The management of these institutes was entrusted to Vladimir Ipatieff by the Scientific and Technical Division of the Supreme Council of the Economy, for they were the spearhead of the Supreme Council's drive for food and chemicals, and often worked in conjunction. Agricultural academies and institutes were formed to cope with successive famines; by 1933 there were no less than 1,233 of them: more than had been opened in the whole world since 1835.[41] One visitor spoke of their staff as 'barefoot, ragged scientific workers'. At Timiryasev, Roger Williams, the son of an American railway engineer, worked at Odessa with T. D. Lysenko, later to bring Russian soil science into grave disrepute in soil-science circles by his mixing politics and science, self-interest and truth. But here the great figure was N. I. Vavilov (1887–1943) who directed the All-Union Institute of Plant Culture from 1924 to 1940.

The production shortage of the basic chemicals (sulphuric acid, nitric acid, chlorine and soda) was desperate; most of the heavy chemical plants had either been destroyed during the war or had worn out. In the plans for its reconstruction further institutes were founded. Near coke plants, institutes were set up to pioneer manufacture of benzol, toluol and ammonium sulphate. Near iron and steel centres others were established for developing nitrogenous fertilizers from ammonium sulphate. In potato-growing areas, plants for the production of synthetic rubber were established using the process pioneered by Sergey V. Lebedev (1874–1934), a professor at Leningrad University, who as Director of the Laboratory of Synthetic Rubber from 1928 to 1930 developed the process for polymering unsaturated compounds which led to basic techniques in the rubber industry. The list goes on—plastics, pharmaceutics, artificial fibres. And all the time ceaseless prospecting went on for sources of new materials. Between 1928 and 1940 the production of sulphuric acid increased sevenfold, from 211,000 to 1,587,000 tons; that of fertilizers increased twenty-fourfold, from 135,000 to 3,240,000 tons; that of artificial fibres increased fifty-fivefold, from 200 to 11,000 tons and that of tyres thirty-fivefold, from 85,000 to 3,007,000 tons.[42]

A Radium Institute which became the centre of such work in the Soviet Union was founded in 1922 by V. I. Vernadsky who with others travelled to the West to pick up ideas. Lenin himself established the Central Institute of Röntgenology and the Bekhterev Institute of the Brain.

The need for coal, petroleum and metals called for the reorganization of the geological institutions. The Geology Committee became in 1930 the Chief Administration of Geology and Prospecting and in 1946 became the All-Union Ministry of Geology and Mineral Resources.

(6)

Perhaps the most outstanding of all were the institutes of physics. Here Munich-trained Abraim F. Ioffe (1880–1960) was outstanding. He worked with W. K. Röntgen from 1902 to 1906 and became Professor of the St. Petersburg Polytechnic Institute in 1913. After the revolution in 1918 he founded the Institute of Physics and Technology of which he was to be director for thirty-three years. Quantum mechanics, crystallography, semi-conductors, all came within his purview.

(He should not be confused with Adolf Abramovich Ioffe (1883–1927), a follower of Trotsky, who initiated peace negotiations at Brest-Litovsk, and later carried out diplomatic negotiations in China (1923), committing suicide in 1927.)

Moving four years later to a handsome building originally intended as a home for retired scientists, the Institute of Physics and Technology became a training ground for directors of other institutes, at Kharkov (1928), Tomsk (1928), Sverdlovsk (1932), Dnepropetrovsk (1933) and the Leningrad Physics Agricultural Institute: men like N. N. Semënov, A. A. Chernyshëv, P. I. Lukirsky and Y. I. Frenkel.[43] Here Ioffe worked on semi-conductors, a rich and promising field. Here too the skills and enterprise of the Cavendish Laboratory were imported in the persons of Chariton and Peter Kapitza. Round Kapitza was later built a special institute of Physical Problems at Moscow.

Ioffe started work on the atomic nucleus in 1930, obtaining large funds to do so. In the same year the Physico-Technical Institute was established at Kharkov by Leningrad scientists. In 1931 an Institute of Chemical Physics was founded at Leningrad to consider chemical problems in the light of new discoveries in atomic physics.[44] Leningrad had by 1934 a strong team of sixty-five scientists[45] who acted as hosts at the first Soviet conference on the nucleus convened at Leningrad, to which Western scientists were invited. At Kharkov too an outstanding team was fast assimilating British experience. Its director, A. I. Leipunsky, had worked at Cambridge and in 1932 four of his colleagues repeated Cockroft and Walton's experiment and built a high-tension laboratory.[46]

I. V. Kurchatov, one of Ioffe's nursery, went on to build at Leningrad the first cyclotron in Europe at the Leningrad

Radium Institute where his activities provided the Soviet Union with an excellent platform from which to launch an expansion of nuclear research in 1939. S. I. Vavilov (1891–1951) organized in 1932 the Lebedev Physical Institute at Moscow and the institute which was later named after him.[47] To the Lebedev Institute came D. Skobelt'syn from Leningrad. Heavy-water and isotope separation also engaged the Dniepropetrovsk Institute of Physical Chemistry.

The integration of the institutes with the enormous programme of industrial expansion necessitated frequent conferences. One such was held in the April of 1931 when *bourgeois* or 'pure' science was attacked as having no contact with reality. The only science from now on was to be socialist science, or science for social welfare. Harnessed to the task of maximizing the natural resources of Russia, a multiplicity and diversity of institutes grew, guided by the academy which participated in all the conferences convoked by Gosplan.

As they grew, these institutes hived off other specialist institutes. Thus from the preoccupation of the Lebedev Physical Institute in Moscow with particle accelerators, cosmic rays, radio-wave propagation, radio-astronomy, luminescence in solids—hived off the Seismological Institute (later the Geophysical Institute) whilst the laboratories of surface phenomena superface layers and of disperse systems joined to become the Colloidal Electrochemical Institute in 1937, later, in 1945, the Institute of Physical Chemistry.

(7)

The new spirit spread to the Arctic, where Soviet exiles organized themselves in 1918 into a committee under the Scientific and Technical Department of the Economic Council. This grew after the withdrawal of the Allied Forces from Archangel in 1920 into the Northern Scientific Industrial Expedition. By 1925 it became the Institute for the Study of the North, and in 1930 the All-Union Arctic Institute.

Meanwhile various governmental and scientific organizations were becoming involved in the Arctic. The Northern Sea Route occupied the Revolutionary Committee of Siberia from 1920 (*Komseveroput*), and after the formation of the Union was made a department in the People's Commissariat for Foreign Trade.

As the economic importance of the Arctic increased, *Komseveroput* was abolished and its work transferred to *Glavsevmorput* in 1934, which became in 1936 the supreme directing and co-ordinating agency for the exploitation of all Russia north of 62°N.

This was the last great unoccupied region of the world. Comprising 5,700,000 square kilometres, it was little less than one-third of the total area of the U.S.S.R. and could absorb all the U.S.A., 24 Englands or 187 Belgiums. Responsible not only for the mastery of the Arctic sea routes and the exploitation of natural resources but also for cultural development, *Glavsevmorput* had 16 departments: politics, culture, maritime and river transport, air service, polar stations, hydrography, geology and mining, agriculture, fur, trade, planning, ice prognostication, finances, mobilization of resources, office administration, cadres. Subordinate to it were the Arctic Institute, the Institute of Economics of the Extreme North, the Hydrographic Institute, the Aviation School, Arktikugol (the coal trust), the Anaderma Fluorine Mines, Nordvikstroy (salt, coal and oil trust operating in the Nordvik peninsula) and Arktikshub (the supply and procurement office). It was administered through Leningrad, Murmansk, Archangel, Omsk, Tobolsk, Krasnoyarsk (Igarka), Irkutsk, and Vladivostok.

Its 'Red Travelling Tents' attacked illiteracy among the corps of reindeer herdsmen, nomads and other Eskimo types amongst the 60 different nationalities to be found in the Soviet Arctic. By the imaginative use of caterpillar tractors, aerosleds and aircraft these 60 nations were integrated into the Soviet Union. As an American student of Soviet affairs wrote in 1938,

> it cannot be denied that the progress made by the Soviets in their endeavour to uncover the hidden wealth which has been lying idle so long is strikingly different from the situation in the Arctic inherited by them from Imperial Russia in 1917.[48]

For with no less than 74 polar stations in the Arctic, the Soviets had established firm bases from the Barents Strait to the Chukchi Sea.

One of the Russian scientists who grew in this atmosphere was Evgeny K. Fëdorov, who worked as the geophysicist at the first Soviet Drifting Station North Arc from 1937 to 1948.

He has been investigating the effects of atomic explosions on meteorological processes.

The science of geocryology—or of frozen deposits—developed from the necessity of building large industrial structures on frozen soils. Here the Permafrost Institute of the Academy of Sciences has been active, where M. I. Sumgin and N. A. Tsytovich are pioneers.

(8)

The scientific general staff of the great leap forward was the Soviet Academy of Sciences, which established branches in the Urals (at Sverdlovsk in Siberia), in the Far East (at Vladivostok), in Tadzhik Base (at Stalinabad) in 1932 and, in the following year, in Transcaucasia (at Tbilisi). Tbilisi itself found its role too great and in turn split into three branches in 1935: for Georgia, Armenia and Azerbaidzhan. A branch for Kola was also founded at Kirovsk in 1934. Separate academies of science had already been opened in the Ukraine S.S.R. at Kiev (1919) and in the Byelorussian S.S.R. at Minsk (1929).

Its close liaison with the Council of Ministers was emphasized by the transfer of its headquarters (a division on its own known as the Presidium of the General Assembly of the Academy) from Leningrad to Moscow in 1934. In the same year Peter Kapitza, who had worked in the Cavendish Laboratory since 1922, was detained in Russia. Round him was established the Institute of Physical Problems, which amongst other things produced cheap oxygen for the Soviet metallurgical industry.

Each department of the academy (physics and mathematics, biology, chemistry, biology and geography, technical sciences, history, economics, philosophy and law, and literature and language) was given its own assembly; a miniature of the General Assembly of the Academy, which met several times a year to elect its Academician-Secretary. Each department was given research groups and institutes to undertake specialized research, to publish findings, to train scholars, to organize conferences, to assist in the 'application' of findings and to fight 'pseudo-scientific' tendencies. Sometimes research units were organized to cross barriers and act as crash groups investigating urgent practical problems.[49]

This gigantic scientific machine was put to the test when in

1941 the Germans seized the Russian granary of the Ukraine and threatened Moscow. Scientists leapt to defence: Tofim Lysenko, then the President of the Lenin Academy of Agricultural Sciences, took over the responsibility of getting in the harvests, and succeeded. The President of the Academy of Sciences, Vladimir Komarov, moved the universities from the Ukraine, Leningrad and Moscow to the Urals, then to Kazakhstan. Similarly, Peter Shirshov, an intrepid ice-floe researcher, was put in charge of lend-lease operations.[50]

Russian recuperation was possible in the East because of its planned exploitation, and certain elsewhere because of the average Russian being involved in it. As an observer from the Australian Government remarked,

> it can be said without fear of contradiction that nowhere else in the world, not even in America, is there such interest in science among the common people, as there is in Russia.[51]

For the philosophy of the Soviet State was so 'complete and uninviting to a materialistically bent mind' that the peasants elevated by its operations surrendered to it completely.[52]

(9)

Siberia was the Russian recuperator as well as the Russian frontier. Unlike the American Far West which was opened up by individualist effort, the Russian Far East was exploited collectively with American techniques. The exploitation of Siberia was intensified as they drove headlong into it to obtain raw materials. The iron and steel of Magnitogorsk in West Siberia was tapped in the thirties. Komsomolsk in far eastern Siberia was, as its name implies, built by the Young Communist League. North of Magnitogorsk another town, Sverdlovsk, took its name from Jakob Sverdlov, the first chairman of the Soviet Central Executive Committee. Its industrial complex was primed by a university, the Urals Polytechnical Institute, and a branch of the Soviet Academy of Sciences, established in 1932. Another complex also in Siberia is the Kuznets Basin which brims with coal, steel and chemicals.

To this expanding economy Russian laboratories were moved before the invading Germans, and new branches of the Academy of Sciences were established. To Saratov on the Volga came the

University of Leningrad, and to Kazan (half-way to Sverdlovsk) came both the Leningrad Physico-Technical Institute and the Moscow Institute of Physical Problems. In this latter place a branch of the Academy of Sciences was established in 1943, followed by a second branch at Novosibirsk, capital of Siberia, and a third at Syktyvkar in the far nothern republic of Komi that stretches into Siberia.

Four more branches of the Academy of Sciences were opened during the war. To probe the icebound northern rim of Eurasia, and cope with the constant incoming and outgoing of war supplies, two were opened at Archangelsk on the White Sea (1941) and Vladivostok in the Far East (1943). South of Kazakhstan, where Asian Russia abuts on China, a branch opened at Kirgiz in 1941, whilst yet another was established at Petrozavodsk in Karelo-Finnish Russia in 1945, where a State university had been founded in 1940.

To these seven branches another six were added in the immediate post-war period: Makhachkala (Daghestan) and Kishinev (Moldavia) in 1946, Simferopol (the Crimea), Sakhalin and Yakutsk in 1947, Irkutsk (eastern Siberia) in 1949 and Ufa (Bashkir A.S.S.R.) in 1951. This made thirteen new branches in all.

(10)

Russia 'will give soul to the world',[53] a Chinaman told Frank Lloyd Wright, the Wisconsin-trained pioneer of the 'prairie school' of American architecture.

'I thought I saw then what he meant', said Frank Lloyd Wright fourteen years later, when he described the U.S.S.R. as 'a heroic endeavour to establish more honest human values in a social state than ever existed before'. He feared, however, that 'pseudo-machine worship used to defeat pseudo-capitalism may become inverted capitalism in Russia itself, and again prostitute man to the machine'.[54] But what really impressed him on a visit in 1937 were the collective farms, which, he forecast, 'are sure to become the most desirable places in which to work and live,' while Moscow, when completed, 'will be the first city in the world'. But he detected the same barrier across the road to culture as in the U.S.A. 'the popular demand for spiritually unearned, luxurious grandeur. But in their case, no wonder nor reproach. The Russians outside the aristocracy and bourgeoisie had less than nothing. Now it is their turn.' He concluded, 'Russia may yet give to this money-minded, war-minded, quarrelling pack of senile races that make up this world the soul they fail to find within themselves; and, I hope, in time to prevent the suicide their nations are so elaborately preparing to commit'.[55]

Such was the response of the 'Wisconsin spirit' to the Russian experiment.

15

Technocrats and the Politics of Power

(1)

THE Dneprostroy barrage capitalized upon the discoveries of the research group of the General Electric Company of America: especially those of Charles Proteus Steinmetz, whose explanation of the phenomenon of hysteresis enabled losses of electrical power due to magnetism to be forecast and enabled generators to be made of iron. Steinmetz's symbolic method of calculating alternating current phenomena enabled it to be commercially employed, whilst his investigations of the travelling waves in lightning phenomena made possible lightning arrestors to protect high-power transmission lines.[1]

Steinmetz saw electrification as the chief agency of Socialism, and on Lenin's seizure of power he offered to assist 'in the technical sphere, and particularly in the matter of electrification in a practical way, and with advice'. Lenin replied regretting that he could not take advantage of his offer but enclosing his picture, which Steinmetz promptly placed in a place of honour in his laboratory.[2] Lenin did not forget Steinmetz, however, and when planning the industrial exploitation of the Kusbas in Siberia, a Russian mission in America sought his advice.[3]

As a member of a little discussion group which used to meet in Greenwich Village, Steinmetz aired his views with Thorstein Veblen, then teaching at the newly founded New School of

Social Research; Dr. Richard Tolman, later Principal of the California Institute of Technology; F. L. Ackerman, an architect who had been the chief housing expert for the U.S. Shipping Board in the First World War; W. Rautenstrauch, a professor of Industrial Administration at Columbia and Basset Jones, the chairman of the elevator standards committee of the American Standards Association. But the most mysterious of the group was Howard Scott who claimed to have worked at Muscle Shoals under Colonel Cooper.

From the discussions of this group, or 'technical alliance' as it was called, Veblen wrote a series of articles in the *Dial*, later gathered into a book: *Engineers and the Price System*.[4] Its theme was that Bolshevism was 'not a present menace to the vested interests in America' and that 'twentieth-century technology has outgrown the eighteenth-century system of vested rights'.[5] Veblen appended a 'Memorandum of a Practicable Soviet of Technicians'. He realized just how Utopian this suggestion was, for the technicians of his generation were just incapable of becoming technocrats: to him they were just a 'harmless and docile sort, well fed on the whole, and somewhat placidly content with the full "dinner-pail" which the lieutenants of the vested interests habitually allow them'.[6] Sadly he concluded that there seemed 'no present promise of the technicians turning their insight and common sense to such a use', since they were 'a scattered lot of fairly contented subalterns, working piecemeal under orders from the deputies of the absentee owners'.[7]

Wise and shrewd Veblen might be, but Howard Scott was neither. When both Veblen and Steinmetz died and Tolman had gone to California, Howard Scott took control of the 'technical alliance' and directed its attention to making an energy survey of North America. A series of charts were prepared which attracted some publicity.[8] Registered as Technocracy Inc. (a name invented by William H. Smyth of Berkeley, California), the group's monistic technological determinism evoked some acid comments. Archibald MacLeish castigated the replacement 'of the economic determinism of Marx by the scientific determinism of Mr. Scott'. 'The infantile cowardice of our times', he lamented, 'demands an external pattern, a non-human authority, it has manufactured a new nurse. And that nurse is the Law

of Physics. One mechanistic nipple has replaced another.'[9]
When their programme was virtually adopted by the New
Deal, Technocracy lost ground. After America entered the
Second World War, a full-scale advertisement appeared in the
New York Times of 8 March 1942, asking for total conscription
of men, machines, material and money: national service from
all and profits to none. It urged the federation of North and
Central America, Bermuda, the West Indies and Hawaii into the
'Technate State of North America', run like 'a continental telephone system' by a self-perpetuating *élite*.[10] Even when the war
ended, the Technocrats were still crying, 'The price system is
doomed. Energy is the only thing that occurs in science. Communism is radical enough for the old world, but here it's
bourgeois . . . we believe in geomechanics . . . we are faced
with the operational problems of a continent.' These operational
problems could, they argued, be solved if energy certificates replaced money and work was limited to those between 25 and
45 for 4 hours per day, for 4 days a week and for 6 months in
the year.

(2)

Latent among both workers and employers were similar
schemes for enlisting the support of this new and ill-defined
group, the technical intelligentsia. For the Industrial Workers
of the World (I.W.W.), Ralph Chaplin toured the country
after the First World War, attempting to supplement the inade-
quacies of the Marxist canon by promoting industrial congresses
and an industrial encyclopaedia. Their purposefully named
journal, *One Big Union*, even carried articles by Howard Scott
signed 'Industrial Engineer'.

Scott was hired in 1920 as the first and only Research Director
of I.W.W. and Chaplin left a most revealing portrait of his
lodgings in Greenwich Village:

> All the time he was discoursing so plausibly about tear-drop auto-
> mobiles, flying-wing aeroplanes, and technological unemployment,
> I was looking at the other side of the studio where an appallingly
> phallic water color painting was displayed among blue-prints and
> graphs.[11]

During the First World War Charles Ferguson, an editorial

writer for the Hearst chain, outlined a similar scheme. Ferguson was an intimate of Colonel House, for whom he embarked for Europe on mysterious missions. 'We are living', he wrote, 'in the gray morning of an apocalyptic day.'[12] He went on, 'There is about to appear on the field of history, for the first time since the world began, a people more concerned to produce goods than to divide them.'[13] He too sighed for the possibility of industrial engineers, 'such men as Harrington Emerson and H. L. Gantt', holding 'the high places of counsel in Washington'.[14] In true St. Simonian fashion he argued, 'modernity in politics is government by sheer stress of organised intelligence. We have lived for three generations under the complete dominance of the theory that democracy is a mere level numerousness—a circle without a center.'[15]

Organized intelligence was the theme of the journal founded by Willard Straight in 1914: *The New Republic*. As preached by one of the editors, Walter Lippman, fresh from serving the Socialist Mayor of Schenectady (the home of General Electric), it involved a division of rulers into Routineers and Inventors. More inventors (or industrial organizers) were wanted but the common man with his 'pseudo-environment of inaccurate news' would not have them. In *The Phantom Public* (1925) Lippman compared common men to a pack of Pavlovian dogs, arguing that only regenerate business men could give a lead out of the impasse. Such comforting words got Lippman his reward—appointment to the staff of the *New York Herald-Tribune*.[16]

The other editor, Herbert Croly, called for a fourth Department of Government, an *élite* of the competent experts who would extract from the bosom of society the immediately available supply of social reason. 'A better future would derive from the beneficent activities of expert social engineers', said Croly in 1925, since they could 'bring to the service of social ideals all the technical resources which research could discover and ingenuity could devise'.[17]

Fortified by contributors like Harold Laski (who, dining with them in 1931, found them 'as solemn as a gathering of Baptists met to do justice to the Scarlet Woman of Washington'[18]), the *New Republic* survived the loss of both Lippman and Croly (who retired in 1928), and warmly applauded the adoption of planning by other groups in the U.S.A.

(3)

Steinmetz was himself the symbol of a technocratic revolution which was taking place in industry. Ever since the white clapboard laboratory was built in 1876 by Thomas Alva Edison in the hills of northern New Jersey, this revolution had been gathering momentum. For at Menlo Park, Edison utilized the services of C. F. Brackett, the Professor of Physics at Princeton, and F. R. Upton, to ransack the scientific journals. Not only did Menlo Park make possible the building of his electric light company (in 1878), his lamp works (in 1880), his dynamo works (in 1881) and his General Electric Company (in 1889), but it was also a hatchery of electrical engineers. Schuckert, a co-founder of the Siemens-Schuckert works in Germany, Kruesi, the Chief Engineer of General Electric, Kennelly of the Kennelly-Heaviside layer, E. G. Acheson, the inventor of carborundum, and Lee Fleming, inventor of the radio tube, were all trained there, and absorbed the Edisonian formula for success: 'to be able to work without regard to expense'.[19]

After Steinmetz joined General Electric at Schenectady, he and other G.E.C. technocrats like E. W. Rice, jun., A. G. Davis and Elihu Thompson agreed that expanding knowledge rather than improving their product was the best policy for the company. 'There is no scientific investigation, however remote from industrial requirements,' said Steinmetz, 'which might not possibly lead to industrially useful developments.'

His arguments were more than proved in the laboratory devoted exclusively to original research that was organized in 1901 under Dr. Willis R. Whitney, formerly of the Massachusetts Institute of Technology. Whitney's high-resistance electric furnace, W. B. Coolidge's ductile tungsten filaments and X-ray tubes and Irving Langmuir's vacuum-tube oscillators and rectifiers of large power output were major breakthroughs. Langmuir was the first industrial scientist to win the Nobel Prize. Then too this laboratory developed the thyratron as a unit of power control (first used in the Chicago Opera to dim lights), and the magnetron (a source of continuous high-frequency oscillations used in the Second World War in radar transmitters), both owing much to A. W. Hall.

Even more massive research activity was needed to cope with

new problems generated by the radio industry and here another associate of Steinmetz, E. F. W. Alexanderson, became the Chief Engineer of the Radio Corporation of America (formed by the amalgamation of General Electric and Marconi). Here S. M. Kintner, Vladimir Zworykin and James Helling came into their own with the electron microscope, enabling further new discoveries like that of the structure of the protein molecule to be made.[20] In 1930 R.C.A. took over the radio research laboratories of Westinghouse too.[21]

Menlo Park and Schenectady were not the only hatcheries of new industries. The Volta laboratories, established by Alexander Graham Bell, in 1880, worked on Helmholz's analysis of the ways in which sound waves could be built up by tuning forks. Bell consulted scientists at M.I.T. and Joseph Henry in Washington and engaged Thomas A. Watson to do research in telephone technology. Watson's laboratory was expanded by Hammond V. Hayes. Bell's manufacturing section, Western Electric, established research laboratories too, whose head, F. B. Jewett, a former president of the A.A.A.S., ended the system of rewards per patent in 1912. As a result the Bell laboratories became one of the largest in the world and compassed much of modern physics and chemistry in its quest for more efficient electrical communications.[22] In 1925 the Bell laboratories came under the control of the General Electric Company which established with the American Telegraph and Telephone Company a non-profit-making corporation to run them.

The Bell Telephone Laboratories at Murray Hill, New Jersey, became the largest of their kind in the world. Here Broglie's theoretical speculation (in 1924) of the electron's wave and vibration properties was confirmed by C. J. Davisson and L. H. Germer in 1927, for which C. J. Davisson was awarded a Nobel Prize twelve years later. The Bell laboratory's most spectacular success was the invention of the transistor by William Stockley, John Bardeen and Walter H. Brattain: all three Nobel Prize winners. Another was the successful trial of the communications satellite: a plastic balloon with an aluminium coat reflecting waves of frequencies up to 20,000 megacycles. This was the work of J. R. Pierce, of Holmdel, New Jersey.

Soon after Edison and Bell began their own independent researches, Dr. William M. Burton was hired by Standard Oil in 1889 to solve the problem of distilling products from the 'sour' oil of Lima, Ohio. Twenty years later he initiated his first 'cracking' process to increase gasoline yields and, with two other Johns Hopkins men, brought the first catalytic stills into operation in January 1913. During the next seven years the catalytic revolution gathered pace as the possibility of changing the size and shape of the natural molecules and the availability of large quantities of cheap reactive hydrocarbon by-product gases attracted the large chemical companies like Du Pont.

Research was now a condition of growth. In 1900 Du Ponts had tempted G. L. Reese (1862–1940) from academic teaching to become an industrial consultant. By 1911 he became the spearhead of Du Pont's advances at Gibbstown, New Jersey, collecting a formidable cadre of chemists and deploying them in five large research laboratories.

Paced by the petroleum companies, Du Ponts expanded still farther. When in 1927 Shell Petroleum decided to establish a research department at Emeryville quite different from normal testing departments of a refinery under E. C. Williams (formerly Dean of the Faculty of Science at the University of London),[23] Du Ponts followed suit in the following year with a new laboratory and an equally bright academic star, W. H. Carothers (from Harvard), in charge.

Carothers's arrival in 1928 was a real event, for he was distinguished enough to attract research students from university research laboratories with the promise of doing fundamental work. On 23 May 1934 he was successful in spinning a superior polymer through a hypodermic needle. To neoprene, already launched in 1931, he added nylon. His death through overwork robbed Du Ponts of a great man. But the demands of the Second World War stretched Du Ponts still farther, so that by 1948 they had 38 research laboratories working on 136 projects. By 1951 8 of these were commercial successes.[24] Their pacemakers, Shell, grew too. Not counting control laboratories, Shell had by the end of 1955, 2,225 people (6 per cent of its total employees) engaged on full-time research and development.[25]

The Standard Oil Company of New Jersey, which had

organized a development department in 1919 to cater for the ever-increasing demand for the lighter fractions to propel motor cars, developed catalytic polymerization and alkylation processes. Soon 75 per cent of gasoline was being produced from crude oil. Catalytic cracking was vastly accelerated during the Second World War, when in addition to gasoline, nearly a million tons of artificial rubber a year were to replace the lost supplies of Malaya.

Similar stories could be told of the Dow Chemical Company, of U.S. Rubber and of Standard Oil of California, of the American Cyanamid Company and of Monsanto Chemicals. Monsanto developed krilium, a fertilizer of which 1 lb. was as efficacious as 200 lb. of peat moss or 500 lb. of compost.

These companies conducted biological research too. Thus the research laboratories of Merck and Company of Rahway, New Jersey, under R. T. Major and W. H. Engels (originally established in 1933) determined the structure and synthesis of Vitamins B_1, C, B_2 (riboflavin), B_6 (pyridoxine), K, E, pantothenic acid, biotin and B_{12}. They assisted in the mass manufacture of antibiotics, synthetic ephedrine and papaverine during and after the war. The Merck Institute of Therapeutic Research now exists by its side to conduct pharmacological trials of new drugs.

The motor car stimulated the growth of other research teams. C. F. Kettering of the Dayton Engineering Laboratories Company, who developed the Delco electric self-starter in 1912 made further advances with tetra-ethyl lead (anti-knock) in petroleum, and the refrigerator. Incidentally, Kettering also established its General Laboratories to work on fundamental organic chemistry and its high-polymer research teams developed new products like Lastex, Latex and Asbestos. The Goodyear Rubber Company even set up an industrial university which by 1932–3 was the largest corporately supported educational institution in the nation, with 1,322 students.

The recipe for growth was research, as George Eastman realized in 1912 when he organized the Kodak Research Laboratories at Rochester with a budget of 54,000 dollars, and chose C. E. K. Mees as director. Mees held the post until 1947. As a by-product of Kodak ingenuity Vitamin A was recovered from fish-liver oil in a concentrated form.[26] By 1950 this research group was spending 18 million dollars a year. Similarly the U.S. Steel Corporation which allowed a budget of 150,000 dollars a year in 1927 for its newly established research laboratory was by 1950 spending 5,250,000 dollars.[27]

American industrial research laboratories increased from 300 (employing 9,300 persons) in 1920 to nearly 1,000 by 1927; to 3,480 (employing 70,000) by 1940 and to 4,834 by 1956. By that time they were spending 30 per cent of the total amount devoted to research and development in the whole of the U.S.A., sums totalling 8,000 million dollars. Their demand for scientific manpower is such that they were employing nearly 20 per cent (167,000) of the total number of professional scientists, engineers and technicians employed in all types of work in the United States (some 916,000). This 167,000 represented 75 per cent of all those engaged in research and development in the United States.[28] Well might three English observers remark in 1958 that research teams 'constitute the most spectacular change in the activities of the industrial corporation'.[29]

(4)

This industrial research completed, to Veblen's disgust, the seduction of the universities as independent arbiters of opinion.

> Anything like an effectual university—a seminary of the higher learning, as distinct from an assemblage of vocational schools—is not a practicable proposition in America under present conditions,

Veblen lamented. Their transformation into research establishments he attributed to

> a sanguine hope born of academic defeat. They had become large establishments, of the nature of retreats or shelters for the prosecution of scientific and scholarly inquiry in some sort of academic quarantine, detached from all academic affiliation, and renouncing all share in the work of instruction . . .',[30]

To Veblen, this 'desperate surrender of the university ideal' was 'the proven inability of the schools under competitive management, to take care of the pursuit of knowledge'.[31]

Since R. K. Duncan (1868–1914) had argued in the first decade of the century that American industry was behindhand in utilizing scientific research, bankers had rallied to back industrial research, notably A. W. Mellon, who had financed Charles M. Hall's patent of 1889 for the electrolytic production of aluminium (thereby generating the Aluminium Company of America), and E. G. Acheson's discovery of carborundum. Mellon claimed that his outlook had been moulded by reading Benjamin Franklin's *Autobiography* and the institute he founded in 1913 was an immediate and timely success. Used by the War Industry Board under Bernard Baruch in 1917, the Mellon Institute converted the other industrialists to the need for fellowships to prosecute specific research problems. One such was the commercial production of aliphatic chemicals generally associated with G. O. Curme, jun., of the Carbide and Carbon Chemicals Corporation.

Total responsibility for university research problems in metallurgy and fuel technology was assumed by a second research institute founded in 1929 by Gordon Battelle. Its annual expenditure in 1948 was $5\frac{1}{2}$ million dollars a year, and it now has branches in Geneva and Frankfurt.

A third, the Armour Research Foundation of the Illinois Institute of Technology was formed in 1936. A number of regional groups also sprang to life in the New England Industrial Research Foundation; the Mid West Research Institute (at Kansas City) and the Southern Research Institute (at Birmingham, Alabama). At Purdue, Chattanooga, Louisville, Wichita, Denver, Syracuse and Austin (Minn.), other industrial research institutes were founded.[32] The numbers of patents made by university staff were such a problem that F. G. Cottrell formed the Research Corporation to handle them in 1912. Up to the end of World War II this gave $1\frac{1}{4}$ million dollars to projects like the cyclotron, the Van de Graaf high-voltage generator, solar energy projects, computing machines and the synthesis of Vitamin B.

Warning notes were sounded by 1947 that professors might not do their normal work adequately. Ten years later it was reported that 60 per cent of the funds going to universities went to such research centres in universities, and only a quarter of this went to basic research.[33]

(5)

Experts were sermonized by other experts on the need for planning. The American Institution of Mechanical Engineers listened to Herbert Hoover on 26 August 1920 saying that

> The time has arrived in our national development when we must have a definite national program in the development of our great engineering problems. Our rail and water transport, our water supplies for irrigation, our reclamation, the provision of future fuel resources, the development and distribution of future fuel resources, all cry out for some broadvisioned national guidance.[34]

Such 'broadvisioned national guidance' needed, in Hoover's view, an agency of the central Government. He also stressed the long-term goal of adequate study and preparation of the plan and method of dealing with these problems over the next fifty years—'viewed', he added cautiously, 'solely in their national aspects'.

In the same year in the preface to *America and the New Era* (1920), Hoover asserted that government always lags behind social development, and to eliminate the lag he transformed the Secretaryship of Commerce into a national intelligence service and later appointed a Committee on Recent Social Trends, the most comprehensive survey of America's material resources up to that time.

Hoover's Committee on Recent Social Trends enlisted a former pupil of Veblen's and of John Dewey's, Wesley C. Mitchell. Mitchell was a veteran mobilizer of the economy from the days of World War I. After it he had organized the National Bureau of Economic Research. Now he and his colleagues on Hoover's committee called for economic planning and recommended that a National Advisory Council should be established to 'consider some fundamental questions of the social economy, governmental, educational, technical, cultural, always in their interrelation, and in the light of the trends and possibilities of modern science'. In simple English, this meant that plans should be made for making plans.

Hoover and Wesley C. Mitchell were not the only experts discussing the advisability of planning to make plans. Gosplan had been placed on the programme of the American Economic Association's annual meeting in December 1928. When it was discussed, a proposal to establish an analogous economic planning council for the United States was made. Similar proposals were made by the American Federation of Labour and the U.S.

Chamber of Commerce. A Bill for the same purpose was introduced into the first session of the 72nd Congress by Senator Robert La Follette in December 1931, and two months later, on 13 February 1932, a similar Bill was introduced in the House of Representatives.

The report of the American Trades Union delegation to Russia[35] (aptly enough organized by the chairman of the New York State Power Authority, Frank P. Walsh) was edited by Rexford Guy Tugwell, who saw that 'the image of the future is becoming visible' in Russia. Tugwell took part in the campaign of 1929 to get a Socialist elected Mayor of New York, and subsequently became the first lieutenant to Henry A. Wallace, Roosevelt's Secretary of Agriculture. Wallace was quite clear where the future lay, and in *New Frontiers* (1934) he wrote:

> The keynote of the new frontier is co-operation just as that of the old frontier was individualistic competition. The mechanism of progress of the new frontier is social invention, whereas that of the old frontier was mechanical invention and the competitive seizure of opportunities for wealth. It is not a musty sentimental frontier but one of hard realities.[36]

Descanting on what he called 'the Engineering-Scientific Approach to civilization',[37] Wallace challenged the American Association for the Advancement of Science to jettison orthodox economic ideas based on competition and to participate in the New Deal. 'If the planning of the engineer and of the scientist in their own field' could be followed by 'comparable planning in the social world', man would be 'freed from economic insecurity'.[38]

Wallace was really responsible for the creation of a Science Advisory Board under the chairmanship of Karl T. Compton, a physicist. Departments other than his own like commerce, the interior and the Bureau of the Budget utilized it from its initial creation on 31 July 1933. But Compton's ideas clashed with those of the National Resources Board so his Board was dissolved three years later.[39]

(6)

The National Resources Board stemmed from the report of Hoover's Committee on Recent Social Trends, and evolved from a research and advisory committee set up in July 1933 under F. A. Delano, Roosevelt's uncle, which became, a year later, the National Resources Committee under Secretary Ickes. Ickes considered that

> Wise and comprehensive planning on a national scale fits into the social vision of the future. If, as I believe, we are now definitely committed to the testing of new social values; if we have turned our backs for all time on the dreadful implications in the expression 'rugged individualism'; if it is our purpose to make industrialism serve humanity instead of laying themselves as victims on the cruel altar of industrialism, then national planning will become a major governmental activity.[40]

Walter Lippman hastened to bless this new movement:

> If you wish to know why the young men are tempted by communism, by fascism, by almost anything which is emphatic and bold and positive, this is the reason: those who sit in the seats of authority are preaching a gospel of frustration.
>
> If we are to have economic liberty we must accept the ancient truth that liberty is not the natural state of man, but the achievement of an organised society . . . it is the artificial product of civilised effort, and is lost almost instantly when the primitive passions of men are unleashed.[41]

Roosevelt himself put his finger on the real reason for planning. To H. G. Wells he was 'the most effective transmitting instrument possible for the coming of the new world order. . . . He is continuously revolutionary in the new way without ever provoking a stark revolutionary crisis.'[42] For Roosevelt said:

> Equality of opportunity as we have known it no longer exists. . . . Our last frontier has long since been reached and there is practically no more free land. . . . There is no safety valve in the form of a Western prairie to which those thrown out of work by the eastern economic machines can go for a new start . . . Our task now is not the discovery or exploitation of natural resources or necessarily producing more goods. It is the severer, less dramatic business of administering resources and plants already in hand. . . . of distributing wealth and products more equitably, of adapting existing economic organizations to the service of the people. The day of enlightened administration has come.[43]

Two years after he took office Roosevelt formally closed the public domain.

On the National Resources Board sat the secretaries of the interior, commerce and labour, together with the federal emergency relief administrator. By 1939, it had become the National Resources Planning Board, advising the President on the long-term planning required to prepare a continuing six-year plan. Its science committee enlisted the National Research Council, the Social Science Research Council, the American Council of Learned Societies and the American Council on Education. On 1 October 1943 it ceased to exist and an even greater apparatus took its place.

(7)

The greatest natural resource was power. All the slaves freed during the American Civil War could not match the power going to waste at Muscle Shoals, Alabama, where Colonel H. L. Cooper's dam was virtually idle. Cooper had built it to provide nitrates during the First World War and afterwards it was the subject of more debates in Congress than any other issue. Farmers wanted it to continue manufacturing fertilizers and manufacturers like Henry Ford wished to buy it as a power source, but a few far-sighted politicians like Senator George Norris and Representative John Rankine wished it to be the nucleus of a states power complex.

Harmonizing the needs of farmers and manufacturers called for some shrewd orchestration, so A. E. Morgan, a civil engineer, indicated to President Roosevelt that if a comprehensive plan were made for flood control, soil conservation, afforestation and power, standards of life would be raised, not only in Tennessee (thrice raped for timber, oil and gas), but in Alabama, Georgia, Mississippi, North Carolina, Kentucky and Virginia as well. Roosevelt took the point that Morgan was arguing for 'national planning for a complete river watershed', touching and giving life 'to all forms of human conduct'. Well might Representative Charles A. Eaton of New Jersey describe Morgan's plan as 'simply an attempt to graft on to our system the Russian idea'. Morgan the visionary got his reward and on 18 May 1933 became chairman of the *troika* appointed to operate the Tennessee Valley Authority.[44]

One of Morgan's two colleagues, the lawyer David Lilienthal, considered it 'vital to maintain the strictest public control' over power. The other, Morgan's namesake, Harcourt A. Morgan, was an agricultural scientist, preferring the more traditional uplift of the land-grant colleges—of one of which he had once been president—to A. E. Morgan's Utopian social engineering schemes of co-operatives. It is perhaps worth noticing that at the beginning of November 1963 Mr. Barry Goldwater described T.V.A. in Washington as 'a socialistic venture which has been perpetrated on the American people without their knowing what they're getting into'.[45]

(8)

'The true pacemakers of socialism were not the intellectuals or agitators who preached it,' wrote one American economist, 'but the Vanderbilts, Carnegies and Rockefellers.'[46] Carnegie set the example. Having made a vast fortune from applying science, he primed pumps to produce more.

Of the six foundations established by him in the first two decades of the twentieth century, the first endowed the teaching and research in Scottish universities, and in doing so, indirectly set precedents for English universities too. The second, modelled on the Royal Institution of London, sustained ten research departments, including one of experimental evolution at Cold Spring Harbour, another for terrestrial magnetism at Washington, a botanical field station at Tucson, Arizona (established in 1905), a marine biological station at Tortugas Islands, a nutritional laboratory at Boston in close relationship with the Harvard Medical School and an observatory for research in the astronomy of the Southern Hemisphere at San Luis, Argentina. As the Carnegie Institution of Washington it aimed at discovering 'the exceptionally endowed man in all specialities, whatever may be their origin, whether they are in the schools or outside, and to give them the necessary financial aid in order to permit them to accomplish the work for which they seem specially designed'. One so encouraged was a young Belgian, George Sarton, whose enthusiastic pursuit of the history of science was brought to a head by the institute's publication of his massive five-volume *Introduction*. Well might Sarton say that this appointment was the most important event of his life, and, certainly, but for their support 'the New Humanism' would not have been as well received. Another of the institute's grants went to Dr. Gregory Breit and Dr. Merle Tuve, who in 1925 discovered that if they could produce very short pulses of radio waves they could utilize the cathode-ray tube as a measuring device for aircraft, i.e. the second step on the road to radar.[47]

The third Carnegie Foundation, for the Advancement of Teaching, sponsored a number of inquiries. Those into medical education in 1910 (by A. Flexner), engineering education in 1918 (by C. R. Mann) and dental education in 1928 (by Dr. William W. Gies), were the most notable. The first prompted R. S. Brookings, a multi-millionaire who had already handsomely assisted Washington University at St. Louis, to raise some 15 million dollars to improve its medical school. The improvement was such that it was 'unexcelled by any in the country'. Brookings himself, in 1916, promoted an Institution for Research into Government. Six years later he induced the Carnegie Corporation to establish an Institute of Economics, and in 1924 he financed a new graduate school of economics and government in Washington. Four years later he conceived, promoted and developed the main institution for Research and Training in the Social Sciences which bears his name.

The fourth Carnegie endowment, for International Peace (1910), was followed a year later by a fifth, the Carnegie Corporation of New York, which had the most massive endowment of all—some 135 million dollars. Incorporated in 1911 as a 'body to receive funds and apply the income to the advancement of knowledge', the Carnegie Corporation assisted technical schools, institutions of higher learning, libraries, publications, scientific research and in 1919 gave 5 million dollars to the National Academy and the National Research Council. Under its wing, the Carnegie Institute of Pittsburgh and some forty colleges and universities in the U.S.A. and Canada found shelter. The sixth, his United Kingdom Trust, virtually refounded public libraries in England.

By 1950 the Carnegie trusts had given 277,958,179 dollars and stimulated the giving of much more.[48] Amongst their major achievements were the building of the Mount Wilson Observatory in the mountains above Pasadena for G. E. Hale, a lead which was followed by the Rockefeller Foundation, which in 1928 provided a 200-inch telescope for Mount Palomar.

(9)

The Carnegie 'civil service' which administered these funds themselves set precedents. In Britain, Richard Burdon Haldane became the dominant member of a committee of four set up in 1904 by the Treasury to administer a grant to the British universities, and Sir William M'Cormick became the chairman both of the University Grants Committee which succeeded it and of the Advisory Committee of the Department of Scientific and Industrial Research set up in 1916. In America Elihu Root and Vannevar Bush deserve special mention. Root, as President of the Carnegie Institution of Washington, helped during the First World War to get scientific research under way in the U.S.A. with the National Research Council. From the same position Vannevar Bush played a similar role during the second in helping to establish O.S.R.D. and, later, the National Science Foundation.

The pumps Carnegie primed became gushers under the massive social welfare schemes of the oil magnate, J. D. Rockefeller. Guided by his 'particular Baptist minister', Federick T. Gates, Rockefeller's charity endowed medical research on the lines of the Koch Institute in Berlin and the Pasteur Institute in Paris. At Rockefeller's expense, a study of medical schools at home and abroad was made by Starr J. Murphy, followed by grants. A laboratory was built on the East River to secure 'unity of aim and the co-ordination and mutual stimulus which are essential to the highest achievements in research'. Meanwhile Rockefeller's son-in-law Harold McCormick had endowed a Memorial Institute of Infectious Diseases in Chicago in 1902. A year later Henry Phipps gave more than a million dollars to establish the Phipps Institute for the Study, Treatment and Prevention of Tuberculosis.

The Rockefeller Sanitary Commission under Wicliffe Rose as secretary, marked the first entry of private philanthropy into the field of public health. In five years hookworm, together with typhoid and dysentery, was vastly reduced. The Sanitary Commission continued as the Rockefeller Foundation, under the leadership of the International Health Commission, still with Rose in charge. In 1918 a school of Hygiene and Public Health was opened at Johns Hopkins, financed by the Rockefeller trustees, who four years later endowed it with 6 million dollars.

As Simon Flexner, its director, wrote, 'Rockefeller and his advisers agreed to a delegation of power such as may never before have existed in an American philanthropic institution.' The trustees were only to look after finance, the policy was to be in the hands of scientists.[49] Using the rebuilding after the fire at McGill in 1907 as a precedent, they widened the issue to help all medical schools in the State to build laboratories or hospital clinics associated with laboratories. By 1910 the Foundation had a hospital (under Johns Hopkins graduates), a clinic for sick animals and a laboratory at Princeton in 1917, whilst a division of plant pathology was begun in 1926 and completed in 1931. Diabetics owe the Foundation a great debt, for it was a Rockefeller grant of 8,000 dollars which enabled F. G. Banting, J. J. R. Macleod and C. H. Best to isolate insulin, the secretion of the pancreas and a vital regulator of carbohydrate metabolism.

Of the subsequent Rockefeller charities the Rockefeller Foundation, chartered in the State of New York in 1914, had a massive function, nothing less than 'to provide for the well-being of mankind throughout the world'. To this Rockefeller gave, in all, 235 million dollars. It provided much help to British universities like London, Oxford and Cambridge, as well as to medical research throughout the world.

Of the 757 largest American foundations, with assets of a million dollars or over, over three-quarters were founded in the third, fourth and fifth decades of this century: 126, 272 and 194 respectively. By 1960 there were 5,202 foundations with total assets of 11,518,019,000 million dollars. Seven own one-fifth of the total assets of all foundations in the U.S.A. The three largest of these are the Ford (now 316 million dollars)[50] and Rockefeller (now 648 million dollars) foundations and the Carnegie Corporation of New York (261 million dollars).

Forty-one per cent of the total grants of all these foundations —a percentage which rose to 47 in the case of the large foundations—went on education. Health absorbed only 15 per cent. Scientific research came third with 11 per cent—some 71 million dollars—though to this the large foundations gave twice as much as all other foundations put together. One trustee thought even this was too much and complained that 'America had been oversold on science'.[51]

(10)

Being 'oversold on science' was but another aspect of the likeness between the U.S.S.R. and the U.S.A. Lincoln Steffens considered they were 'more alike, essentially and politically, than any two countries I had seen', and asked, 'Wasn't it this, that these two young peoples, the Russians and the Americans are driving, the one consciously, the other unwittingly, towards the same end?'[52] What he meant was that politics was now a matter of operational research.

Steffens knew both countries well. He was an American and had visited Russia first with Charles Crane in 1917, then two years later, with W. C. Bullitt and thirdly, with the La Follettes in August 1923. 'I have seen the future and it works', he declared after one visit, and he spent years lecturing on it. By 1935 he was writing, 'our old culture is finished, we all have got to turn to welcome the new culture, which covers everything, the arts, science, business and life'.[53] He saw clearly that the leaders of the Russian State trusts were of the same mind as the Vice-President of General Motors, whom Steffens reported as saying,

> We may think up a theory, but we don't act on our theories any more. We send our theories or our need into the laboratory and so have it tried out. If it doesn't work, we change the theory, scrap it. But if a theory modified, works, we may make it into an engine or a car and put it out for trial on the market, but—even then, it's only a sort of working hypothesis. We go on monkeying with that and other theories and hunches to improve the car on trial.

'This', continued Steffens, 'is revolutionary'.[54]

American intellectuals of the inter-war generation were strangely like the Russian nihilists of the 1860s. Whereas the advanced Russian nihilist had looked to the American as a model of liberty, now advanced Americans looked to Moscow as a model of planning. And paradoxically, the influence of Russia became greater as the American Communist Party became weaker. The Communist Party divided in 1927 into two camps, the Stalinists (led by W. Foster) and the Trotskyites (led by Lovestone). Since the Anarchists and Socialists refused to join the third international, the American intellectuals of the twenties were rootless. As Malcolm Cowley remarked, 'During the last years before the Depression, the desire to escape became the compelling emotion that dominated the world of American letters.'[55] T. S. Eliot, Ezra Pound and Gertrude Stein were expatriates all, and those who stayed at home like H. L. Mencken and Sinclair Lewis were bitter critics. The correspondent of the *Christian Science Monitor* reported a 'proletarian poet' as singing:

> I'm always thinking of Russia
> I can't get her out of my head
> I don't give a damn for Uncle Sam
> I'm a left wing, radical Red.[56]

Many influential figures in the American churches took a kind view of Russia. Thus Lewis O. Hartman, editor of *Zion's Herald* and another visitor to Russia (in 1923), wrote on 4 July 1923:

> Soviet Russia constitutes the greatest social experiment in the history of the world. Never before in the life of mankind has there been an attempt on so vast a scale to equalise opportunity and to promote the genuine brotherhood of man.

Or again, on 17 November 1926:

> the Communist leaders with all their mistakes are sincere, honest men working for what they conceive to be the good of humanity.

By 8 October 1931 an editorial in the *Christian Register* could say:

> No-one who studies the religious press steadily and carefully can doubt that American Protestantism has gone over in its sympathy to the Russian experiment and the basic idea of the Russian philosophy. . . . These ministers, true to the traditions of the prophets, are aware of the moral evil beneath our economic and social order, and are satisfied that Russia's fundamental principle of a non-profit making and co-operative commonwealth is true to the teachings of Jesus and square with the pretensions and professions of all the churches.[57]

Charles M. Muchnic, of the American Locomotive Sales Corporation, gave it as his view that the new order in Russia had developed a more human and more humane relationship between the various classes in everyday life.[58] Perhaps the most significant of all was the planner of some regions of the T.V.A., of

Washington and of some sixty towns and cities of the U.S.A., Jacob L. Crane. After planning Nizhni-Novgorod in conjunction with the W. J. Austin Company of Cleveland, he said at Pittsburg on 16 November 1932:

> Two of the strongest 'drives' motivating the western world are, first, the impulse to extend our imaginations and our activities farther and farther outward in space, and, second, the impulse to exert conscious guidance over our future. State planning is in direct line with the tendency to forecast and predesign the circumstances of our living; and it represents the movement to deal with the future in a larger and larger way.[59]

Two years later he prophesied:

> We may foresee each state with its State Planning Board, groups of States associated through their planning boards to handle inter-state matters, and a set of planning agencies in Washington offering counsel and guidance and funds to the state planning project. This whole plan for planning plainly requires heading up at some one point.[60]

(11)

The great laboratory of Russia provided American engineers with an opportunity to see large-scale social engineering in action. After four years there designing steel mills, Henry J. Freyn returned to address the Taylor Institute, a body formed to promote the ideas of Frederic Winslow Taylor on management.[61] After listening to him Edmund Wilson (author of *To the Finland Station*) remarked in the *New Republic*:

> As he proceeds it becomes apparent that the ideals conceived by the Soviets are precisely those of the Taylor Society and that it is their aim to put them into practice on an unprecedented scale. In all this, he rarely mentions Communism, but as he goes on, one begins to get the impression that he is as much sold on it as any class-conscious proletarian rallying round the Thirteenth Street headquarters. He talks with conviction and emphasis—he is defending the Soviets, one realises, he is giving expression to his admiration for them, he seems even to have ended after four years in catching something of the fervency of their faiths.[62]

The most fervent American Taylorian was Morris Llewellyn Cooke[63] whose 'deeply religious' nature (Copley calls him 'a sort of modern knight errant')[64] led him to organize 'pilgrimages' to Boxly, Taylor's home near Philadelphia. Taylor employed Cooke to reorganize the American Society of Mechanical Engineers and later to investigate the possibility of organizing university education on Taylorian lines. Cooke's findings, published in *Academic and Industrial Efficiency* (Bulletin No. 5 of the Carnegie Foundation, 1910), led Taylor to suggest that college and university officials should undergo a course similar to that advocated for industrial managers. Earlier Taylor had approved of H. W. Schneider's experiments in 'sandwich courses' (workshop and college alternating) at Cincinnati in 1908. Later, Taylor suggested that Cooke should become director of public works in Philadelphia.[65]

Cooke directed a Power Survey of Pennsylvania and though unsuccessful in pressing his ideas on Hoover, succeeded with Hoover's successor, Roosevelt, who had heard them on the New York Power Authority. He commissioned Cooke in 1933 to make a survey of the Mississippi Valley for the Public Works Administration. Cooke subsequently became administrator of the Rural Electrification Administration, established by Roosevelt on 11 May 1935, where in the face of hostility from private power companies he helped non-profit-making co-operatives to establish themselves. In this he was succeeded by another Taylorian, John M. Carmody, who carried out his policy with even greater vigour. By 1950 nine out of every ten farms in the U.S.A. had been electrified. Before Cooke took office, the proportion was one in ten. The results of their work has been authoritatively summarized by a distinguished modern historian:

> No single event, save perhaps for the invention of the automobile, so diminished the aching resentment of the farmers and so swiftly closed the gap between country and city. No single public agency ever so enriched and brightened the quality of rural living.[66]

Yet that same historian, when discussing the 'logic of the machine' made so explicit by Charles Beard (when in *Whither Mankind*: (1928) and *Toward Civilisation* (1929) he acknowledged 'the imperative necessity of planning' and the 'conscious rationality triumphant' of science 'controlling unlimited power, mastering the nature of materials, adapting them to mankind, and mankind to them',) declared that 'this was an entirely indigenous faith. It had no relationship with experiments in totalitarian planning currently in operation in Italy and Soviet Russia and soon to come to Germany. It was if anything a reversion to the Utopianism of Edward Bellamy and *Looking Backward*'.[67]

16

◇◇

Science and Social Recuperation
in Britain

◇◇

(1)

As the Russian experiment got under way a debate on its significance developed amongst British scientists. Amongst those who considered that a similar experiment would redress the swing of the geographical balance against Britain was J. B. S. Haldane whose *Daedalus—or Science and the Future* (1923)[1] was answered by Bertrand Russell in *Icarus, or the Future of Science* (1925). 'Much as I should like' said Russell 'to agree with his forecast I am compelled to fear that science will be used to promote the power of dominant groups rather than to make men happy.'[2]

Russell recognized the religious nature of Communism, considering its aims 'as admirable as those instilled by the Sermon on the Mount, but . . . held as fanatically and as likely to do as much harm'.[3] Yet Russell was no abject pessimist, for he thought 'science offers a possibility of far greater well-being for the human race than it has ever known before'. But the possibilities depended on abolition of war, even distribution of ultimate power, and a limitation of the growth of population.'[4] Russell's support of dissentient groups like N.C.F. (No Conscription Fellowship), and the W.B.C.A. (Workers Birth Control Association) indicated his opposition to large-scale corporations. The latter were to him 'the inevitable outcome of modern technique and technique tends increasingly to make competition wasteful . . . the solution lies in public ownership of the organisation'.[5]

Russell's main target was the modern addiction to mechanism, which he found 'indistinguishable from Calvinism'. 'Put the machine in place of God, the efficiency of the machine in the place of the glory of God, the rich and the poor in place of the saved and the damned, inheritance in place of predestination; you will then find', he wrote, 'that every tenet of Calvinism has its counterpart in the modern religion of industrialism.'[6]

Russia also appealed to H. G. Wells, who thought that 'Lenin, under the stresses of a more pressing reality, was steadily evolving an extraordinarily similar scheme', to his own idea of a scientific Samurai. After a visit to Russia in 1920, Wells returned anxious to help them: the Society for Cultural Relations with the U.S.S.R. (S.C.R.), was one tangible result of his efforts. Wells advocated a variant of the Russian plan, called the 'Open Conspiracy' to 'hive, cherish and multiply . . .' the company of scientific men which he described as 'less like a host of guiding angels than like a swarm of marvellous bees—endowed with stings'. Such hiving was to be undertaken by a revolutionary *élite* of high I.Q. and competence.

The conspiracy was to be 'open' since it could be joined by any managers, engineers, scientists, students or teachers simply by their forming local associations. Its aim was the immortality of the species through world unity. Wells emphasized that 'every step to world unity must be taken in the daylight, or the sort of unity that will be won will be found to be scarcely worth the winning'. These steps would all be taken by the associations: birth control, resistance to military service and ultimately, world government. From modest beginnings, as the common creed took form around the aim of a world directorate, the conspirators would advise, diffuse and infuse, through 'a great multitude and variety of overlapping groups, all organised for collective political, social and educational as well as propagandist action'. They would 'be definitely and obviously attempting to swallow up the entire population of the world and become the new human community'.[7]

So too Beatrice Webb now began to argue for 'an Order', as she called it, 'of dedicated persons, something resembling the

Jesuit order of the Russian Communist Party'.[8] Similarly Ernest Bevin, who had also, like Beatrice Webb, been impressed by L. B. Krasin, told his fellow-unionists in August 1931 'there can be no doubt that the Russians have an entirely new economic philosophy, a philosophy which is in direct contact with the rest of the world', and he urged the International Transport Federation to send a delegation to the Soviet Union to establish relations with them, not to pursue what he called an 'ostrich policy . . . by not studying the situation in Russia'.[9]

Some scientists, however, were virtually frightened into mysticism as the 'planning' of Russian science looked like creeping into Britain. As one young Russophile physicist remarked in 1931:

> just as the growing free thought of English Dissent in the eighteenth century had been frightened into emotional Methodism by the French Revolution, so the mechanistic Darwinism of the triumphant capitalism of the nineteenth century was being frightened by the growing strength of the Soviet Union into the popular scientific mysticism of Jeans and Eddington . . .

Bernal also posed the problem as to whether it was 'better to be intellectually free but socially totally ineffective' or 'to become a component part of a system where knowledge and action are joined for one common social purpose.[10]

In the same year a party of thirty British scientists visited Russia in 1931. Amongst them was Julian Huxley. He noted that Russia spent more on its Geological Survey than all the rest of Europe together. Its Institute of Plant Industry seemed to him to embody proposals he had made earlier for a British National Genetical Laboratory. He pointed out that the vast scale and world-wide basis of the operations in Soviet Russia would have enormous advantages in the next generation. When he revisited it in 1945, though he criticized the distortion of science for political ends, he emphasized that the status of a Russian scientist was far higher than his English counterpart. 'I anticipate', he wrote in *Nature*, 'that they will soon be leading the world in some fields.'[11]

Even the English apostles of 'scientific management' admired the 'combination of the Russian revolutionary sweep with American efficiency.'[12] The words are Stalin's, himself an admirer of American efficiency, describing it as 'that indomitable force which neither knows nor recognises obstacles; which continues at a task once started until it is finished, even if it is a minor task; and without which serious constructive work is inconceivable . . .' Colonel Urwick, the leading British apostle of scientific management, cited M. V. V. Obolensky-Ossinski, the chief of the Soviet delegation to the World Congress on Social and Economic Planning at Amsterdam in August 1931, as saying:

> the plan . . . cannot base its methodology on anything else but science—the quintessence of social thought and experience.

For Colonel Urwick, rationalization, rather than nationalization seemed to be the purpose behind 'the large scale experiment . . . in process in Russia.'[13]

(2)

'American efficiency' became much more evident in Britain, too, after the First World War as American financiers hastily bought up British firms in order to duck the tariff screen set up against them. To rubber, sewing machines, Linotype presses, electric lighting and telecommunications, they now added automobiles as the General Motor Corporation of New York bought Vauxhall in 1927. Goodyear and Firestone Rubber began manufacturing in Britain in 1928 and Ford opened what was virtually a European factory at Dagenham in 1929. Monsanto Chemicals had by that time completed their purchase of Graesons and were set to become the largest Anglo-American firm of their kind in the United Kingdom.

But for the crisis of the early thirties, the tally of British firms coming under American tutelage might have been far greater. Amongst the firms sold back to British interests were Boots Pure Drug in 1933 and Electrical and Musical Industries in 1935. But the trend continued: Proctor and Gamble (1930), Hoovers (1931), Standard Brands (1932) and Remington Rand (1937) were four of many that had swelled the total value of U.S. manufacturing investments in Britain by 1940 to 275 million dollars and of business investments to 530 million dollars.[14]

With these American companies came new attitudes towards research, development, planning and administration. The ratio of non-operative to operative workers increased from 1 : 12 in 1907, to 1 : 5 in 1951. Cumulatively more American research was made available to Britain, so much so, that one observer wrote:

> in *real* terms the parent companies of the 100 most important U.S. financed firms manufacturing in this country devote more of their resources to research and development each year than the whole of British industry combined.[15]

Moreover, by pioneering in the establishment of consultant and factory organization departments, of training facilities for customers staff and of after sales servicing, U.S. firms have profoundly influenced the structure of British industry.

The *femme libre* of American managerialism was Mary Parker Follet, a Cambridge graduate who returned to England in 1926 and 1928, and stayed here from 1929 to 1933. She held that

> the time is fast disappearing when we need ask ourselves whether we believe in an 'autocratic' or 'democratic' leadership, for we are developing something that is neither, something that is better than either . . . I think business management by far the most interesting activity at present . . . because we are working out something new in human relationships.[16]

She pleaded for greater respect to be given to the expert, whose information

> not only forms a large part of the executive's decision; it is becoming an integral part of the decision-making machinery. We have experts on more matters and the expert is taking a different place in the organisation.[17]

or yet again:

> control is fact control rather than non-control, and central control is coming more and more to mean the correlation of many controls rather than a super-imposed control . . . The opposite of *laissez faire* is co-ordination . . . an auto-controlled activity.[18]

As one of her ablest expositors in Britain, Colonel Urwick, maintained:

> To principles sooner or later, the subtlest craftsman has to bow his head, or be left behind; for, even while his hand is on his tools, by theory contingency and complications are being detected and eliminated, and processes shortened and economised.[19]

Labour, too, began to appreciate the value of large unions and of management. Ernest Bevin, after visiting America, considered that the managerial type

> is becoming of far greater importance. He is the man who has to get the job done and to be continually inspiring, organising, directing the affairs of his great undertaking. I frankly confess in my job, the large scale organisation of labour, I feel more akin with this type than I do with the so-called director.[20]

Logically extended, managerialism involved conversion of the worker to the religion of industry. A rich and variegated group life designed to evoke interest in, rather than rewards from, the job, was consciously planned in the Hawthorne works of the American Telegraph and Telephone Company, and it became a model for many countries, especially in Britain where the Institute of Industrial Psychology also began to see how 'the maximum energy of each worker, from the managing director to the office boy (could) be aroused and directed in the best interests of the firm'.[21] The spirit was well caught by George Orwell: 'all mechanical progress is towards greater and greater efficiency; ultimately, therefore, towards a world in which *nothing goes wrong*'.

Industry as a whole is more technocratic in America than in Britain. Of all American managers in 1950, 78·5 per cent had been to college and 62·5 per cent had taken degrees,[22] whereas in England only 30 per cent of their counterparts were graduates.[23] This slow upward rise in the proportion of 'administrative employees' to 'production employees' in Britain (from 8·6 per cent in 1907 to 20 per cent in 1948)[24] was actually deplored by Stanley Baldwin as due to growth of joint stock companies. This rise, thanks to the American pacemaking, continued.[25]

Perhaps one of the forces that gave scientists further corporate strength was the overt attack on science and research deemed to have been made by such public figures, amongst them Sir Josiah Stamp.[26]

(3)

'Management' techniques were applied in the experiments in collective organization begun in 1919 with the establishment of H.M. Forestry Commission. This was to create State forests.

By providing grants for local authorities and landowners, it secured the planting of a quarter of a million acres, and acquired another quarter of a million for planting.

Two even more powerful aggregates of expertise took shape in the Central Electricity Board and the British Broadcasting Corporation. The first bought power and distributed it to existing undertakings whether private or municipal and within 7 years had completed some 4,000 miles of the high-voltage transmission lines of 'the Grid'.[27] The second began a network of some 21 national and regional radio stations on the proceeds of a 10s. tax. Both maintained research organizations.[28]

Seven more experiments in collective organization in England took shape during the years 1931–3. The Traffic Commissioners (1931) co-ordinated passenger traffic by road and rail. The Coal Mines Reorganization Commission (1931) formulated schemes for the amalgamation of private collieries. The Hops Marketing Board (1932) controlled the sale of hops; the London Passenger Transport Board (1933) unified all metropolitan transport facilities. The Milk Marketing Board (1933) purchased all milk for resale to distributors and other users. The Pig Marketing Board (1933) provided efficiency services on similar lines for pigs. The Bacon Marketing Board (1933) fixed selling prices, and grades of British bacon.

British industries as well as becoming more oligopolic, were increasingly to act in concert. As a very real legacy of the First World War, the Federation of British Industries (formed in 1916 by Sir F. Dudley Docker, a Birmingham car manufacturer) soon gobbled up two previous employers' associations: the Employers' Parliamentary Council (a pressure group founded in 1898), as well as the British Manufacturers' Association (founded in 1908), and began collectively to worry as to whether 'the existing organisation of industry was capable of meeting present-day problems'.

The F.B.I. appointed a Commercial Efficiency Committee to consider ways in which this could be done. The committee came up with suggestions for centralizing research, interchanging statistics, standardizing details of costings, plant, machinery and products, interchanging of methods of working, pooling facilities for propaganda, allotting of orders to those best fitted to carry them out, avoiding undue competition and regulating prices 'based on efficiency not on monopoly designed to exploit the consumer'. Its report emphasized the need

> for the individual to subordinate his views to those of Industry for the achievement of a common policy, and for co-operation between industries on a scale that pre-war conditions did not so insistently demand. Public considerations today place upon each industry a collective responsibility for efficient and economic production.[29]

By the Second World War the F.B.I.'s Industrial Research Committee was emphasizing the need for more research, an attitude stigmatized by the Association of Scientific Workers as 'a sort of talisman for getting quick results cheaply, for producing good "selling lines" with a minimum of modification to existing plant'.[30]

But it was to industry that H. G. Wells looked to

> supersede existing governments by disregard; making them negligible by replacing their functions . . . What is useful of them it will use; what is useless it will efface by its stronger reality; it will join issue only with what is plainly antagonistic and actively troublesome.

As an aggregate of industrial scientists, engineers and managers, I.C.I. (thinly disguised as Romer, Steinhart and Crest in *The World of William Clissold*) would 'grow around and over existing institutions . . . inconspicuously reducing them by degrees to useless appendages, tolerated, like so many features of the British Constitution, for old times sake'.[31]

It looked as if Wells as usual, had interpreted the times aright. For the Royal Society invited Sir Alfred Mond of Imperial Chemical Industries, and Lord Weir, head of a big engineering firm, to meet representatives of the T.U.C. General Council on 12 January 1928, to discuss 'the finance and management of industry; new developments in technology and organisation, the organisation of industry itself, nationally and internationally; and means for assuring the status and security of the workers'. Significantly, the employers came mostly from the new industries: oil (Sir John Cadman), electricity (Sir Hugo Hirst), rayon (Samuel Courtauld), engineering (Sir Charles Parsons), automobiles (Sir Herbert Austin, Sir Edward Manville), steel (Sir Arthur Dorman, Sir Ronald Hadfield and

Sir Frederick Mills), transport (Sir Josiah Stamp and Lord Ashfield) and of course, I.C.I. (Sir Harry MacGowan). Even more significantly, both sides agreed that a National Industrial Council should be established, that larger units of production be formed, that a national development fund be established and that better credit facilities for modernizing firms should be set up. For Sir Alfred Mond was a great admirer of the General Electric Company with its expenditure of £200,000 a year on research, and openly said:

> There is only one possible policy. Rightly or wrongly we must pin our faith to the scientists of this and of future generations. On their work and discoveries the race must stand or fall.

or again:

> The future prospects of the world, the solution of its economic difficulties, the security of its teeming millions, depends far more upon its scientific progress, upon its increased power to produce wealth by the application of scientific thought and method to its industrial process, than upon any other form of human effort.[32]

Responsible trade unionists were in full agreement with this. In 1937 Ernest Bevin expressed his conviction that

> precision and foreknowledge of the significance of scientific discovery in all fields of research will be of incalculable value.

Speaking on behalf of the General Council, he cordially welcomed

> the opportunity to consult with representative scientists by means of such an advisory council and panels of scientific workers from whom we can obtain the information and advice we need in dealing with our problems.[33]

Following this, the Secretary of the T.U.C. arranged for Sir Richard Gregory and Ernest Bevin to discuss the establishment of a Scientific Advisory Council for the T.U.C., together with the President (H. H. Elvin) and Professor P. G. H. Boswell. At a second meeting other scientists were brought in by Gregory and Boswell: Professors P. M. S. Blackett, F. G. Donnan, J. B. S. Haldane, Lancelot Hogben, Sir Frederick Hopkins, Sir Daniel Hall and Sir John Orr. These, with members of the Finance and General Purposes Committee of the T.U.C., met and agreed to ask the British Association to nominate members of the committee. This the British Association did. So on 13 July 1939 the Scientific Advisory Committee of the T.U.C. held its first meeting at Transport House under Gregory's chairmanship, with ten trade unionists and eleven scientists.[34]

(4)

Such initiative on the part of the scientists concerned reflected their increasing awareness of the social implications of their work. Having established their own professional associations they had also established in 1919 a National Union of Scientific Workers. In the twenties, no voice spoke louder on their behalf than Wells, who told his friend Sir Richard Gregory:

Science *will endure and rule*, but that Labour with a capital L, as the name of a class of human beings organised for distinctive class ends, will *pass away*. I am at one with Soddy in believing that if the Spirit of Science is to be carried right through human affairs, it means a complete organisation of human society for all common ends, educational and economic, and a common general administration of the whole world and all its resources.[35]

Wishing him to speak for them in Parliament, the National Union of Scientific Workers tried to secure his election for a university seat. Their letter of support to the University of London argued that 'the advent of a Labour party will mean a greater obligation to sustain and extend scientific subjects and research . . . not only in physical, but also in financial, economic and social science'. Though Wells was not elected, the secretary of the National Union of Scientific Workers was, thanks to the initiative of Professor Hyman Levy. By fine irony Church became P.P.S. to Sidney Webb in the first Labour Government: irony since Webb was now disinclined to press for more scientists in government.

As his union's spokesman, Church advocated the formation of a body of scientists analogous to the British Medical Association:

Hitherto [he said] scientists have been denied the opportunity of directing or sharing the control of affairs of a civilization for which they are mainly responsible. . . . They could, if they were united in a great resolve, make the nation understand the contributions they

270

have to offer to its problems. . . . It is essentially their function, and not primarily that of a government department, to state the aims and needs of science, and how best these needs can be met.[36]

Church also vigorously pressed, with Gregory, for a Minister of Science with a seat in the Cabinet and his own civil service. Both also advocated the admission of science graduates to the administrative Civil Service[37]—a proposal amplified by the Bridgman Committee on the Post Office in 1932. This agreed that engineering experience was 'insufficiently brought into the consideration and formulation of general policy'.[38] The case was kept alive by the Institution of Professional Civil Servants whose chairman called for a reform of entry into the administrative grade, 'so as to ensure a larger quota of entrants familiar with the history and methods of science and sympathetic to the scientific outlook', and for scientists to be able to take a 'direct and effective part in the moulding of state policy'.[39]

With the help of the Institute of Physics, and the engineering associations, Gregory and Church led the Association of Scientific Workers and the British Science Guild in joining forces with a number of scientific societies and professional associations to form the Parliamentary Science Committee; 'an authoritative body, able to present to Parliament and the country, the collective opinion of the scientific community on matters affecting the country's interests'. Reorganized in 1939 as the Parliamentary and Science Committee, it embraced, by 1962 a total of 127 scientific societies and professional institutes and over 130 Members of Parliament, equally balanced between both parties. Its influence over thirty years has been considerable.[40]

(5)

The need for scientists in government led the Haldane Committee on the Machinery of Government to recommend in 1920 that a new Department of Research, together with others of Production and of Employment should supplement conventional ones like Finance, Defence, External Affairs, Supplies, Health and Justice.[41] The need of such a Research Department was re-examined twelve years later by the Economic Advisory Council, which turned it down because it would 'cut across the ground already being covered and prove harmful to industrial research as a whole'. Nor did the Economic Advisory Council endorse the idea that industries should be given general powers to impose compulsory levies for research. It did, however, suggest that a fund should be available for financing new ideas and tests—an idea later (1948) adopted when the National Research and Development Corporation was established.[42]

From the Haldane Committee's approval of the five years' working of the Advisory Council on Scientific and Industrial Research stemmed three other research councils: for Medical Research (1920), Agricultural Research (1931) and the Nature Conservancy (1949). All have grants in aid; their members are appointed after consultation with the President of the Royal Society. All three, unlike D.S.I.R. are constituted by Royal Charter, can make independent scientific decisions and negotiate directly with the Treasury.

To help redress the increasing swing of the geographical balance against Britain other schemes of enlisting expertise were ventilated. National industrial councils, proposed by a committee of the Ministry of Reconstruction under J. H. Whitley during the First World War, to discuss production methods, training, welfare, wages and hours, were set up, but only in the smaller industries.[43]

A social Parliament, responsible for industry and working through committees, equal and parallel to the existing political parliament, was canvassed by the Webbs, and ventilated in the House of Commons.[44] Though this was abortive, a National Industrial Conference of 500 workers and 300 employees was convened and urged by the Minister of Labour in Central Hall Westminster on 27 February 1919 to form a permanent National Industrial Conference. This was done—with little effect. For two years later it came to an end in July 1921, leaving, as its legacy on the employer's side, the British Employers' Federation and on that of the unions, the T.U.C. General Council (replacing the old Parliamentary Committee that had existed since 1871).

Eight years later the proposal appeared again—this time as an annual National Industrial Conference—endorsed by the Balfour Committee on Industry and Trade in 1929. The Balfour Committee really emphasized the lack of expertise, instancing the need for managers to obtain insight based on higher education and research. Indeed, some members of the Balfour Committee advocated a 'planned acceleration of what has already begun in collective economic organization' through a National Economic Committee which would draft and correlate plans for industrial reorganization, and empowered to initiate and implement them.[45]

A National Planning Commission (with a Bureau of Statistics), a Planning Centre in each industry and a 10-minister Cabinet was proposed by an organization formed in 1931 and known as PEP: Political and Economic Planning. Its members included Julian and Aldous Huxley, Sir Basil Blackett, an ex-Civil Servant and Director of the Bank of England, Kenneth Lindsay, later to be M.P. for the English universities, I. M. Sieff (vice-chairman of Marks and Spencer), who became chairman and Lionel Elmhirst (founder of Dartington Hall), its vice-chairman.[46]

Attacked by the *Daily Herald* as Fascist and by the *English Review* as Communist inspired, PEP's *ad hoc* working groups explored approaches to a 'national plan'. The Economic Division's report on the British Iron and Steel Industry (1933) was an unprecedented attempt to examine the structure of the industry in the light of its technology and exerted great influence on its reorganization in subsequent years.

These groups embodied 100 or more experts, and set a new pattern in politics:

> It has been a conspicuous weakness of parliamentary democracy [ran a broadsheet, No. 23 on *What PEP is For* of 22 March 1934] that organised interests with big axes to grind possess influential 'lobbies' while those on whose service technical civilisation depends—the administrators, the managers, the engineers, scientists, teachers and technicians—have been able to make little direct and continuous contribution to government outside the particular pigeon-hole in which chance has placed them.

PEP aimed not to be a new political party or indeed to capture an existing one, but

> . . . to create non-party groups outside the political arena, continuously surveying what is really happening in their own subjects and their own neighbourhoods, making known the facts and drawing conclusions from them in a detached and objective spirit.

273

It hoped for

> a rich growth of enquiring constructive groups [putting] the vast fund of skills now sectionally and locally applied at the disposal of the whole community. The idea of an exploratory group . . . committed to no narrowing thesis, is still comparatively fresh in Great Britain. A scientific outlook and some political maturity make it possible to look forward to the spread of this pattern, and to the growth, through its constructive and pervasive influence, of something that we can really call democracy.[47]

PEP's technocratic destination led Aldous Huxley to drop off before it got there. His *Brave New World* is a virtual explanation of why he did so. Set in the seventh century after Ford, *Brave New World* pillored the feeling that America was the paragon to be emulated.[48] His brother Julian, on the other hand, provided the first description of the Tennessee Valley Authority for readers of *The Times* in 1935. Describing it as 'the early growth of a new and hopeful type of social organism' combining science and vision 'in a way and on a scale new in human history', he expressed a hope 'that an experiment of comparable scale along the same sort of lines, combining vision and science in the same fruitful way, might be initiated here in Britain'.

Two years earlier, Julian Huxley accepted a commission from the B.B.C. to survey British science. He found that 'our existing structure and hope of progress' were based on science, 'the serious feature of our political situation' was 'the lack of appreciation and understanding of it amongst business men, financiers, education authorities, politicians and administrators'. 'Almost equally serious', he added, 'is the absence of a broad scientific outlook on life to be noted in the scientific specialist.' Huxley stressed the importance of the scientific *spirit* in government and urged that planning should 'always be in touch with scientifically ascertained fact'.[49]

Such a National Economic Committee or an Industrial Development Board or Central Economic Council, composed of representatives of more than 100 industrial councils together with economists, scientists and technicians,[50] was also canvassed by Harold Macmillan, then a back-bench Tory M.P. and secured many signatories. Its drawbacks were pointed out by PEP:

If it were not in practice advisory, it would certainly leave Parliament high and dry on many first-rate social issues, while if it were advisory there would be the difficulty, which has arisen elsewhere, of its decay through the various parties refusing to put all their cards on the table until the ultimate authority in the background was reached.[51]

This, too, came to fruition as the National Economic Development Council, when Harold Macmillan was Prime Minister.

The idea of a 'functional' House became a favourite theme of Conservative politicians and was ventilated, with intermissions up to 1949, when Christopher Hollis envisaged it as playing

in industrial affairs which the Church Assembly plays in ecclesiastical affairs. Legislation on the technical details of industrial matters should in the first instance be passed by it . . . it would be hoped that, as in ecclesiastical matters, the House of Commons would not challenge detailed technical legislation, being satisfied that it had been properly considered by qualified persons in an atmosphere as little partisan as possible.[52]

(6)

Engineers, too, were anxious to ensure that their professional opinions were represented in the councils of the State. Reinforced by new bodies like the Institutions of Production Engineers (1921), of the Rubber Industry (1921), of Chemical Engineers (1922) and of Highway Engineers (1930), they much impressed contemporary sociologists, who remarked:

nothing short of the onset of a glacial age in the history of human mental activity could now check the onward march of these sciences. The scientific professions are obviously borne along by the progress of the knowledge upon which they are based. . . .

These new associations, forecast the sociologists, would prevent the 'professions whose technique is institutional' from stagnating, since

where institutional professions are practised alongside others, it is most unlikely that they will be uninfluenced by those which have this safeguard against stagnation. . . . Therefore it is reasonable to anticipate that the progressiveness shown by the scientific professions will in future be characteristic of all.[53]

Two case-histories illustrate the political activities of these engineers. The first centres round D. N. Dunlop, an electrical engineer, who believed that 'national efficiency' could best be provided through a national industrial federation to 'encourage the work of scientific investigation and foster inventions by ways and means which only a thoroughly representative body could undertake'.[54] Like Krhizhanovsky, the Russian electrical engineer, Dunlop saw the magic of industry 'as the *direct* application of energy', and convened the first of the World Power Conferences in 1924.[55]

Nor was this the only evidence that engineers were acting in concert. The Civils, Mechanicals, Electricals, Naval Architects and North East Coast institutions joined to protest over the exclusion of engineers from executive rank in the navy. The pages of the engineering Press reverberated with protests and the associations went on a joint deputation to the First Lord of the Admiralty. 'Never before', wrote *Nature* on 6 February 1926, 'have the four founder engineering institutions taken so notable a step.'[56]

Two months later, engineers took steps to establish a council of their profession analogous to the B.M.A. A Bill 'to provide for the registration and to regulate the qualifications of engineers', was introduced to the House of Commons on 29 April 1926 by an electrical engineer (Sir Herbert Williams), a pioneer of radio telegraphy, torpedoes, aircraft and the tank (Rear Admiral Sueter), a gas engineer (Mr. Clarry) and a Royal Engineer (Colonel Crookshank). They were beaten by the general strike.[57]

But the idea lingered. 'Is there any hope', asked Sir Daniel Hall, the great agricultural chemist, 'of obtaining a body of men of science who will express a corporative opinion on public affairs?'[58] He realized that by charter and custom both the Royal Society and the British Association were debarred from participation in politics. His opinion was shared by Sir Richard Gregory who considered that the nation 'could not afford to leave administrative control in the hands of those who have no first hand knowledge of science. Modern technical achievements and scientific thought foreshadow a new scientific structure for society in which they should be used to exercise decisive influence upon the major policies of the State as well as upon their administration.'[59]

(7)

The war answered Hall's question. All scientists were mobilized to cope with problems of defence. Before the war, Sir Henry Tizard was consulted by the Air Council; in its early stages Winston Churchill brought in Professor Lindemann, later Lord Cherwell, as a private scientific adviser. When he became Prime Minister, Cherwell was at his side. His Cabinet also appointed its own Scientific Advisory Committee. But above all, the Services adopted scientific advisers, men like P. M. S. Blackett and J. D. Bernal, who lived alongside the controllers of the operations, doing the research necessary for them and so often consulted that they became part of the policy-making machine.[60]

The pattern continued after the war when Sir Henry Tizard was appointed Scientific Adviser to the Ministry of Defence and chairman of the Defence Research Policy Committee, whilst a senior scientist was appointed in each of the Services. Parallel to this, an Advisory Council on Scientific Policy was created to appraise civil science with a number of sub-committees (e.g. on manpower and technical information). Both the Defence Research Policy Committee and the Advisory Council on Scientific Policy had no executive authority—merely advisory.

'Civil' research was perhaps an understatement of the role of the Advisory Council, which was officially defined as 'to advise the Lord President of the Council in the exercise of his responsibility for the formulation and execution of Government scientific policy'. This Government scientific policy included the organization of scientific manpower, overseas scientific relationships, space research, resources devoted to research and development, the organization of Government research and various other matters. Its important power was that of initiating the discussion of problems.

The answer, of course, was a Ministry of Science, which was what the Lord President of the Council had virtually become. Describing him as 'a kind of de facto Minister of Science', J. D. Bernal pointed out in 1945 that

the habit of attaching scientific advisors and scientific advisory committees . . . is now spreading . . . the outline of a new system of research organisation is becoming visible . . . The addition of a scientific section means that the activity of the Ministry need no longer depend on the routine of an office, on the vagaries of a minister's career, or on the vigour of critics in the House of Commons.[61]

But the Association of Scientific Workers, whilst aiming for a Central Scientific Office at Cabinet level with further co-ordinating machinery between Government, university and industrial science,[62] rejected the suggestion of a Ministry of Science on the grounds that

if all scientific work were done in a single ministry, the rest of the Ministries would be divorced from science and the valuable responsibility of Ministers for an essential element of their own work would be lost.[63]

In fact the scientific services of the various ministries did increase considerably. The number of specialist advisory committees increased from 200 in 1939 to 700 by 1949, and to 850 by 1958.[64] In mere numbers, the standing advisory committees attached to central Government departments were by then considerable. Agriculture (54), Supply (41), Labour (39), the Board of Trade (38), the Home Office (30) and the Colonial Office (29), led the field, followed by Health (23), the Treasury (20), Transport (20), Works (19), Power (18), Education (16), the Admiralty (13), the War Office (13), the Air Ministry (12) and Housing and Local Government (10).

In addition further bodies, like the National Research and Development Corporation (1948) and the Nature Conservancy (1949) were also set up: one to encourage and finance the adoption of new ideas (like the Hovercraft), the other to provide scientific advice on the conservation of flora and fauna. The latter was, if anything, a tribute to the tireless public work of Sir Julian Huxley who had not only advocated it for over a quarter of a century but was a member of the Hobhouse Committee which recommended its establishment. And with the Nature Conservancy came Nature Reserves and National Parks.

(8)

An even more influential public authority was created in 1954—the Atomic Energy Authority. This was to be 'an incubator which will hatch the ideas of the research people and those will be followed up by industry'.[65] Originating in a secret project undertaken by 'The Directorate of Tube Alloys' during the war which was transferred to the U.S.A., work on atomic energy was resumed in Britain after the war under the Ministry of Supply. The successful detonation of the first British atomic bomb in 1952, led the Conservative Government to appoint a committee under Lord Waverley to examine the situation. Their recommendations were embodied in the Atomic Energy Authority Act of 1954 which transferred the work from the Ministry of Supply to a self-contained authority with its own administrative organs.

Under Sir Edward Plowden as chairman it was planned to operate in conjunction with the Electricity Authorities and the manufacturing industries, to assist universities or firms with loans for research, to provide training in education in atomic energy. It was to be primarily a research and development authority to reinforce a 10-year plan of constructing 12 nuclear power stations. It was organized into three groups: the Research Group under Sir John Cockcroft, the Weapons Research Group under Sir William Penney and the Industrial Group under Sir Christopher Hinton.

With these three technocrats sat a fourth physicist, Lord Cherwell, and a number of industrialists as part-time members like the chairman of Fords and of Tube Investments. Between them they controlled about 20,000 staff.

The authority enjoyed the best of two worlds: 'certain powers and privileges normally reserved for the Crown, combined with the freedom of operation and internal structure of an industrial enterprise'. For as the custodians of the country's most cherished military secrets, as well as a prime competitor in the international scientific race, they were hedged physically, legally and financially from the more obvious disadvantages of 'popular control'.[66]

In 1956, the Advisory Council of D.S.I.R. became an executive council, appointed by the Lord President of the Council after consultation with the Royal Society.

Increasing costs of research in nuclear science led to the creation of the National Institute for Research in Nuclear Science (N.I.R.N.S.) in 1958, also by Royal Charter, to provide universities with common facilities. Financed through the Atomic

Energy vote, and virtually governed by the universities, this brought science education still further into the Government's vision.

Such accumulations of responsibility made it necessary to review the position of the Lord President of the Council, so in 1959 he was appointed Minister of Science. Yet another reason for the crystallization of his title were the increasing responsibilities for participation in established international agencies like C.E.R.N. (the European Organization for Nuclear Research) or projected ones like E.S.R.O. (the European Space Research Organization). Other bodies, like the International Atomic Energy Agency, or the Overseas Research Council (created in 1959 to advise the Privy Council Committee on Overseas Research), laid even heavier burdens on the new ministry.

Three new agencies (a Science Research Council divided into six divisions, a new Natural Resources Council and a new Industrial Research and Development Corporation) were recommended by the Trend committee in 1963. The first was to control the royal observatories, to finance post-graduate awards in science and technology and N.I.R.N.S., and to supervise space research, and the scientific aspects of the national commitment to C.E.R.N. and E.S.R.O. The second was to take over the functions of the Nature Conservancy and other environmental problems concerning geology, forestry and oceanography. The third was to take over the research stations managed by D.S.I.R. as well as the work of N.R.D.C. Though these three new agencies would involve the dissolution of D.S.I.R. they would not affect the Agricultural nor the Medical Research Council.

Above all, this Trend report recommended the strengthening of the Ministry of Science. It was to take over from the other Privy Council committees under which existing research councils operate the powers of appointing governing bodies and of issuing formal instructions to them. Moreover he was to obtain a new advisory body, half of whom were to be scientists. He was to take over responsibility for co-ordinating research agencies, the National Lending Library for Science and Technology, and A.S.L.I.B., whilst his staff was to be strengthened by new members and by exchange with the various agencies under him.[67]

The spirit of these recommendations was adopted when in 1964 a new Department of Education and Science was established.

(9)

How far has the trend to technarchy gone? Have they become what H. G. Wells called 'a new body, a new force in the world's history'? Part of the answer must be left till the last chapter. Here it is necessary only to point out that 'much of what Wells has imagined and worked for', as George Orwell remarked, was 'physically there in Nazi Germany' in the shape of 'the order, the planning, the State encouragement of science', 'but', added Orwell, 'all in the service of ideas appropriate to the Stone Age. Science is fighting on the side of superstition.'[68]

Orwell also attacked the hypertrophied sense of order affecting the Marxists. 'What they desire', he wrote, 'is to reduce the world to something approaching a chessboard.' They so identified Socialism with mechanical progress that ordinary men and women recoiled from it. 'This essentially fat-bellied version of "progress" ' was, to Orwell, 'not an integral part of Socialism, but it has come to be thought of as one, with the result that the temperamental conservatism which is latent in all kinds of people is easily mobilised against Socialism'.[69] So 'the only possible course is to examine the Fascist case, grasp that there is something to be said for it, and then make it clear to the world that whatever good Fascism contains is also implicit in Socialism'.

In *Animal Farm* (1945), Orwell parodied Socialist Russia's parody of Socialism. There Science had replaced Farmer Jones's god and Squealer demanded that brain-workers (mainly pigs) needed all the milk and apples to prevent Mr. Jones's return. For wanting the farm scientifically improved, Snowball, the hero, was chased away by the dogs.[70] Scientific research, as Orwell showed in *Nineteen Eighty-Four* (1949), could cover two great anti-democratic approaches: methods of mass production and the control of thought. By doing so, he forecast, it would enable three great power blocks to emerge: the British Empire merged with the Americas in Oceania; China, Japan and the neighbouring powers in East Asia, and the rest in Eurasia. These three superstates would be in a continuous state of war, shattering materials or pouring them into the atmosphere or sinking them into the sea, lest they might be otherwise 'used to make the masses too comfortable or too intelligent'.[71] These masses would by 1984, he suggested, comprise 85 per cent of the population.

What was the spirit of the 'new men' ten years after Orwell wrote? An inquiry into some twenty firms in the Manchester area found in 1958 that proportionately more science graduates and scientifically trained men were being used more in types of work other than merely technical ones, and that they exhibited no lack of 'leadership'. The investigator commented:

> The group from grammar schools and redbrick university science courses continues to grow in social esteem and, as it rises, the status of its individual members within industry improves. It may be still too amorphous to be described as an élite, yet, despite the divisions that may be observed between physicist and chemist within the same laboratory, it has a mythology and principles of its own, and increasingly it is conscious of common interest which stimulate attempts to organise it.[72]

In the same year a detailed PEP study failed to identify in the scientific community

> the unity and cohesion displayed by some trades and professions, nor do its political and social attitudes differ markedly from those of the rest of the country. But [added the Report] if circumstances develop, however, when such differences become significant, then the power of the scientists will become politically important.[73]

Three years later another study of some sixteen firms in the Scottish electronics industry indicated that in Britain, perhaps more than elsewhere, the industrial scientist 'conceives himself as a member of a professional group the bounds of which extend over the institutions of higher education and government service as well as business'. Indeed much of the study was concerned with their expanding control over sectors of the concern previously under the control of production and higher management.[74]

That this expansion had not gone far enough by 1964 was evidenced by the controversy over the V.C.10 aircraft. The administrative gamesmanship exhibited in this affair was to one Canadian scientist 'a luxury which Britain can ill afford'. He added:

Public debate in Britain of technical affairs is beset by technical incompetency, and I am left with the strong impression that Britain badly needs more men at the top administrative levels, of business and government, who have both technical and economic training.[75]

(10)

The chief complaint against the technocrats was that though they make themselves accessible to the public, 'they do it in such a way that the public can put up no effective resistance'. A writer in the *Daily Telegraph* suggested that committees of laymen should be set up to control the technocrats whom he described as 'good servants, but mischievous masters' who 'left to themselves can get up to all sorts of mischief', which only 'the quiet firm murmur of the establishment' could control.[76] Whilst agreeing with him, A. P. Herbert nevertheless favoured each Department of State having a research and technical section, charged to look ahead and consider the answers to problems likely to arise in the future or at present only 'in the air'.[77]

Then too, the mere size of the technarchy in government alone was considerable, for by 1963 the scientific class of the Civil Service was four times as large as the administrative, and with the professional and technical classes, half as large again as the administrative and executive classes put together.[78] It was this which led the all-party Parliamentary and Scientific Committee to propose on 30 July 1964 that a select committee should be created to examine the annual reports from scientific and research bodies receiving public funds, hoping that by this means Parliament 'could establish more effective control over scientific and technological policy'.

For the first Minister of Science, on his own admission, construed his role as that of a patron, not as the chief of 'scientific planning staff' with a science budget.

> The tidy, ambitious, and grandiose schemes which I am constantly being invited to adopt for the aggrandisement of my office, and the enhancement of my personal reputation [he said] would in effect be reactionary and restrictive of my true activities. [He insisted that] it is important not so much that there should be a Science Minister as that all Ministries should learn to regard the application of science, each in its own particular sphere, as one of its main responsibilities.[79]

His opposite number on the Labour Front Bench considered that during the Second World War Britain 'was probably the best governed country in the world' and openly advocated a return to the practice of that time whereby scientists of every kind were recruited 'round the firm scaffolding of a permament civil service'. To secure 'a continuous and purposeful adaptation to its environment' he insisted that 'British Establishment must become "science-based" '. To R. H. S. Crossman, the pitifully small number of M.P.s—less than 20 out of the total of 625—possessing any scientific qualification was emphasized by the paucity—7 per cent—of assistant principals in the Civil Service, equally qualified. The second could be remedied, the first could not.

Crossman advocated the provision of professional scientific advice for every ministry, and the opening of channels to ensure that advice gets through 'in time to influence decision'. To avoid difficulty he urged not only 'a sharp increase in the size and status' of the Scientific Civil Service, but 'a full recognition of the vital role of the outside specialist on temporary assignment to Whitehall'. He envisaged investigations to precede 'really sensible and accurate planning'.[80]

The leader of the Labour Party was even more explicit: asked by a newspaper as to what above all he associated with Socialism in this modern age, he replied: 'if there was one word I could use to identify modern socialism it was "science" '.[81]

(11)

Such identification of socialism with science became complete when a Labour Government took office in 1964. In reorganizing the clumsy *ad hoc* set of mutually independent dispensers of government money for science into a group of interdependent research councils, the Labour Party was doing no more than Trend recommended. That the Medical and the Agricultural Research Councils should be augmented by a new Natural Environment Research Council and a new Science Research Council; all within the Department of Education and Science, was to be expected. What was not, was the replacement of the Advisory Council on Scientific Policy by a Council of Scientific Policy (C.S.P.) from which the adjective 'advisory' was deleted. On this now sit the technocrats from the universities and industry, reinforced by secretariats and information services. A second innovation was the creation of a new Ministry of Technology with the N.R.D.C., the Atomic Energy Authority, the National Physical Laboratory and the research stations and associations of now-extinct D.S.I.R., under its wing. Its new council had, aptly enough, a trade union official as chairman and Professor P. M. S. Blackett as vice-chairman. This new ministry was to work by crash techniques—sending teams of experts to selected industries to speed up the assimilation of new ideas. One of the first industries to be selected was electronics.

A third change was itself a response to the first two: the replacement, in 1965, of the British Employers Federation, the Federation of British Industries and the National Association of British Manufacturers by a new Confederation of British Industry. As its first Director General was chosen a member of the new National Economic Development Council and of the new Energy Advisory Council: Mr. John Davis the Managing Director of Shell-Mex and B.P. Little wonder that his philosophy should be that industry and Government are 'strongly intermeshed'. Such 'strong intermeshing' is, as we shall see, no less a feature of the two leviathans between which Britain was increasingly sandwiched.

Let us now consider them.

17

The Two Leviathans

(1)

As two great land powers, the U.S.A. and the U.S.S.R. are
astonishingly alike. Both believe in groups as agencies of social
change. Both envisage such change as limitlessly possible.[1] Both
countries have vast frontiers to manage, so both have rejected
the amateur. Both vehemently criticize their own bureaucracies:
the Americans for being agents of 'creeping communism' and the
Russians for being a 'pernicious remnant of capitalism'.[2] Both
bureaucracies are in fact modifying the systems of their respective countries. Some critics indeed, like James Burnham, consider that Russian institutions, 'more fully than any other in the
world, give the direction towards the future: that direction
being towards technocracy—'established and consolidated managerial society'.[3] To W. W. Rostow Russian economic development was 'remarkably similar to that of the United States, with
a lag of about thirty-five years in the level of industrial output,
and a lag of about half a century in *per capita* output in industry'.[4]
Even the content of the debate over Communism seemed to
Daniel Bell to have been 'forgotten by friends and foes alike'.[5]

(2)

Both the likeness and the lag are best seen in the five constituent republics abutting on India and China: Turkmenia,

Uzbekistan, Tadzhikistan, Kirgizstan and Kazakhstan. For Russia these became in the sixties what Siberia was in the thirties: a new frontier.[6]

Boltholes for Russian science in war, these five republics became shop-window exhibits in peace. The recuperative potential of institutions like the University of Odessa, which was evacuated in 1942 to Turkmenia, was astonishing. In a State that was 99 per cent desert, scientists designed the Karakum Canal, 256 miles of which were completed by 1959. When finished it will irrigate more than a million acres. A new Academy of Sciences, founded at Ashkhabad, in 1951, on the borders of Iran, is busy devising techniques for the full exploitation of native oil, gas and ocerite deposits.[7]

Even more generously endowed with natural gas is Uzbekistan, where a pipe line, 1,300 miles long, is being built to Sverdlovsk. Here, too, canals like the Ferghana are fighting back the deserts. Its Academy of Sciences, established since 1943 at Tashkent, has over 1,000 research workers.[8] Tashkent has become a mecca to which over thirty different Indian delegations came during the years 1954 to 1956.

Through the third of these Soviet republics, Tadzhikistan, a series of rocky enclaves on the roof of the world, flow the rivers that make up the Amu-Darya—the biggest river system in Central Asia—giving the republic the second largest hydroelectric potential in the union, now being intensively harnessed by multi-purpose hydro-electric schemes. Hence the importance of its State university, founded in 1948, and its Academy of Sciences, founded in 1951, at Stalinabad: a city of a quarter of a million people created out of the village of Dyushambe. These also serve Leninabad, another centre of work on guided missiles.[9]

The fourth republic in this group, Kirgizia, has the third largest hydro-electric potential in the Union in the Naryn river, now the hub of the projected Central Asian Power System, the first section of which began operations at Uch-Kurgan in 1961. Since 1954, an Academy of Sciences at Frunze with thirty-four research institutions, is busy in tapping the Central Asian treasury of the Kirgiz Mountains, with its coal, gas and nonferrous metals.[10] Sixty elements in the Mendeleevian table are reported. Aggregates of smoke-filled tents are disappearing before blocks of modern flats as this is being written.

The fifth of these Central Asian republics calls for special comment, for here many enterprises evacuated from the West during World War II have stayed to grow. Eleven times the size of Britain, the million square miles and more of Kazakhstan are flanked by China on the east and by four Soviet republics on the west. As an integral part of the Virgin Lands Scheme it furnished the Soviet Union in 1956 with 16 million tons of grain: a figure which Terenty Maltsev of its Academy of Agricultural Sciences is bent on increasing. It is also a vast storehouse of minerals, mapped by their Academy of Sciences (founded at Alma-Ata in 1946) and contains practically every element in the Mendeleevian table, including big deposits of molybdenum and titanium. By 1959 it had 107 scientific research institutes including its own nuclear research centre. To these come not only native Khazakhs, but mature people from China and Mongolia, Vietnam and North Korea.[11] Its Karaganda coalfield is the Soviet Union's third largest, its Sokolovsky-Sarbay iron mills will have an annual capacity of 19 million tons. Copper, aluminium, gold and silver are similarly being exploited, together with hydro-electric power. Krushchev himself referred to 'the gigantic scale' of this new development. Nor in the picture of this vast humming, developing republic should a town like Semipalatinsk be forgotten; for it is a testing centre for nuclear bombs.[12]

(3)

Atomic power had also acclimatized the United States to 'megabuck science', and convinced them of the necessity for organizing their own intellectual resources.

> The intellectual banks of continental Europe, from which we formerly borrowed, have become bankrupt through the ravages of war. No longer can we count upon these sources for fundamental science . . . in this modern age, more than ever before, pure research is the pacemaker of technological progress.

So concluded a report on Science and Public Welfare prepared for the U.S. Government at the end of the Second World War. With one eye cocked at Russia ('other world powers intend to foster scientific research in the future'), the other on the inadequacy of private enterprise (in the form of endowments, grants, foundations and appropriations) to support American science, Vannevar Bush urged the Federal Government to establish a National Science Foundation. The 'modern way to do it,' he said, 'was to accept new responsibilities for promoting the flow of new scientific knowledge and the development of scientific talent in our youth' and to 'foster the openings of new frontiers'.[13]

Having witnessed in the 'Manhattan Project' what could be achieved by governmental support, Americans warmed to his theme. The warmth was not, however, one of agreement. There ensued a five-year wrangle as to whether or not there should be a National Science Foundation established at all.

Three wartime expedients extended and expanded into actual establishments. The Naval Office of Research and Invention became the Office of Naval Research (O.N.R.) in 1946. The Federal Security Agency (embracing the U.S. Public Health Service and the National Institutes of Health) continued. The Atomic Energy Commission exploded, bringing the universities into yet closer touch with Federal needs, via five national laboratories: Berkeley (which existed before 1939), Los Alamos, Argonne (connected with the universities of the Chicago area as a reactor laboratory carrying on pure research), Oak Ridge (Tennessee) and Brookhaven (established after the war for the universities of the New York area).

When at length the National Science Foundation was established in 1950, its director, Alan T. Waterman, was only given a budget of 3·5 million dollars. It became a para-academic body with James Bryan Conant as its chairman. By discharging its role (to foster basic research in the mathematical, physical, engineering and biological sciences, to establish scholarships or graduate fellowships and to initiate and sustain a register of research and researchers), the grant crept slowly up to 16 million dollars by 1956. One of its most effective inquiries was a study of Soviet scientific manpower.[14] Congress more than doubled its grant as a result—from 16 million to 40 million dollars. It undertood fresh responsibilities when the President set up a national committee for the Development of Scientists and Engineers in 1956.[15]

Soviet scientific manpower had for some time before this been carefully scrutinized. One of the first responsible groups to do so was the first Trade Union Delegation to Russia in 1928.[16] A National Manpower Council (established at Columbia University in 1951 with a grant from the Ford Foundation) had been trying to kindle public interest in improving the supply and utilization of American scientific manpower, organizing conferences and publications.[17] Some politicians, like William Benton (publisher of the *Encyclopaedia Britannica* and a senator from Connecticut between 1949 and 1953), introduced a Bill popularly known as a call for a 'Marshall Plan of Ideas'. Benton visited Russia, and described her classrooms and libraries, her laboratories and teaching methods as a greater threat than her hydrogen bombs or guided missiles. The latter indeed were 'tactical and even diversionary' to their 'schooling for export of the scores of thousands of indoctrinated and capable engineers, scientists, schoolmasters and technicians of all kinds'. Benton put his finger on the missionary quality of these technologists, describing them as 'being trained to help develop the resources of countries outside the present Soviet orbit. . . . The advance guard is now in India, to which a technological institute has also been offered: and enticing inducements have recently been advanced to Egypt, Afghanistan and Latin America.'[18]

(4)

More ominous than this army of technological Jesuits were the Russian spies whose betrayal of scientific information stimulated reciprocral Western efforts to prevent them doing so. Following the discovery that Fuchs was giving information from 1941 to 1948, that Greenglas had disclosed the atom bomb's detonating mechanism, that Pontecorvo gave himself and that A. N. May gave them small samples of U233 and U235,[19] Western states organized their atomic research in conditions of greater secrecy. Meanwhile Russia had obtained from the occupation of East Germany the personnel and equipment of the Kaiser Wilhelm Institutes of Physics and Chemistry; the uranium manufacturing company for the German efforts in this field together with unranium mines and a heavy-water product. The captured German scientists included Baron von Ardenne, Dr. H. Barwich, Professor G. Hertz, Professor R. Rompe,

Professor Schintlmeister and Dr. Volmer. Ardenne is now back in Dresden with his own research institute.

By 1947 the Russians had built their first reactor. Thanks to I. V. Kurchatov, A. I. Alikhanov and D. I. Blokhintsev, A. I. Leipunsky and V. V. Vladimirsky, further developments were undertaken. In Moscow nine reactors were built; one at the Academy of Sciences (1947), two at the Thermal-Electrical Institute (1949), two at the State University (1953 and 1958), one at the Atomic Energy Institute (1957), one at the Engineering and Technical Institute (1958) and three at the Power Station (1955, 1956 and 1958). Eight others were spread out over the Union: the Physico-Technical Institutes of Leningrad and Kharkov, at the Tashkent Institute of Nuclear Research, the Alma-Ata Institute of Nuclear Research, and at Sverdlovsk and Minsk. It is again significant that the reactors at Alma-Ata, Tomsk and Tashkent were sited both where nuclear materials are situated and also where they can be brought to help Asian countries.

In the 'satellite' states of eastern Europe similar activities went forward. The work of Professor Infeld of the Theoretical Physics Centre at Warsaw was greatly accelerated by the creation of an Institute of Nuclear Research at the Polish Academy of Sciences. At Swierk a research reactor and linear accelerator together with numerous research laboratories have been set up, whilst at Cracow further buildings have been constructed. To service industrialization, an increased number of graduates— 9,177 in engineering and 1,435 in pure science—were provided in that year. In Czechoslovakia the Research Institute of Radiology, founded in 1923, as well as the Charles University, owed much to Petrizilka's visit to England. With Russian help, nuclear physics laboratories are also opening in East Germany, Rumania, Hungary, Bulgaria and Albania (where the Tirana Institute of Sciences is showing unwonted life).[20]

The centralization of Russian science, which had reached ridiculous heights under Stalin, began to moderate. Lysenko, as the President of the Lenin Academy of Agricultural Sciences, had denigrated Western science as 'bourgeois' 'idealistic' and 'backward' compared to Russian science, which he described as 'proletarian' 'materialistic' and 'advanced'. But Lysenko's ideas (Lamarckism reduced to absurdity) were not accepted by the majority of his colleagues at Moscow. Similar restiveness greeted the declaration, at a joint session of the Russian Academy of Sciences and the Academy of Medical Sciences in 1950, that Pavlov's doctrines were fundamental for medicine, psychiatry, physiology, psychology, pedagogy and animal husbandry. Though S. I. Vavilov, then President of the Academy of Sciences, approved the declaration, protests intensified. In 1954 Soviet scientists were allowed to participate in outside conferences, and two years later, at the twentieth Party Congress, Lysenko had resigned and been succeeded by P. P. Lobanov.

The 'new look' in Soviet scientific organization was sketched by the new president of the Academy of Sciences, A. N. Nesmayanov. 'Comrade Krushchev,' he said, 'is quite right in having pointed out the abnormality of concentrating scientific institutions in Moscow. . . . It is absolutely necessary to increase the importance of existing scientific institutions on the periphery: universities, institutes, the branches and institutes of the U.S.S.R. Academy of Sciences, and especially the academies of sciences of the national republics.' He cited the case of the Armenian Academy of Sciences which received only 500,000 roubles a year. 'This,' he said, 'is quite insufficient. Only two or three up-to-date and rather simple apparatuses can be obtained for this amount.'

The increase of the intelligentsia was a major decentralizing influence in Russia. Between 1940 and 1952 the number of those who received higher professional or technical education increased from 2,500,000 to 5,940,000.[21] These were spread over a greater area of the Union than ever before and gave great vitality to the academies of the various republics.[22]

Such decentralization was also economically and administratively necessary. Industry on 30 March 1957 was freed from some thirty Moscow ministries and reorganized into over a hundred regional economic councils, each with considerable autonomy. Agriculture followed suit in 1961. Even the most elementary considerations of national defence indicated that dispersal was a wise policy.[23]

Decentralization spread to the Academy of Sciences. The most powerful advocate of autonomous academies undertaking the intensive acceleration of production and leaving the central academy free to pursue pure research was Professor Semënov. Physical chemist and Nobel Prize winner, he was opposed by Professor I. P. Bardin, a metallurgist. Semënov's point of view was victorious on the very day in which Major Yury Gagarin was hurled into space. In April 1961 the Academy handed over its supervision of institutes and branches of the various State Committee of the Council of Ministers. It reserved to itself the training of scientists and general methodological supervision of research. A new State Committee of the Council of Ministers under Mr. M. V. Krunichev was to look after automation, machine building and major scientific and technical problems in the economy. On this committee sit the Ministers of Education, the Chairman of the State Committee on Inventions, the President of the Academy of Sciences and the Deputy Chairman of the State Economic Council and Gosplan.

(5)

The ascent of the first Russian sputnik was a portent of great change for America. The President's Committee on Scientists and Engineers and the Benton Foundation sponsored a conference at Yale on 'America's Human Resources to meet the Scientific Challenge'. 'The significant feature of Russia's scientific progress and technical competence,' said the chairman of the President's Committee, Howard L. Bevis, 'lies not in the fact that she manufactured an atomic bomb years before we thought she would be able to do that or that she beat us to the draw in launching a satellite. The significant—and disturbing— feature is the rate of speed at which this competence was acquired.' Nicholas de Witt once more emerged to emphasize that whereas the U.S.A. only spent from 3 to 3·5 per cent of its gross national product on education the U.S.S.R. spent 8 per cent (one-third of which was spent on specialized training), and, in addition, another 2 per cent on research alone.[24] The budget of the National Science Foundation was dramatically increased from 50 million to 136 million dollars for 1959 and to 150 million dollars for 1960.[25] A Department of Research and Engineering (under Herbert York, a physicist) and an Advanced Research Projects Agency were created in the Department of Defence. The National Advisory Committee on Aeronautics was upgraded to become the National Aeronautics and Space

Administration, and a new National Aeronautics and Space Council was created.

For the first time Congress created for itself a single committee concerned with basic science: the Committee on Science and Astronautics. Senate followed suit with a Standing Committee on Astronautics and Space Science. Even more important, Congress gave authority to governmental departments and agencies to make grants for scientific research in addition to their existing power to award contracts.

Next, the President was given a special assistant for science and technology to sit on the National Security Council and to be called to the Cabinet when needed. The office had never existed before, except in wartime. First holder was J. R. Killian, the former president of M.I.T.[26] The Presidential Science Advisory Committee was also reconstituted. It now became a federal centre for the scientific bodies and the Government. On it sat the President of the American Association for the Advancement of Science, the Director of the National Science Foundation, the Director of Research and Engineering of the Department of Defence, the Chairman of the Defence Science Board and the Scientific Adviser to the State Department.

The Office of Scientific Adviser to the State Department, which had lapsed in 1954, after a three-year existence, was not only reactivated with the appointment of Wallace R. Brode, but science representatives were sent to ten major overseas capitals to advise members of the embassy staffs.

To cap this technarchy, a Federal Council for Science and Technology was created in 1959. Representatives of all the Federal departments sat on it: Defence, Interior, Agriculture, Commerce and Health, Education and Welfare, the National Aeronautics and Space Administration and the Atomic Energy Commission. The A.A.A.S. were reassured on 30 December 1958 by Killian himself that these multiple creations

> have been directed at multiple objectives: to enhance the excellence of our science, both basic and applied, and to add to our effort, relatively in basic research; to extend the recognition of science as a creative activity that augments man's dignity and understanding and afford him intellectual adventure of the highest order; to recognise that outstanding accomplishments in science appeal deeply to the hopes and aspirations of men everywhere and contribute to the

prestige and goodwill of nations to demonstrate that the democratic environment of the free world is the best for achievement in
science; to improve the ways in which our Government uses and
supports science; to apply it more effectively to improve our
environment, to strengthen our economy, to improve the health
and welfare of our citizens and the peoples of the free world; to
promote international understanding and good-will; to ensure that
science and technology contribute their maximum to the defence of
the United States and the free world.[27]

A new element in the power structure surfaced in 1962 with
the creation of an Office of Science and Technology. Its director
was the Presidential Science Adviser, who, as chairman of the
Federal Council on Science and Technology now had a fresh
source of authority. Thus equipped he was, according to the
President's message to Congress on 29 March 1962 to advise
and assist on

(1) Major policies, plans and programs of science and technology of the various agencies of the federal government,
giving appropriate emphasis to the relationship of science
and technology to national security and foreign policy, and
measures for furthering science and technology in the
nation.

(2) Assessment of selected scientific and technical developments and programs in relation to their impact on national
policies.

(3) Review, integration, and coordination of major federal
activities in science and technology, giving due consideration to the effects of such activities on non-federal resources
and institutions.

(4) Assuring that good and close relations exist with the
nation's scientific and engineering communities so as to
further in every appropriate way their participation in
strengthening science and technology in the United States
and the Free World.

(5) Such other matters consonant with law as may be assigned
by the President to the office.

Such powers, coupled to his budgetary responsibilities and
inevitable involvement as a consultant for top-level scientific
posts, led the editor of *Science* to write on 22 November 1963:

Means should be found to separate functions of the P.S.A.-C.O.S.T. complex into logical packages, with no one man asked to perform more than is humanly possible. The job of President's Science Adviser is a big one which merits full-time effort. A full-time director should lead O.S.T., and he should have a far better staff. Finally, we need a Planning Office headed by a man who can think and who can marshal the wisdom of his nation in attempting to give guidance for the future.

(6)

To buttress this elaborate Federal structure, greatly increased Federal subventions to science education were given under the National Defence Education Act of 1958.

Teams of American visitors departed to Russia to see what lay behind their technical achievements in space. The U.S. Commissioner of Education went over in 1958 and reported hearing everywhere the slogan, 'Reach and overreach America'. All bore witness to the sheer numbers of students in the Soviet institutes of higher education (1,178,000 full-time, 127,500 part-time and 756,000 taking correspondence course) and to 'the most dynamic element in Soviet education and technology' being the Academy of Sciences. It possessed, reported the Commissioner's team, 'the means for broad subsidisation of brain power by the State on a scale beyond any . . . that we had known before'. Its 'international activities' were strengthened by a huge force of 260,000 researchers, 96,000 of whom were either Masters or Doctors of Science. They concluded:

> It was of special interest to us to note the virtually unlimited support for basic research that the Soviet Union is providing through the U.S.S.R. Academy of Sciences and the Republic Academies. Apparently the Soviet Government considers basic research to be the most practical investment it can make. This attitude, along with the high prestige accorded brain power in the Soviet Union, makes the Academy of Sciences the most powerful scientific institution that many of us have ever known.[28]

A second team sent to the Soviet Union in the following November by the American Society for Engineering Education, agreed that 'nowhere are the engineers and scientists held in higher regard than in the U.S.S.R.' 'They are among the aristocracy of Soviet Society,' reported F. C. Lindval of the California

Institute of Technology. 'Their research degrees,' he added, 'could be, and were, obtained through institutes and industrial ministries rather than through engineering institutions and universities.'[29]

Faced with cumulative evidence of their own relative slowness to match the Soviet scientific beanstalk, some Americans had been criticizing the by now traditionally instrumental curriculum of their own public schools. Widely publicized books like *Educational Wastelands* (1953), *Quakery in the Public Schools* (1953) and *The Diminished Mind: A Study of Planned Mediocrity* (1954) were utilized by critics like Admiral Rickover (promoter of the nuclear submarine). Well-timed punches were aimed at what was increasingly considered to be the soft underbelly of American life: its schools.

More serious critics even pointed out that the current climate of opinion in America really debilitated efforts being made to overmatch the U.S.S.R.[30] Even Russian *émigrés* in the U.S.A. and Europe admired Soviet technocracy. Seventy-eight per cent of a sample of them examined and psychoanalysed in depth by Harvard research workers confessed themselves as

willing to consider keeping some aspect of the Soviet system, such as the social-welfare provisions, the educational system, or the State-ownership of basic industries and the means of transportation and communication.[31]

The sputnik represented Soviet science in the heavens. Even more significant were its activities on earth. A cultural offensive of major intensity was launched in industrially backward countries in Asia and Africa in 1953, had, by the end of 1957, cost nearly 1·9 billion dollars and by 1961 3·6 billion dollars. Over twenty-four countries have either received Soviet technological missionaries to help their major projects or have sent students to Communist bloc countries to study and be trained. Two-thirds of Russian aid went to the United Arab Republic, India and Indonesia, and over 6,500 scientists, engineers and technicians from the Sino-Soviet bloc were working in these areas at the end of 1960.[32] This was in addition to the numerous trainees for whom the Soviet Government offers training facilities.

Though Soviet aid was only a fraction (some 3 or 4 per cent) of the amount given by the West it was proportionately more effective. It was preferred as a 'liberation' from imperialism, no visible 'strings' were attached to it, and it came from a country rapidly hoisting itself up to the position of technological dominance by its own system of scientific and technological training.[33]

For in the contemporary Sino-Soviet world, science has become a religion, and technology its good works. Its adherents have made a social theory out of science. It is not so much from Marx as from Ostwald and Mendeleev that the effective ideology of Soviet Russia has been compounded: these and the iron determination to adhere to plans. Nor was it Marx, but a product of the École Polytechnique, August Comte, who asked: 'Men are not allowed to think freely about chemistry and biology, why should they think freely about political philosophy?' This is why Communism has been described by Arnold Toynbee as the last great Christian heresy: its heresy is technological charity to underdeveloped countries.

(7)

These Soviet offers of technical assistance to underdeveloped areas stimulated America to organize special agencies for the same purpose. Here a pre-war precedent existed in the Inter-Departmental Committee on Scientific and Cultural Exchange, set up as a result of the Buenos Aires Convention of 1936, which developed a variety of technical assistance programmes in Latin America through the Institute of Inter-American Affairs.

This precedent was broadened and intensified by President Truman in 1946. 'I'm tired of babying the Soviets', he told his American Ambassador to Moscow, Averill Harriman. Together they agreed that Communism could only be stopped by the development of 'sound economic conditions' in backward areas. So the Foreign Assistance Act of 1948 (Public Law 472, 80th Congress) established the Economic Co-operation Administration to provide assistance for Europe.

In 1949 President Truman called for 'a bold new programme for making the benefits of our scientific advances and industrial progress available for the improvement and growth of underdeveloped areas'. This was followed by an Act for International Development in 1950 (Public Law 535, 81st Congress). To improve the living conditions of Latin America, non-Communist Asia and most of Africa, by loans, treaties, trade policy, but above all, technical assistance, a Technical Co-operation Administration was organized as a Department of State. Three years later its functions were absorbed by the Mutual Security Administration, set up as a result of Mutual Security Act of 1951 (Public Law 165, 82nd Congress). This was designed to provide help both to Europe and some Asian countries in which technical assistance was necessary.

By 1953 it was considered necessary to unite the work of these various agencies. So the Institute of Inter-American Affairs, the Mutual Security Administration and the Technical Co-operation Administration were brought together as one: the Foreign Operations Administration. This became, two years later, part of the Department of State, when its name was changed to the International Co-operation Administration (I.C.A.).[34] By 1957 the I.C.A. was spending 240 million of the 476 million dollars appropriated by Congress for various agencies. In various parts of the world it was fostering community schools and colleges, introducing improved poultry or livestock strains, demonstrating new techniques and fertilizers, building public health services, improving communications, and providing advisers of all kinds. But its programme, working through education, training, demonstration and pilot-plant operation, badly needed trained personnel. One administrator complained:

> We are already having great difficulty in the United States finding suitable, experienced, mature, technically competent and willing people to live abroad for a period of years. . . . The difficulty of recruiting personnel is apparently one of the great barriers to any large increase in international efforts to promote economic and social development.[35]

He then went on, significantly enough, to remark that though 'some amelioration is possible by a greater use of contracts with private organizations, such as universities and engineering firms', the 'only way to surmount this barrier is to establish a Foreign Technical Service Corps'.

Under the I.C.A. a contract system with American universities was initiated whereby they undertook direct responsibility for technical training.[36] These contracts provided life blood for the universities' growth for, as President Eisenhower said on 25 May 1956,

> the whole free world would be stronger if there existed adequate institutions of modern techniques and sciences in areas of the world where the hunger for knowledge and the ability to use knowledge are unsatisfied.

As a result of this, an Inter-Agency Committee was established and in 1957 the Development Loan Fund was established to supplement technical assistance by finacing development projects and programmes.

By 1961, however, it was officially admitted that 'in several important aspects' American aid programmes had not produced 'the hoped-for effects'. 'Some of the policies governing the programmes, the increasingly heavy machinery of the responsible agencies, the complexities of our legislation', confessed President Kennedy's Administration, were 'certainly to blame'. So was the way in which U.S. aid was received and used.[37]

So, realizing that 'the desire for modernization and individualization is active and intense among the nations of Africa, Latin America, the Middle East and Asia', and that Communism exploits this demand for change, President Kennedy decided to establish a Peace Corps of trained personnel to help developing nations at their own invitation. A new Agency for International Development, co-ordinating the I.C.A. and other aid agencies was designed 'to express the new concepts of the aid program'.

Two of these new concepts were first, the formulation by the recipient nation of a national development plan; and second, the facilitation of the growth of 'strong and viable' institutions in the country concerned. The A.I.D. was to be organized under an administrator with the status of Under-Secretary of State, with four assistant administrators responsible for the Far East, the Near East, Latin America, and Africa and Europe.

The most novel proposal of the U.S. programme was that a concerted, continuing programme of research, development and scientific evaluation should be initiated to increase the effectiveness of the aid.

Intellect was now organized in the U.S.A. as well. But there was one major difference between it and the U.S.S.R., since the U.S.S.R. has largely escaped what Dr. Nove has called 'the large scale commercialization of the moron' with its encouragement of mental laziness and ignorance.[38] Signs were not wanting that the larger implications of an authoritarian cultural régime were being imaginatively considered.[39]

(8)

To reconcile the demands of planning with the normal process of deliberation in American government had become increasingly acute. The Senate debate of the summer of 1962, as to whether the control of the communications space satellite should be in the hands of the American Telegraph and Telephone Company or the Federal Government was so rending that, for the first time in thirty-five years, the Senate had to apply the closure. Other problems, like atomic power, scientific agriculture, the employment of displaced workers, and the need of medical care for an increasingly geriatric society introduced problems of State regulation.

'Evidence is now becoming overwhelming', remarked Edward T. Chase, 'that the traditional market mechanism of supply and demand, for all its uncanny power to articulate the public will, simply is not up to reflecting the long-range values that have to be weighed if a rational use is to be made of the new technology. The point is that this is not a doctrinaire matter, a sly triumph by creeping socialists; it is the result of technological change.'[40]

Both the presidential science advisers, Dr. James R. Killian and his successor Dr. Jerome Wiesner, were seized of this need. Killian urged scientists to run for Congress so that science would be 'in the public arena'. Wiesner has an 18-man Panel on Civilian Technology which reports to him as well as to the economic adviser and the Secretary for Commerce as to how new technology can be harnessed for economic growth.

The sheer scale of Federal expenditure in research and development since the war is perhaps best expressed by the fact that in 1963 alone more was spent for this purpose than in the whole period from the Revolution to 1945. Wiesner pointed out that since 1950 it had grown by a factor of 10, and that industry, universities and private foundations together only spent half as much. In itself this poses a need for a planning authority, which American Labour, represented by the American Federation of Labour and the Congress of Industrial Organizations suggests should be 'a Permanent Commission on Technological Change'.[41]

The solution of this problem may well lie in the problem itself. For to provide the necessary technical personnel and to retrain others jettisoned by the changes they are bringing about an Office of Manpower, Automation and Training has been created. The sheer numbers resulting from such massive preparations to produce technical personnel might well produce a 'new constituency' of scientists that might well overwhelm those ideologues of the mystique of the market—the businessmen.

To outsiders, the drive of both the U.S.A. and the U.S.S.R. towards the same technical mastery looks like producing even more curiously similar societies in both countries. Reflecting in public on the Soviet doctrine that Communism would be achieved within twenty years, a British Minister of Science remarked, 'should it come, I fancy that it may not turn out to be so different from the American way of life as the inhabitants of the Kremlin or the White House might expect'.[42]

Russia's acceptance of the technocratic principle was made starkly manifest by the emergence to supreme power in 1964 of Leonid Brezhnev and Alexei Kosygin, one the successful initiator of the virgin lands scheme in Kazakhstan, the other the chairman of Gosplan. Since the other nine members of the supreme presidium have had similar careers, one might be excused for seeing in this the apotheosis of the technocrats. Soon afterwards Sir Leon Bagrit remarked

'Recent examination of changes in communist Russia indicate that under the impact of automation, even communist dogma is beginning to undergo a reformation. Due to the creation of a new technological class on a world wide scale, orthodox political theories are now beginning to be amended, if not to crumble, and the process must inevitably continue. So it is possible that both capitalism and communism will find common denominators as a result of the forces let loose by the productive power of automation.'[43]

PART V

The Diaspora of Technology

18

❖❖❖

The Conversion of the Mandarins

❖❖❖

(1)

THE *rêve chinois*, or cult of the Confucian Sage, undoubtedly contributed to the rise of the spirit of rationalism in Europe. So culturally and politically advanced was China, according to the accounts brought back by sailors and missioners, that the *avant-garde* of European thinkers regarded it as a kind of Utopia. The traffic was two-way, however. At the same time as Bernard Palissy was active in the Tuileries, a 31-year-old Jesuit Matteo Ricci (1552–1616) opened a scientific stall of clocks, mathematical instruments, prisms, maps and oil paintings at Kwantung in 1583. This marked the first breach in the wall of indifference erected by the first Ming Emperor, who nearly two centuries earlier had decreed that his people 'should not go down to the sea in ships'. Though the persistent Portuguese had been kept at arms distance in the port of Macao by Chinese pirates, it was their cosmographers in Portugal and Goa that enabled Ricci to become a cartographer.

The mandarins were divided. Some admired Ricci's instruments, others suspected them, and it took Ricci twenty-two years to penetrate Court circles and obtain an audience with the Emperor at Peking. The Emperor had his own 200-strong Board of Mathematicians, who tendered advice about the calendar—a necessity in an agrarian economy. This Ricci was determined to undermine. He translated the *Elements* of Euclid into Chinese and in 1606 imported a skilled astronomer, Sabbatina de Ursis, to help him. The Board, quite naturally, expelled both of them from Pekin in 1611.[1]

It was not the Gospel of the pale Galilean but that of the swart Galileo that the Jesuits relied on in their second assault on the Board of Mathematics some eighteen years later, led by 53-year-old Father John Terrentius (1576–1630), a member of the Italian Academy of the Lincei. They endeavoured to point out the obsolescence of Moslem techniques in astronomy. Terrentius's younger colleague, J. A. Schall, actually penetrated the mandarinate to become President of the Board of Mathematics.

The Jesuits were now in the singular position of advising the Emperor on military affairs, especially on the making of cannon to fight the Manchus. And when the Manchu emperors replaced the Mings, Schall remained at the Chinese Court, as did his successor, Father Ferdinand Verbiest, who to the presidency of the Board of Mathematics and Mastership of the Ordnance added that of general consultant on mechanical matters.[2]

(2)

Paradoxically, Western imaginations were fired by the Jesuits' reports on China and a wave of Sinomania broke over the West.[3] Gonzales de Mendoza, an Augustinian, enthusiastically eulogized the Middle Kingdom in 1585[4] and for the next two centuries the Jesuits increasingly did so: Trigault (in 1615), Semedo (in 1645), Kitcher (in 1667) and Duhalde (in 1735) all published major works of this kind. So did the anti-Jesuits like Navarette (in 1676). All of them nourished a growing Sinophilia which found its best-known exponents in Leibnitz[5] and Voltaire.[6]

Leibnitz really articulated European admiration for Chinese culture. Reading the newly-translated maxims of Confucius, his imagination was so fired by the literature of the Orient that he dreamed of a new culture formed by fusion with the Occident. To effect this fusion he looked first to the Society of Jesus, then to Peter the Great.

Voltaire's admiration for Confucius was so great that he kept a picture of him in his library at Ferney, facing him as he worked. His Sinophilia was of long showing. The Professor of Rhetoric under whom he had studied was much interested in Chinese science and carried on a correspondence with Father Joachim Bouvet, who sent over treatises on Chinese algebra. Voltaire's chief English friend Falkener was a merchant with interests in the East, whilst another friend, Father Jean-Francois Fouquet, had spent twenty-two years in the Church in China.

From these and other contacts Voltaire aimed at making the Chinese a counterbalancing force to Judaism and the Bible. But especially was he interested in their cult of justice and their freedom from fanaticism, superstition and dogma. He admired 'le culte simple ou maitre du ciel', and again 'leur religion était sage, auguste, libre de toute superstition et de toute barbarie, jamais déshonorée par des impostures; jamais troublée par des querelles de sacerdoce de l'Empire; jamais chargée d'innovations absurdes'.[7]

In Confucian deism Voltaire hoped to find a religion which would oppose the Christian Church. This led him to accept Jesuit panegyrics and to suspend his usual critical judgement and greatly to enthuse on Chinese progress in science and the arts. But when any suggestion of Chinese miracles appears, as for instance the legend that the Manchu Dynasty sprang from a Virgin who conceived after eating a red fruit dropped from heaven, he was immediately on guard.

This Sinophilia led him to reject the doctrine of the perfectibility of man, and the superiority of science over tradition. China was for him a Utopia, much the same as Moscow was for Western intellectuals in the 1920s.[7]

The dissolution of the Jesuit Order in 1773 left few Western bridgeheads in China. The Chinese had no respect for Western ways and twenty years after the society was dissolved a British envoy was told, 'We have never set store on strange or ingenious objects, nor do we need any more of your country's manufactures.'

(3)

But China did need opium and raw cotton from India, and this was of great importance to Britain. So when the import of opium to China in 1836 was prohibited, the British secured the opening of four treaty ports: Amoy, Foochow, Mingpo and Shanghai. Hongkong became a British colony, and an island in the river beside Canton remained in their hands.

To these little enclaves of the West flocked Chinese merchants, anxious for security and a high standard of living. Amoy, Foochow, Mingpo and especially Hongkong and Shanghai also attracted Europeans interested in trade. In the 1840s Rutherford Alcock (1809–79) served at Foochow and Shanghai and Thomas Wade (1818–95) at Hongkong. Other ports obtained by later treaties in 1858 and 1860 included five north of Shanghai (Newchang, Tientsin, Chefoo, Nanking and Chinkiang) and one between Amoy and Hongkong (Swatow). From these foreigners were now allowed to travel into the interior.

To facilitate intercourse the *T'ung-Wen Kuan* or Interpreters' College was established by the Empress Dowager T'zu-hui ('Old Buddha', as she was nicknamed), as a belated concession to the Europeans seated at her doors. Plagued by internal rebellions, she had already been obliged to ask them to collect her customs dues in 1858, and it was from this money that the college was financed. Its purpose was to staff the Chinese Foreign Office with young Bannermen trained in foreign languages.[8]

That she took these and other steps, too, was in no small way due to the persuasion of Alcock and Wade, and of Robert Hart, organizer of the customs service at the ports from 1859 to 1863, and Inspector General until 1906.[9]

The Interpreters' College extended its scope. Branches were established in Shanghai (in 1863) and Canton (in 1864). It acquired momentum after 1869 under the 20-year presidency of Dr. W. A. P. Martin, who not only visited various foreign countries and reported on their systems but initiated programmes of translation. An American Presbyterian minister adept both in local dialects and Mandarin, Martin had played a part in the treaty negotiations of 1860. By 1898 his standing was such that he was chosen as president of the newly created Imperial University.

(4)

Endowed by the treaties of 1860 with permission to carry on their work in China, other missionaries founded schools, hospitals and universities. Presbyterian colleagues of Dr. Martin established in 1864 what became, in 1882, Cheloo University at Tengchow. Six years later the American Episcopalians established what became the Hua-Chung or Boone University at Wuchang. They exchanged ideas by promoting general conferences: one such, held at Shanghai in May 1877, showed how strong was their desire to introduce the sciences and arts of Western civilization to China.[10]

The four most colourful and energetic missionaries were Samuel Isaac Joseph Schereschewsky (1831–1906), Calvin W. Mateer (1836–1908), Devello Zelotes Sheffield (1841–1913) and Duncan Main (1856–1934). Schereschewsky, formerly a Lithuanian Jew, became an American Episcopalian bishop in China, where he founded in 1879 what became in 1890 the St. John's University at Shanghai. Mateer, a missionary at Tengchow in Shantung Province, founded what became Shantung Christian University, building a laboratory and collecting a museum of mechanical equipment as well as writing a primer of Mandarin. D. Z. Sheffield, formerly of the U.S. Army, organized North China College in 1889, and constructed a typewriter for the Chinese language as well as much apparatus. Duncan Main, known to the Chinese as 'Dr. Apricot of Heaven's Below', founded the Medical Centre at Hangchow, where many Chinese were trained. Indeed, in most of the leading cities universities and medical schools were founded by missionaries.

No less than 12 universities were founded by Christian missions in China up to 1911; 4 by the Presbyterians—Shantung Christian University (1882), Lingnan University (1893), Hangchow College (1897) and North China Union College for Women at Peking (1905); 2 by the Methodists—another at Peking (1886) and Soochow University (1901); and 1 each by the American Board, the Episcopal Church and the Baptists—North China College at Tungchow near Peking (1889), St. John's University at Shanghai (c. 1890) and Shanghai Baptist College (1907). The remaining three were jointly sponsored by collaboration between the above and other missions. Thus the Episcopalians and the American Board joined the London Missionary Society to found Boone University in Wunhang (1903), the Methodists and Presbyterians joined the Disciples of Christ to found the University of Nanking

(1909) and the Methodists and Baptists joined the English Society of Friends to found West China Union University at Chengtu (1910).

Missionaries also ensured that some of the indemnity paid by the Chinese Government in compensation for the Boxer rising was applied for educational purposes: Timothy Richard, for instance, persuaded the authorities in Shansi to set aside half a million taels from the Boxer indemnity to found the University of T'aiyüanfu.[11] The Tsinghua University was founded in 1911 to prepare 'indemnity students' before they left for America.

These men really hoped that modern science would help dissipate Chinese superstitions, and help the Chinese to help themselves. As D. Z. Sheffield remarked,

> A man of culture and ideas declines to be the servant of other men, simply because he feels in himself the power of self-government, the exact feeling that we want to develop, and must develop, before we have a church that can stand by itself.[12]

(5)

Similar cues from the West were taken by the 'Scholar-generals' who ruled the various regions of China. To strengthen imperial authority in his area, Tseng Kuo-fan (1811–72) established an arsenal at Kiangnan in 1865 and two years later a school of mechanical engineering under Yung Wing. The works translated at Kiangnan, it is said, 'exceeded in quality those translated in all China during the subsequent half-century'.[13] Tseng Kuo-fan also published a Chinese translation of Euclid's first fifteen books—the completion of the one begun by Ricci 200 years before. One of Tseng's pupils, Li-Hung-Chang (1823–1901) even considered establishing a modern university at Tientsin in 1887.[14] Although this was not immediately accomplished, mathematics and science were introduced into the traditional public examinations of China in that year. Li Hung-Chang engaged a Columbia graduate, John Adams Church, to introduce modern mining methods into China.

Li Hung-Chang and Tseng Kuo-fan also persuaded the Empress to send Chinese students abroad. Yung Wing, Tseng Kuo-fan's adviser, was put in charge of the operations, as he had been educated at Yale. From 1872 onwards 30 students a year were sent to America. The practice was discontinued in

1881 and a number of 'service' institutions on Western lines were set up, like the Military School at Tientsin (1885), the Imperial Naval College at Nanking (1890), the Medical College at Tientsin (1893) and the Mining College of the Hupeh Board of Mines at Wuchang (1895).

In the Moslem north-west, Tso Tsung-t'ang (1812–85) built a naval yard at Foochow in 1866 where, three years later both the French and the English established naval schools.[15] Both had boards of translation. The Kiangnan Arsenal and the Foochow Shipyard also represented something quite new in Chinese life. The technological training given in them impressed Europeans and they set a fashion.[16]

Europeans operating the treaty ports needed trained Chinese as salesmen and engineers for the products they were selling; so to train them they promoted scientific and technological schools. These were often associated with the scholar-general's arsenals. Thus at Shanghai, where Li Hung-Chang had established an arsenal in 1864, a polytechnic was organized in 1874 and endowed two years later with optical apparatus by John Bourne and Company.[17] The British Navy provided two professors for the Chinese Imperial Naval College at Nanking in 1890. When Hongkong University was founded in 1912, Sir Frederick Lugard thought its curriculum should be practical and utilitarian, and the U.S.A. offered not only equipment but staff as well.[18] Schemes for bringing the Chinese over to Europe and America for training were initiated. The intervention of the Japanese, who, after a short war in 1894–5, had been allowed to establish a number of industrial firms in their ports, accelerated this trend. Japan's success stimulated other nations to wrest concessions. Russia obtained Port Arthur and Dairen; Germany, Kiaochow Bay; France, Kwangchow Bay; Britain, Weihaiwei, plus more land adjoining Hongkong.

True to her nickname, 'Old Buddha' tactically allowed K'ang Yu-wei (1856–1927) to assume full powers to deal with a crisis in 1898. He began by condemning the 1,000-year-old Chinese examination system and proposing the establishment of agricultural and technical schools. When it looked as if he were going too far she imprisoned the Emperor and restored the examinations. Soon anti-foreign feeling erupted in the Boxer risings of 1901, which led the foreign powers to occupy the Chinese capital. They only handed it back to the Emperor on payment of an indemnity of £67 million. This indemnity, on the initiative of the United States, was to be expended on the purchase of industrial equipment from abroad and on educational facilities. In this way the Tsing Hua (or American Indemnity College) was founded in Peking in 1911 to prepare students before they went to America.

(6)

Meanwhile the mandarins continued to westernize China. Chang Chi-tung (1837–1909) published an *Admonition to Study* in 1898, and founded colleges of agriculture, languages, mechanics, mining and military science for which he engaged professors from America, Belgium, England, France and Germany.[19] He wished to convert Buddhist temples and Taoist monasteries into schools. 'Sooner or later', he wrote, 'we shall perish through our own stupidity.' Shang Hsuan-Huai (1844–1916), who managed the railways, financed two other Western-type institutions: the Sino-Western Academy at Tientsin in 1895 (where the first military school had been founded in 1885) and the Nanyang Public Institute at Shanghai. The first developed into Peiyang College, the second into an Imperial polytechnic in 1907 under the Ministry of Posts and Communications, producing engineers and politicians like Wang Ch'ung-hui and Ch'en hi-fu. Also associated with this second school was a translation bureau for Western technical and political works.

The greatest obstacle to the cultivation of science was removed in August 1901 with the abolition of the literary examinations. Provincial colleges (*Shu Yan*) were converted into modern universities on the lines of the Peking National University. Middle and primary schools on the Japanese model were established to feed them.

(7)

From these three types of institutions—governmental, scholar-general and missionary, a new type of student emerged. Perhaps the best individual example was that of Sun Yat-Sen (1866–1925) who entered the Po-chi Hospital School at Canton in 1886. Later he wrote:

I began to make up my mind to overthrow the Ch'ing dynasty, and from that time on I was using the (Po-chi Hospital) school as headquarters for propaganda, and using medicine as a medium for entering the world.[20]

Marrying the daughter of a former Methodist minister, Charles James Soon (later Soong), he began to prepare for the revolution of 1911 whereby the Manchu Dynasty was overthrown and he was elected president. He held office long enough to found the Kuomintang and appoint his friend Tsai Yuan-p'ei as Minister of Education. Sun Yat-Sen's fall was followed by Tsai Yuan-p'ei's translation to the chancellorship of the Peking National University, the first non-missionary institution of higher education, formally established in 1898, and in 1901 incorporated with the Tung-Wen Kuan, or Interpreters' College.

The Peking National University under Tsai Yuan-p'ei was based on the German idea; a centre of research and forum of opinion. Under his régime[21] it became the centre of the Chinese Renaissance. The students started a magazine with that name (Hsin Chao) in 1919, which urged the Chinese to recognize the superiority of Western learning. Here, too, the movement for writing the spoken language began when Hu Shih invented a modern simplified Chinese language Pai hua writing poems in it as a prelude to establishing a 'literature of realism'.[22] Hu Shih grasped the fundamental truth that 'civilization which makes the fullest possible use of human ingenuity and intelligence in search of truth in order to control nature and transform matter for the service of mankind, to liberate the human spirit from ignorance, superstition and slavery to the forces of nature, and to reform social and political institutions for the benefit of the greatest number—such a civilization is highly idealistic and spiritual'.[23] It found an enthusiastic supporter in Liang Ch'i-chao (1873–1929), a friend of Sun Yat-Sen who was to spend the rest of his life putting Western ideas before his fellow-countrymen.

But perhaps the strongest and strangest bond between the University of Peking and modern China was to be found in the inner recesses of its library. There a young assistant was, at the close of the First World War, charging his intellectual batteries. His name was Mao Tse-Tung.

(8)

Meanwhile Russian interest in China had been growing. 'Russia', wrote Mendeleev, 'should conclude the closest political and every other alliance with China, which is an awakening country of 430 million inhabitants and possesses, like Russia, every opportunity to become the most powerful state in the world.'[24] After the revolution of 1917 Russian 'missioners' began to cosset and foment the dreams of the Chinese intelligentsia. Some of the Chinese intelligentsia were already tuned to the new waveband.

> We must understand that from now on [remarked the librarian of the University of Peking, on 15 November 1918] the world is going to become the world of workers. We must therefore take hold of this trend as an opportunity to make everybody a worker and not to make everybody a bandit. All those who eat without working are bandits.[25]

This librarian, Li Ta-chao, took with Chen Tu-hsiu, the first steps to form the first cell of the Communist Party in China. Another Peking library assistant, and an organizer of youth groups in Tientsin joined it: Mao Tse-Tung (b. 1893), and Chang T'ai-Lei (1898–1927). The former was to conserve the Russian creed in exile for the next thirty years, the latter to organize the Chinese Communist Party.

China needed talent, and Russia sent it in good measure. A. A. Ioffe (1883–1937), a trained physician with literary gifts and considerable diplomatic experience, came as a 'missioner' of the new Leninist creed that only by planning could overcome out of chaos. By renouncing all her rights and privileges in China, Russia could then send M. M. Borodin (1884–1953) with a strong cadre of Soviet advisers and technicians to Canton. Borodin had taught in Chicago before coming to China, and in four years he organized the Kuomintang into a political party based on cells and training cadres.

A programme for Communist revolution in Asia was drafted by M. N. Roy (1898–1954), an Indian with an American wife, who had lived in the U.S.A. and Mexico, and was now in Russia. As approved by Lenin, China was to be the spearhead, and to sharpen the technique of Chinese Communists, special schools were established in Russia: the University of the Toilers of the East at Tashkent, the K.U.T.V. *(Kommunisticheskii Universitet Trudiash Chikhsia Vostoka)*, and the Sun Yat-Sen University (later the Communist University for the Toilers of China) in Moscow.

Chinese students who went to these institutions returned as dedicated Marxists. Amongst the 600 or so who passed through the Sun Yat-Sen University in 1926 was 30-year-old Chang Wen T'ien, a political demonstrator (in 1919), who had been exiled in Japan and America. He was later to teach at the Institute of Red Professors and the Lenin School.

Chinese students were also enrolled at the former Lazarev Institut in Moscow, at the Eastern Institute at Leningrad and at the Universities of Baku, Kazan, Samarkand and Vladivostock. A central organization, the Scientific Association for Eastern Studies, encouraged this trend. 'We must see to it', wrote Professor D. Anuchin, 'that in the future, Russia will appear to Asia as a spiritual force enjoying the respect of the Asian peoples and promoting their cultural development'.[26]

By using Sun Yat-Sen's Kuomintang as a Trojan horse the Russians hoped to make China the agent for capturing Asia. As a reservoir of raw materials China would, according to Dmitri Manuilsky in 1926, evoke a Japanese-American quarrel that would 'put the great imperialist war of 1914–18 in the shade'. Equally confident was that prestigious Party theorist Nicolai Bukharin, who opened the first session of the Comintern Seventh Plenum in the same year with the words, 'We promise in the name of the entire Communist International, in the name of the whole working class of the world, that we will support this world historical struggle (i.e. Chinese Communism) with all means, with all forces, at any price.'

The Chinese did not assimilate Communism as a religion. As a Communist official Chen Po-ta remarked, 'Bolshevism has been victorious because it is a correct science', and it was in this spirit that the Chinese Communists plotted the seizure of power.[27]

(9)

During the First World War, China sent 175,000 labourers to work on the Western Front. In spite of this she did not obtain, at the peace, the Japanese-held German interests in the province of Shantung. Students of the National University of Peking staged a great national demonstration on 4 May 1919, so great that over 1,000 of them were imprisoned. This accelerated an anti-Western movement (interpreted as anti-Christian) among them.

The President of the Chinese Republic, Dr. Sun Yat-Sen, virtually confined to the treaty ports, saw in Lenin's revolution an analogue of what he might himself achieve. Meeting Ioffe in January 1923, he then had sent his future son-in-law, Chiang Kai-Shek to Russia. On Chiang's return the Whampoa Military Academy was established in Canton to train officers for the Chinese Revolutionary Army. Sun Yat-Sen also reorganized the Kuomintang to fight as a revolutionary party. Through his many addresses he emphasized that

> European superiority to China is not in political philosophy, but altogether in the field of material civilization. . . . If we want to learn from Europe we should learn what we ourselves lack—science—but not political philosophy.[28]

As generalissimo of the Southern Army, Chiang Kai-Shek began to establish Kuomintang government at Wuchang and Nanking. In 1927, he strengthened his relationship with Sun Yat-Sen by marrying his sister-in-law, a graduate of Wellesley College, U.S.A. He then declared war against the Communists. But some Chinese, like Chou En-lai, sided with the Russians.

(10)

Chiang Kai-Shek took over the government in 1927. As leader of a warfare State he established a Ministry of Railways, a Chinese National Aviation Corporation, posts, telegraphs and a native customs service. He flirted with the French-Japanese idea of a National University of the Republic of China (*Ta Hsueh Yuan*) in 1928, which was to be a Ministry of Education as well.

How much Chiang cared for Sun Yat-Sen's statement quoted above may be judged from the effectiveness of the Academia Sinica (*Chung Yang Yen Chiu Yüan* or National Academy) established in 1928 under Dr. Ts'ai Yuan-P'ei, the former Chancellor of the University of Peking. As financial support was never forthcoming—it all went to the army—many Chinese students went abroad for research facilities. Nor did those whose patriotism kept them there find the presence on the Board of the Academia Sinica of the Chief of the Metropolitan Police particularly exhilarating. So the National Research Council established in the year of the Japanese invasion of Manchuria—1931 —had an almost impossible task.

That apostle of goodwill, Lionel Curtis, argued at length for giving it extensive aid. 'No greater adventure awaits human endeavour', he told his British readers, 'and none in which we are fitter to partake. It cannot be achieved through armies and navies, and does not call for expenditure of money, factors in which we were once strongest and are no longer.'[29]

Eating steadily into the coast, the Japanese in six years had swallowed most of industrial East. Tumbling back before them into the unindustrialized West of their country, Chiang Kai-Shek's Government now learned the bitter truth, that to get the weapons to fight back, industry would have to be built up in West China. So a National Resources Commission was organized. But help given by the Western Powers was dissipated. The universities derived more benefit from hardship than from Government aid. Driven from the comfort of their academic chairs, the best of them came to grips with problems hitherto evaded or ignored. In losing scientific books, specimens and equipment, they were forced back to empirical techniques. Above all, they acquired a sense of adventure.

Just how effectively they came to grips with these problems can be seen from the report of a British representative who arrived in China in February 1943 to extend Anglo-Chinese relations in the scientific field. He found 143 universities with 70,000 students doing 'a great deal of first-class work',[30] together with 10 research institutes of the Chinese National Academy. He also found a mass education movement to reduce the percentage of illiteracy of the population, and that the numbers of children at elementary schools had risen from 20 per cent (in 1932) to 75 per cent (in 1944).

All this was tilling the soil for Mao Tse-Tung. Like Lenin, he found the ground prepared for him. By making education a State concern the Kuomintang had cut still farther into the roots that tied the scholar gentry to Confucianism. The universities had done their work only too well; China had acquired a certain autonomy in technology. As the coastal universities were driven up the Yangtse, the Academia Sinica came with them, both uprooted from their cosmopolitan hot houses. The Japanese knew that this would take place; that's why they began the war in 1937 by bombing Nankai University at Tientsin. Indeed war, far from lowering the number of institutions of higher learning, increased them. In 1936 there were only 108, in 1937 they dropped to 91, but by 1941 there were 113, 132 in 1942 and 145 in 1945.[31]

From their loess caves in Yunan, the Communist Government under Mao Tse-Tung was also organizing the intelligentsia. After the outbreak of the Sino-Japanese War, they absorbed them into the People's Anti-Japanese Military and Political University (K'ang-ta). Three more institutions were founded which became North China University in 1939. Propaganda, by means of group discussion varied by threats of violence, built up a party of 1,200,000. When Mao began to move against Chiang Kai-Shek the Kuomintang disintegrated before him. Many Chinese looked with favour if not with fervour on Mao's moves. After a brief civil war in which Nationalists fell away like flies, Chiang Kai-Shek fled to Formosa, and the Chinese People's Republic was founded.[32]

No one remembered the prophecy of sage old Henry Adams, made forty-seven years earlier:

> The only country now on the spot is Russia, and if Russia organizes China as an economical power the little drama of history will end in the overthrow of our clumsy Western civilization. We can never compete with Asia. . . . In that event I allow until 1950 to run our race out.[33]

18

◇◇◇

Science and the Samurai

◇◇◇

(1)

THE first English blue print for an institute of scientific research, Bacon's *New Atlantis*, owed something to the experiences of William Adams, the first English resident in Japan. For, like Bensalem, Japan was an exclusive, indeed, after 1738, a secluded, economy.

This seclusion fostered the growth of the Japanese plantocracy, and of their botanical gardens too. Near the capital Yedo, two were established in 1638 at Azabu and Otsuka, near Yedo (now Tokyo). Forty-three years later they were merged, and a second garden was started in a suburb of Yedo in 1720. The Shogun ordered his feudal lords to make inventories of their plants and sent investigators out to collect specimens for his cabinet. The feudal lords did as they were told: the Lord of Owari in 1744 began to cultivate Chinese plants at Nagoya, thereby helping one of Japan's first notable naturalists to make his name: Matsudaira Kunzan. Another lord, Hosokawa Juken of Higo, established a medical college in addition to his garden in Kumamoto.

Being interested in the natural products of their estates, the feudal lords established bureaux. That of the Lord of Shimazu embarked on a 100-volume study of agricultural botany, but the great fire of Yedo in 1806 burnt the woodcuts and the manuscripts. A similar project from a similar bureau, established by the Lord of Kii in 1792, produced 39 volumes by 1833 and ultimately 85, whilst a third from a bureau at Mito produced 100 volumes on the products of mountains and seas, and 20 volumes on cage birds.

Exhibitions were also held. One was organized at Yushima in Yedo by Tamura Ransui, who also held a conversazione or symposium on the virtues of plants. This now became an annual event.[1]

Such preoccupation with the edible and aphrodisiac properties of their gardens was inevitable since they were hermetically sealed off from the outside world by the Shogun to whom chrysanthemums seemed less dangerous preoccupations than firearms or even ships. The year in which the first botanical garden was founded, 1638, was also the year in which the Shogun prohibited all Japanese, on pain of death; from going abroad, and foreign vessels from entering Japanese ports. Yet even this could not prevent the establishment at his head-quarters at Yedo of an academy for their sons which, in 1690, became the University of Yedo.

(2)

Through the Shogun's curtain crept the Dutch. On their trading station of Nagasaki on the island of Deshima Japanese officials and interpreters imbibed scientific ideas from Leyden-trained doctors. For though the Shogun was anti-Christian, he was not anti-improvement. Such useful acquisitions as the astronomical encyclopaedia of Father Adam Schall, a Jesuit in China, led him to relax restrictions on Western science after 1720.[2]

With the experience of Dutch botanists behind them a group known as Rangakusha, or Dutch Scholars, began slowly to acquire a knowledge of medicine.[3] The first European work to be printed and published by Japanese in Japan was Johann Adam Kulmus's *Anatomische Tabellen*. Following its instructions, Sugita Gempaku and his friends dissected a body.[4] The head of the Dutch factory, Isaac Titsingh, helped in the years that followed. Further books on mathematics and botany were translated. A school of interpreters grew up at Nagasaki which by 1808 was ordered to study English and then Russian.

As Dutch employees, individual European scholars had

already broken through the Shogun's *cordon sanitaire*. The German, Engelbert Kaempfer, spent the years 1690–2 in Japan. The Swedish botanist Thunberg came in 1775–6. P. F. von Siebold, a German who influenced a group of Japanese during the years 1823–30, needs extended mention, for he influenced young Takano Nagahide (1804–50), a great translator of Dutch works on chemistry and mineralogy. 'Indeed,' it has been said, 'the very names of some of the European sciences were new to the Japanese when he wrote.'[5] Siebold was such a disturbing personality that the Shogun pounced on his followers and Takano had to flee for his life. When the fuss died down, Takano came to Yedo where he formed a group which avidly studied Western knowledge and actually included Shogunate officials. This group began to question the official policy of sealing the country from Western learning. Again the Shogun pounced. This time Takano refused to flee and was caught and imprisoned. Escaping after five years he became a secret teacher. His friend, Watanabe Noboru, was also arrested and committed suicide in 1841.

(3)

Since guns were coming into the country in spite of the closed-door policy, the Shogun commissioned Takashima Shuhan (1798–1866) to make ordnance, even though he had been previously gaoled for his 'Western knowledge'. One of his pupils, Sakuma Shozan (1811–64), went farther and urged that large merchant ships should be built, together with schools to provide a modern education. With the aid of a Dutch encyclopaedia, Sakuma also conducted experiments in chemistry to show how valuable knowledge from other countries could be to Japan. His pupil Yoshida Tōjiro (1830–59) even tried to stow away on an American boat in 1854.

Dissection of stray dogs or dead criminals in medical schools led on to the copying of Dutch books and experimenting in electricity. A pupil of one such school established at Osaka in 1838, Fukuzawa Yukichi, was to be the major force in the Westernizing of Japan. For as the pores of Japan were increasingly opened, the internal enemies of the Shogunate multiplied. Young Samurai sent abroad returned as would-be emulators of the material progress of the West. Feudal lords found that mining and industrial enterprises bolstered up their personal power.

When Japanese officials saw the miniature locomotive and tender (running at 20 miles an hour), a set of telegraph apparatus, *Webster's Dictionary* and some scientific books, brought by Commodore Perry from America to Japan in 1854, they were enchanted. The door was opened: two ports (Shimoda and Hakodate) were opened to American vessels by treaty. Other treaties were quickly signed, with Britain (October 1854), Russia (February 1855) and Holland (November 1855). Two of those who took part in the Japanese negotiations with Perry were taught by Ronald MacDonald, the first American teacher in Japan. One of the members of Perry's expedition, Jonathan Goble, later returned as a Baptist minister.[6]

The Japanese also set up an 'Office for the Study of Barbarian Writings' *(Bansho Torishirabe-dokoro)* in 1855. Here Kato Hiroyuki (1836–1916), the first Japanese to learn German, taught. A school for the study of foreign medicine was also established. So was a shipyard with a navigation school at Akuura with 22 Dutch instructors.[7]

In 1862 the *Kaisei-jo* or 'place of liberal culture' was opened as a centre for the study of European sciences. Groups of students went abroad, one to Holland, another to Russia and a third to England. Some of the liberal-minded barons followed suit. Fukuzawa Yukichi (whom we have met as a medical student at Osaka) went to America in 1860, and to England, France and Prussia in 1861. On his return he bent his energetic elbow to describing *Conditions in Western Lands*, a book which was widely pirated. Fukuzawa had founded a school in 1858 which became Keio University. So much indeed was he identified with Western ideas that all books seeking to acclimatize them were known as Fukuzawa Books *(Fukuzawa-bon)*.[8]

(4)

Seven of his books appeared before, and eight in the first year after, the abolition of the Shogunate in 1867. Their exposition of western physics and geography were permeated with a perfectibilist optimism. 'This golden age' he wrote 'is no vain dream. It is simply fortelling the future on the basis of past experience. Our hopes for the future are like a vast spring sea. To call this present age degenerate is like mistaking east for west, morning for evening, or the rising for the setting sun'.

Strengthened by the translation of Buckle in 1874, and the popularization of the ideas of Darwin and Spencer by Edward Morse (a professor of Zoology at Tokio), a materialist ethic grew which dismayed the Christian missionaries. Yet though they regarded it as more threatening than Buddhism or Shinto, yet indirectly they helped spread it by their own activities. Thus a Dutch-born American missionary with an engineering background was invited to Yedo where in 1869 he established an institution which later became the Imperial University. This missionary, Dr. H. F. Verbeck (1830–98), advised the Government to appoint a mission to America and Europe. This was duly sent in 1871, under Prince Iwakura, and indirectly led to the arrival of more Americans.[9] As their national superintendent of schools and colleges from 1873 to 1879 the Japanese acquired David Murray (1830–90), and W. S. Clark (1826–86), the President of the Massachusetts Agricultural College, came over in 1876–7 to establish a similar foundation at Sapporo, now the Hokkaido University.

Sapporo was a major technical key to the opening up of the island of Hokkaido. It grew from the efforts of the former U.S. Commissioner of Agriculture, Horace Capron, who had come to Japan in 1871 with a chemist, Dr. Antisell, and an engineer, A. G. Warfield. Between them these three introduced new crops, like corn, potatoes, blue grass, apples, onions and cabbages and new machinery, and they also made surveys. Indeed, the surveys of B. S. Lyman during the years 1873–9 were blueprints for the future Japanese oil and coal industries, whilst those of Colonel J. V. Crawford made possible the railways.[10] Study in America sharpened the utilitarian, pragmatic spirit of those studying there. Tokyo University was organized in 1876 out of a congeries of technical and medical institutions in the capital, and nine years later the American system of postgraduate schools and colleges was established by the creation of the Imperial Universities at Tokyo (1886), followed by Kyoto (1896), Sendai (Tohoku, 1907), Fukuoka (1910) and Sapporo. Similar ones were later established in Korea and Formosa. German polytechnics *(Senmongakko)*—some 139 of them—also grew up.

The American model influenced men like Fukuzawa Yukichi, the founder of Keio University in Tokyo, and Joseph Deshima who founded Doshisha, the American Mission University in Tokyo. American Roman Catholics established Jochi Daigaku, and the American Episcopalians a college at Rikkyo (in 1883). In Tokyo was established Waseda University (in 1882), after Keio the first private university. Five medical universities were also founded.[11] The 18 private and 4 Government universities in Tokyo offer an interesting example of the way in which Shogunate institutions were adapted to fit Meiji needs.

Round the universities was built, in French style, the whole educational system. The whole country was divided in 1872 into 8 university districts (reduced to 7 in the following year), each with a university. Each university district had 32 middle school sections and each middle school section was subdivided into 210 primary school districts based on a unit of 600 people. The Ministry of Education (*Monbusho*) had branches in each university district. It will be remembered that the Shogunate established the Office for the Study of Western Writings at what was then Yedo. The Meiji oligarchy engaged foreign teachers for it and converted it into a Government college (*Kaisei Gakko*) under the presidency of Kato Hiroyuki (whom we have already met as the first Japanese to study German). Kato Hiroyuki presided over its transformation into the Imperial University of Tokyo. In this he was helped by the American missionary Dr. Guido Verbeck. For the missionary movement was able to operate freely, following the policy of toleration adopted after 1873.[12]

(4)

From the time the Japanese came to the International Exhibition at London in 1862, through to Gilbert and Sullivan's *Mikado* in 1885 up to Puccini's *Madam Butterfly* in 1900, the Japanese were delightful figures of fun in England, as in America. The more serious side of these industrious little Orientals was seen by *Nature* on 18 April 1878 when it drew attention to the 'quartet' of Japanese students in Berlin—and described the ophthalmic skill of one of them—Dr. Dirokitao—as manifested in his invention of the leucoscope.

For the Japanese who came to England had serious intentions.

Those who came in 1872 returned to recommend the building of an engineering college in Tokyo with the first laboratory in the world for teaching applied electricity, and successfully persuaded three leading English engineers, Henry Dyer, W. E. Ayrton and John Perry, to teach there. This laboratory evoked the tart comment of Norman Lockyer[13] that a similar institution should be established in England. By 1889 Rudyard Kipling could remark that 'the cultured Japanese of the English pattern will corrupt and defile the tastes of his neighbours till . . . Japan ceases to exist as a separate nation and becomes a button-hook manufacturing appanage of America'.[14]

Romantic reaction against 'progress' and Victorianism probably accounted for the numerous and exotic pictures of Japan as the land of gentle sensitive people living in mist and lotus blossoms sketched by an Anglo-American who arrived in Japan a year after Kipling: Lafcadio Hearn. For though he won a literary name as an interpreter of 'old' Japan, Lafcadio Hearn was to be one of the most effective diffusers of the ideas of Herbert Spencer in the 'new' Japan. 'I am trying to get all my friends to read him', he told one friend. 'He has completely converted me away from all "isms" or sympathy with "isms".' And again, 'I am an Evolutionist and as thorough a disciple of Spencer as it is possible for one not a practical scientist to be.'[15]

Powerfully affected by Charles Pearson's prophecy that the future did not lie with the Anglo-Saxon races, nor the whites ('I think this is almost certain', he wrote),[16] Lafcadio Hearn married a Japanese woman and became a Japanese citizen under the name Koizumi Yakumo. He 'strongly advised' one Japanese friend

> to direct all (his) studies towards a scientific profession—something really practical—engineering, architecture, electricity, chemistry etc. . . . What Japan needs are scientific men and she will need more and more of them every year.[17]

While to another he wrote:

> The systems of Spencer and others have been much better followed out in Eastern Massachusetts than in England, where religious conservatism persists in loading the mind with perfectly useless acquirements. The future demands scientific education—not ornamental.[18]

A year after Hearn died, his adopted country showed how thoroughly it had assimilated the technological gospel by decisively defeating Russia in 1905. Financed by British and American money, Japanese industry now expanded rapidly. Ten years earlier, it had defeated China. Ten years later, when the Western Powers themselves began to tear each others throats, it cemented its hegemony of Asia.

(5)

Aristocratic Japan, however, still held its appeal for Western men of letters in the twentieth century. W. B. Yeats found his 'first model—and in literature if we would not be parvenus, we must have a model—in the Noh stage of aristocratic Japan',[19] whilst Ezra Pound in his *Guide to Kulchur* defined civilization as 'Listening to Incense' which to him was 'a pastime neither for clods nor illiterates'.

> In the Imperial Court of Japan [he wrote] the companions burnt incense, they burnt now one perfume, and now another, or a mixture of perfumes, and the accomplishment was both to recognise what had gone materially with the perfume and to write apposite poems.[20]

Kokka no tame—'for the state'—was the theme of Japanese industrialism. Under the principle *Kokutai*—'the state body corporate'—scientists and technologists were absorbed, and though the feudal system was formally abolished in 1871, they became instruments for its survival. Under the Emperor (who was Director of the official religion of Shinto), the Japanese technocrats, like the Samurai, unquestionably accepted the code of *Bushido*—with its stress on 'loyalty', 'unity' and 'humility', and the transitory nature of life. To the *Daimyo* or feudal lords, succeeded the *Zaibatsu* or big industrial lords, like Mitsui, Mitsubishi, Sumitomo and Yasuda. These four great family trusts or *Zaibatsu* had State support from the Nippon Kogio Ginko, or Industrial Bank of Japan, founded in 1900. They further benefited from the nationalized railways (from 1907), the cheap electricity supplied by the swift-flowing mountain streams, the virtual absence of trade unions and the near doubling of the population from 30 million in 1850 to 50 million in 1910.

Above all, the Japanese early grasped the interrelation between technology and war. They had observers at the Opium War in 1842, the Crimean War in 1855 and at the Franco-Prussian War in 1871. By 1885 they were building their own torpedo boats and by 1895 their own light cruisers. And in the interval they were building up their own empire. First the islands like the Kuriles (1875), the Bonins (1876), the Ryu-Kyus (1879), Formosa (1895) and the Vulcans (1891), then nibbling at the mainland of China, the Kwantung peninsula (1905) and Korea (1910).

(6)

By industrializing Manchuria and the mainland of China, the scientific Samurai flexed their technological muscles. With over 100 learned societies, many observatories, an Imperial Academy of Tokyo and, in 1920, a National Research Council, they could stage the third Pan-Pacific Scientific Congress at Tokyo in 1926 when more than 150 foreign delegates attended.[21]

The skill of the Japanese technocracy wedded to *Bushido* was demonstrated in 1941 when it destroyed the Pacific Fleet of the Power that had done so much to build it up. This was a disastrous decision. Separated from German technicians and factories (they had tried seven times to reach the German naval base at Brest), deprived of surpluses of crude oil coal and potatoes with which to make rubber as the production of the captured plantations fell, and facing a producer country with a secure position on both sides, Japan finally capitulated after a uranium bomb was dropped on 6 August 1945 at Hiroshima and three days later a plutonium bomb was dropped on Nagasaki.[22] Since then, Japan has rebounded. By 1965 its rate of economic growth, already over three times greater than Britain's, was reflected in its position as the leading shipbuilder and largest producer of cameras and optical goods. In these and other complex technological fields, its commanding position has been ascribed to the sophistication of their new samurai—the managerial class: 80 per cent of whom are university graduates.[23] That the comparable figure for Britain should be 36 per cent shows how much more in the hands of the technical intelligentsia Japanese industry really is, or, perhaps more justly, how congenial science is to the Samurai.

20

Mao's model: The Red Expert for Export

◇◇◇

(1)

REJECTING the Confucian addition to literary studies, Mao Tse-Tung affirmed:

> The culture of New Democracy is scientific in character. It opposes all feudal and superstitious thoughts and advocates searching for truth from concrete facts, it advocates objective truth as well as the unity of theory and practice. In this point, the scientific thought of the Chinese proletariat may form an anti-imperialist, anti-feudal, and anti-superstition united front with the materialism and natural sciences of the *bourgeoisie* that are still progressive in character, but it can never unite with the reactionary idealism.[1]

Of the 200 or so institutions of higher education inherited from the Nationalists, only 5 had more than 2,000 students.[2] Most interesting was the utilization of psycho-therapy to re-orientate possible 'deviationists'. For in addition to directing graduates to places where they would be most useful, prohibiting theology and religion, and shortening courses, discussion groups were established to promote 'self-criticism'. Syllabuses had to be submitted to small discussion groups of the party.

> The people's educational policy [said the Communist paper *Wen Wei Pao* on 28 October 1949] aims at revolutionizing the teachers

328

for the benefit of the pupils. Teachers are the executives of an educational policy; they are the guides of the pupils in thoughts, activities, work and learning. In the minds of these formerly employed teachers, many unsound notions still remain, and if their minds were not thoroughly reshaped and adapted to the needs of a new education in the people's democracy, not only would it be impossible for them to maintain their posts by state approval, but they would not even be tolerated by the pupils.

Much was said about the training of personnel for national construction. At the first All-China Conference on Higher Education in 1950 the Minister of Education said: 'Our institutions of higher education must therefore systematically develop a scientific educational theory that is united with practice, and must, on such a basis, carry on specialised scientific and technological education.' He also added that they 'must from now on throw their doors open for members of the peasant and working-classes, so as to produce for our nation a large group of intellectuals of peasant-worker background'.[3]

(2)

In the light of this remark it is significant that when a separate Ministry of Higher Education was created in 1952 two of its departments should deal with Industrial, another with Agricultural and Health, and another with Middle Technical Education. This new ministry at first shared the administration of the universities with the six greater administrative regions but when those regions were abolished in 1954, the ministry came into its own. Such centralization did not work, and by 1958 the ministry was absorbed once more by the Ministry of Education.

Meanwhile the process, involuntarily initiated by the Japanese invasion, of moving the coastal universities inland was accelerated. By 1957 they had increased to 62 in 1959 as opposed to 27 before 1949.[4] Of these 27, all but 3 had been founded and supported by foreigners, and this support too was cut off. The subsequent discrediting of their teachers made it easy to absorb them by 1952.

In Mao's new pattern three new types of institutions were set up, new in the sense that they were native variants of Soviet practice. The first was the monotechnic, created by the simple expedient of elevating a department to monotechnic status or building an institute round a speciality. The Shanghai Medical Institute was moved to Chungking. Chiaotung University was moved to Sian, where a new institute for Civil Engineering was set up. Others included Wuhan (for Surveying and Mapping), Lanchow (for Petroleum), Chenchow (Motive Power), Taiyuan (Chemical Engineering) and Chengtu (Chemical Engineering), created by moving specialists from the engineering institutes in large cities. The Inner Mongolia University and the Inner Mongolia Medical School were established at Huhakot.

The second was the polytechnic, like Tsinghua, the largest in China, at Peking. The third was the comprehensive university, like Peking, with a full range of faculties. Defined in 1953 as occupying 'a special position, differing from the other two types', they were to train specialists for research and teaching in the theoretical and practical sciences (both social and natural). In other words comprehensive universities were to train the élite.

In all, by 1959, there were 229 colleges and universities with 444,000 students, as opposed to 207 colleges and universities with 155,000 students in 1947.[5]

(3)

The traditional reverence felt by scholars towards Peking was strong. Not only did it become the capital once more, but here out of the Yenching University (founded by Protestants in 1870) was built the new Chinese People's University. Amalgamation with Peking National University and the old Tsinghua produced the Tsinghua University—the largest polytechnic in China.[6] Yet a third, the Chinese University of Sciences and Technology, was opened in 1958 with an élite of 1,600 students, all concentrating on nuclear physics, electronics and eleven other major growing points: a nursery of researchers for the Academy of Sciences.

The Academy itself was formed in a similar way by grouping the Academia Sinica (founded in 1928) with its eleven research institutes, and the Peiping Research Institute (founded in 1929) with its 10 institutes, a private research institute and the Chian-Shong Institute of Biological Survey, into a National Academy of Sciences. By 1958, 68 research institutes and 14 branches were established. As in the U.S.S.R., a centre of post-graduate training was developed as well.[7]

(4)

To establish science in the Constitution, articles 42 and 43 of the Common Programme of the Chinese People's Consultative Committee, adopted on 29 September 1949, read:

> Love of the fatherland, love of the people, love of labour, love of science and care of public property shall be promoted as the public spirit of all nationals of the People's Republic of China.
>
> Efforts shall be made to develop the natural sciences in order to serve industrial, agricultural, and national defence construction. Scientific discoveries and inventions shall be encouraged and rewarded and scientific knowledge shall be disseminated among the people.

No leading Chinese scientist had worked for the Communist Party before this. All but a very few did so after.[8] A Bureau for the Dissemination of Scientific Information was established in the Ministry of Culture a month after the Constitution was adopted, while the All-China Science and Technology Dissemination Association worked in the provinces. By 1957 the latter had established 27 branches and 983 sub-branches. In 1958 it joined the Federation of All-China Natural Science Associations to become the Chinese Science and Technology Association.[9]

Until its own seed-beds of scientists were established, China had to lean heavily on the U.S.S.R. Some 6,500 selected Chinese students were sent to Soviet universities, and 7,100 workers to Soviet factories. In the return direction, 10,500 Soviet experts and a further 1,500 from East Europe came to help some 336 new enterprises.[10] Even greater co-operation was envisaged by a Sino-Soviet Economic-Technical agreement, signed in Moscow on 18 January 1958. Another on 4 July 1958 provided for 'a mutual exchange of scientific and technical information and a mutual commandeering of specialists for studying production experience and achievements in science and technology'.

By these means, native Chinese scientific and technical personnel trebled: from 58,000 in 1952 to 175,000 in 1957. It was coupled with an increase of from 6·15 million to 10·19 million in industrial employment.[11]

(5)

A 12-year plan for the development of science was inaugurated in 1956 when a National Science Planning Commission was established under the State Council, with overall responsibility for co-ordinating the training and employment of scientists to serve major projects, like agriculture and power. A directive issued by Chou En-lai on 14 January 1956, entitled *Report on the Question of Intellectuals*, set a fast pace.

We must catch up with this advanced level of world science [he wrote] We must give our best to this task. Only by mastering the most advanced sciences can we insure ourselves of an impregnable national defence, a powerful and up-to-date economy, and adequate means to join the Soviet Union and the People's Democracies in defeating the imperial powers, either in peaceful competition or in any aggressive war which the enemy may unleash.

Concluding, he used words which, to anyone who knew Russia in the twenties, must have sounded familiar:

our country is now in the stage of transition, a stage of the most penetrating transformation of society . . . The system of exploitation in existence for several thousand years is to be permanently wiped out. All men are to be changed into labourers of various types . . . Our programme in the struggle to carry further the re-education of the intellectuals is as follows in the present stage: to root out completely the counter-revolutionary elements still hidden in the ranks of the intellectuals, to reduce to a minimum the number of backward elements, to lead as many of the middle-of-the-road element as possible to become progressives, and change the progressives into full socialist intellectuals.[12]

To secure even tighter co-ordination between them, the Government encouraged the universities to find their laboratories outside their walls. Thus Tsinghua University had by 1958 established 55 factories and workshops, 3 designing companies and 5 construction companies, and was, through its Department of Hydraulic Engineering, designing and constructing 40 dams to irrigate a million acres.[13]

Lacing the sequence of three 5-year plans, from 1953 to

1967, was a 15-year long-range programme of scientific research into China's natural resources, under the direction of the National Science Planning Commission. An Australian, noting their targets, observed:

> If present plans are implemented, in 1962 Communist China will begin to approach Britain in the number of students per head of population and may already be ahead of Britain in the number of engineering enrolments.[14]

Success up to 1958 was marked. The production of coal and cement doubled (from 64·7 million to 130 million metric tons and from 2·9 million to 6·9 million tons) and that of electricity nearly trebled (from 7·3 billion to 19 billion kWh.).[15] To increase Chinese food production agro-technical institutes, research centres and training classes were set up which by 1957 employed 11,000 research workers and teachers.[16] With Soviet help, a heavy-water atomic reactor, a 25-million volt cyclotron and a high-pressure electrostatic accelerator were built. Following the 5-Year Plan came the great leap forward. These achievements were not mere propaganda figures. Contrasted with that of India, Professor Mandelbaum found 'economic developments overwhelmingly favourable to Chinese effort, both with respect to actual performance and with respect to future growth'. His figures for overall aggregate production for the increase in the production of coal and in the increased production of electricity are revealing.

CONTRAST BETWEEN INDIAN AND CHINESE RATES OF
INDUSTRIAL GROWTH

Year	Aggregate Production		Electricity generation (in million kWh.)		Coal Production (in million tons)	
	India	China	India	China	India	China
1950	85	37	5,112	4,580	32·5	40·9
1951	96·5	76	5,856	5,790	34·3	50·8
1952	100	100	6,192	7,261	36·1	63·5
1953	102	129	6,708	9,165	35·8	66·6
1954	109	152	7,500	11,001	36·8	79·9
1955	118	166	8,496	12,278	38·3	93·6
1956	128	226	9,636	16,588	39·4	105·9
1957	133	244	10,836	19,025	43·5	130
1958	137	288	12,198	23,000	44·8	165

Furthermore, as he pointed out, India was producing in 1955 18·4 engineers and 8·1 doctors per million of the population, whereas China was producing 30·9 engineers and 11·2 doctors per million of the population. He concluded:

> The continuation of these rates would within ten to twenty years reverse the more advanced position which India had in these professional fields in 1955.[17]

This increase is also reflected in the schools, where the percentage of children in the 6–14 age range in schools in China increased from 22·5 per cent to 60 per cent, whilst in India it increased from 33 per cent to 45 per cent.

(6)

But 600 million hungry peasants cannot wait for talent to ripen, or farms to be electrified, whilst their households are erupting with children needing food. And since Mao's revolution was based on the peasant, and not, like Lenin's, on the urban proletariat, emergency steps had to be taken to provide it.[18]

So began in 1958 'the Great Leap Forward'. Communes were set up both in the country and in the towns to mobilize human and material resources. Greater decentralization made possible the winning of autonomy in matters concerning higher education so that communes and factories could run colleges for training specialists. With the merging of the Ministry of Higher Education with the Ministry of Education, the communes could operate primary, secondary and technical schools with an occasional post-graduate school. To encourage the workers to attend, they were given from 2 to 4 hours a day to study, which would improve productivity.

Communes, whether in farm or factory, offered opportunities for the study and bettering of equipment and techniques. In them biology could be caught as well as taught. It was hoped that by various self-directed projects engineering would improve too. The advantage of factory and commune schools was thought to be that teachers and students would not be isolated from the rest of the community and would learn by doing.

After 1958 'Productive Labour' was introduced into school curricula. All students above the age of 9 were required to spend a certain amount of time working in a socially useful job, and primary children were soon working 4, middle school 6, and senior middle school 8 hours a week at such operations.

Finally, in 1960 the usual 12-year primary-secondary school cycle was reduced to 10, to enable children to become 'full manpower units' at 16 or 17. This was accompanied by snips of the syllabus pruner's shears:

> Much of the mathematics, physics and chemistry now taught in middle schools, in particular [it was said] is old stuff from the nineteenth century which in no way represents the science and technology of today.

So an earlier introduction of mathematics and languages was planned, more advanced physics and chemistry was envisaged and to find space in the timetable, history and geography were to be merged into a social studies programme. The object of all this was not only to 'ripen' more college entrants, but industrial manpower units as well.

Crossing the hierarchy of schools is an even more fundamental programme: the elimination of illiteracy. A specially rapid course, invented by Ch'i Chien-hua, was tried out in the armed forces. Part-time peasants' and workers' schools at all levels were established, 680,000 at the primary level, 90,000 at the lower middle and 30,000 at the upper level, plus 5,000 night colleges. These enrolled 31 million, 4 million, 1·5 million and 610,000 students respectively. With the 20 million students in 340,000 'red and expert' colleges, they gave a massive total of 60 million altogether. A factor in this change has been the dissemination of Latin letters for Chinese characters.

A virtual explosion took place in higher education itself. Enrolments increased from 444,000 (1957) to 810,000 (1959), while colleges and universities increased from 229 (1957) to 1,408 (1958). This astounding increase was due to the creation of what are called Red and Expert colleges, to fulfil the official policy of ensuring that a high ratio of students are of peasant origin. People's Universities (like the one at Peking) aim at broadening the concept of higher education. As Professor Hu of Columbia observed,

> While the discrepancy between a full-fledged university and a Red and Expert College operated by a commune may be as wide as

between heaven and earth, the fact remains that both are giving their students some form of education and technical skill. Therefore at a time when higher education is still beyond the reach of so many in underdeveloped areas, and when the very term of higher education is intimately associated with the idea of social and personal advancement, the present Chinese experiment, if successful when measured against other goals, such as industrialisation, will prove to be a powerful attraction indeed.[19]

(7)

And China too has a frontier. The Mongolian pantry on her doorstep might yet save her from a meatless future. Sun Yat-Sen said forty years ago, in words which have acquired significance with the passage of time,

> As Argentina has superseded the United States in supplying the world with meat, so the Mongolian pasture will some day take the place of Argentina, when railways are developed and cattle raising is scientifically improved.[20]

Before this, however, the storehouse of mineral wealth in Sinkiang is being tapped. And Sinkiang may do for China what Siberia did for Russia and the West for America.[21]

The Mongolian Peoples' Republic possesses, in Oliver Lattimore's opinion,

> a real intellectual interest in such concepts as organising and planning from one evolutionary stage of society to another without passing through an intermediate stage. With this goes the idea of planning a program in development economics for the purpose of catching up, not just imitating.[22]

China realizes that a nation with the appearance of world scientific leadership also enjoys unparalleled (and unexpected) political importance.[23] Her own scientific *élite* is growing with the problems posed by the population explosion, the arms race, the lunge to the frontier and the contest to aid backward nations.

China also can enjoy the invalidation of the Keynsian theory that only investment can create new opportunities,[24] by showing that research can do this too, research backed by power.[25]

The very mobility of applied science has helped them at the right time, for not only has there been a remarkable local increase in scientific work in regions remote from world centres of learning, but the spirit of rationality, so important for the advance of economic progress, has spread.[26]

(8)

Technical aid in Asia has become hot politics. Since the Colombo Plan was pioneered by Foreign Ministers of the British Commonwealth after the Second World War, the scale of such aid has grown enormously. Then the individual plans of India, Pakistan, Ceylon, Malaya, Singapore, North Borneo and Sarawak[27] were based on the more effective application of science to agriculture, the elimination of waste and the promotion of scientific knowledge in these areas. Britain's generous contribution of £750 million in 5 years was almost certainly one of the reasons why the pound had to be devalued—so great a strain did it put on her economy. It was a race against India's birth-rate of 5 million a year to increase agricultural output by 10 per cent, electricity by 67 per cent and irrigated land by 17 per cent.[28]

Forty per cent of the population in underdeveloped non-Communist lands live in India. Its iron ore reserves, the largest in the world, lie relatively untapped; only 8 per cent of its hydro-electric power has been developed, and its steel works are crippled by lack of technical manpower, which Barbara Ward asserts 'is not yet available in India. It is scarce abroad, yet without it even the most modern plants cannot work to capacity'.[29]

China's experiment is crucial. If Mao Tse-Tung can really make his great leap forward he will displace the Asian hero of earlier decades, Mahatma Gandhi, saint of the spinning wheel. According to one student of affairs,

> There are many backward countries in the world in a similar position to India and China, attempting to develop a modern industrial economy within the shortest possible space of time. If they come to believe that the speed of development in China, has, over a period, been faster than that achieved elsewhere under different systems of government they may tend to draw ideological conclusions from the fact.[30]

This emphasizes the intensity of American attempts to establish 'multipliers' of science and technology in Asia,[31] and the endless missions sent to effect this. The first Asian-wide study of problems of scientific development in those areas was begun by Farrington Daniels and R. E. Cleland.[32] Solar energy and plant genetics are the present modern missioners' gospel in those parts.

It was at Jokarta University in February 1960 that Premier Krushchev announced the formation of the Patrice Lumumba University. This opened in Moscow on 1 October 1960 with 600 students of the first national cadre to 'understand correctly the interests of their country'. It was to have accommodation for 4,000 by 1963 in a former military academy. The accommodation was evidently of such a kind that the African students marched to Red Square in protest. The Patrice Lumumba University offers a 4-year course in engineering, agriculture, economics and education. No previous qualifications are needed, though a special 3-year preparatory course is put on. Students are accepted up to the age of 35: 30,000 applications were received. In 1961 the Czechs opened a similar university. A Chinese Institute for African Affairs was also founded in September 1960, following the National Afro-Asian Solidarity Committee and the China-African People's Friendship League, created some six months earlier. By 1961 a Union of African students in China had been formed. The Chinese especially concerned with these developments are Ny Yung Chen, Lao Cheng-Chi and Lui Chang-Sheng respectively.

By 1964 Chou En-lai was visiting Africa. Here Soviet Russia aids projects like the Aswan Dam (Egypt) or the Volta Hydro-Electric Project (Ghana). Electrification on the Soviet model needed planned economies and the nationalization of private companies. 'No other country', wrote an observer, 'can compare with the Communist bloc in exploiting the African need for technical experts.'[33] Six thousand of the total of 12,000 Soviet experts at large in the world were in Africa. Among these few were actually Russians. Poland had an office for Technical Services abroad, whilst the normal Czech universities had increased their intake of African students to 3,000, as well as opening a special school at Teplice. The complete polytechnic institute given by Russia to Guinea will be the largest establishment for teaching technology in Africa, whilst the technical college which the Czechs are building in Somalia will be of the same order. Soviet science teachers at Addis Ababa University College were also concerned with a technical school for 1,000 pupils there, opened in October 1963.[34]

That China should turn to Africa, where the problem is so like her own, its industrialization of a peasant economy hitherto exploited by the West, is no surprise. That she should be pacing Russia there is even less so. It shows that the Mao model is now ripe for export. And the struggle was, for both China and Russia, 'not against capital but against the survivals of the Middle Ages'. So African workers, peasants and intelligentsia were urged to co-operate with 'that part of the national bourgoisie which is interested in the independent political and economic development of its country and is ready to defend its independence against any encroachments by the imperialist powers'.[35] China's very inability to feed her own population adds lustre to what one observer has called 'the uniqueness and purity of her image'—the image being one of 'a formerly backward *peasant* nation, shamelessly exploited by the avarice of the West, who are realizing the underdeveloped world's vision of the bootstrap self-elevation—attaining a shimmering technology, immaculate organization, and apparent prosperity unaided saved by native wit and the collected works of Marx and Lenin; a purity untainted by the European blood of everyone else from the Urals to Seattle'.[36]

The history of this particular cultural offensive is now in full swing.

21

✧✧✧✧✧✧✧✧✧✧✧✧✧✧✧✧✧✧✧✧✧✧✧✧✧✧✧✧✧✧✧✧✧✧

An Operational World?

✧✧✧✧✧✧✧✧✧✧✧✧✧✧✧✧✧✧✧✧✧✧✧✧✧✧✧✧✧✧✧✧✧✧

(1)

'I can only hope', wrote Oswald Spengler 'that men of the new generation may be moved by my book to take up engineering instead of poetry'.[1] In his book, *The Decline of the West*, Spengler also considered that more intelligence, taste, character and ability could be found among the technical staff of a first-rate engineering plant than in the entire collectivity of painters and musicians.[2]

Spengler might be regarded, in view of such statements and his general scepticism, as a spokesman for the emergent technocrats; but his thought brings to a close a long line of Eurocentric social theorists whose ideas about the nobility of savages[3] so often served as an indictment of civilization. Such ideas owed much to the travellers.[4]

He is most significant, however, as a predictive fantast, or to put it more kindly, as having operational thoughts about the future. Such thoughts are of the essence of a technarchic world, and appear significantly enough, in the mid-eighteenth century, when Brindley's first canal was being cut and the French chemists were unlocking nature's treasury. What has recently been described as 'the first serious attempt in the English language to describe the shape of things to come'[5]—*The Reign of George VI 1900-1925*—was published in 1763. Seven years later came the even more significant French work *L'an 2440* which envisaged a spacious city lit by street lamps, 'optical cabinets' with shifting scenes, machines for imitating the human voice, improved breeding and above all, a new religion where the 'first communion' consisted for looking at the stars through a telescope and then at animal life through a microscope.[6] The rapid exfoliation of such predictive fantasies, especially in the twentieth century,[7] is an expression, as Arthur Koestler saw, of deep unconscious needs, since these new nightmares or vistas are really attempts to ingest the discoveries of the age which 'weigh like an undigested lump on the stomach of mankind'. A second reason for their popularity Koestler finds in the concern of people with 'the possibility that human civilization may be approaching its end. . . . And together with this may go a dim, inarticulate suspicion that the cause lies deeper than Communism or Fascism, that it may lie in the nature itself of *homo sapiens*.[8] Or as a recent broadcast talk had it 'one of the chief points of science fiction in a literal and sceptical age is to loosen the hobbles that have been put on our imagination by the scientific attitude itself'.[9]

The 'impersonal, non-ideological, relentless and possibly overwhelming' impact of technology on politics led E. T. Chase to voice 'a growing awareness that tomorrow's political convulsion will be different from what doctrinaires obsessed with dated rhetoric about socialism, and U.S. capitalism have led us to expect . . . (since) our political adaptability and inventiveness are being challenged by technology'.[10] In darker, more apocalyptic terms Ortega y Gasset saw technocrats bursting like barbarians on to the political stage 'as through a trap door'. To him they symbolized, and to a great extent constituted, 'the actual dominion of the masses', whose 'barbarism' was 'the most immediate cause of European demoralization'. 'The worst is', he added, 'that with these turnspits of science, not even the real progress of science itself is assured.'[11] 'Who rules in the world?' he asked, dismissing America as 'a primitive people camouflaged behind the latest inventions'. These technocrats were changing the very essence of the State.[12] 'With automatism', wrote F. G. Juenger, 'comes the rigidity which is the essence of all precision machinery geared to high speed. Man not only becomes dependent upon the functioning of the state organization; he is also set in motion by it', even his ideology becoming 'superfluous'.[13]

The amorality of scientists led C. S. Lewis to dramatize a good man, Dr. Ransom, embroiled with the sinister scientist, Dr. Weston, both on Mars and in a little English university town. Lewis was protesting against what he called, in yet another book, the *Abolition of Man* (1943).[14] Or, as O'Brien said to Winston in Orwell's *Nineteen Eighty-Four* six years later, 'If you want a picture of the future, imagine a boot stamping on a human face—forever.'

(2)

'It is in some ways surprising that such control is not even greater than it is' confess two Americans. That it is not, they attribute to the underdeveloped skill of persuasion and lack of 'keen insight into the ways of men and organizations'[15] exhibited by the technocrats. Here the sheer process of training them seems to inhibit their development of these qualities, since utilitarian habits of mind tend to relegate such 'humane' studies to the periphery of the curriculum. For as education is caught up in central planning, it becomes more instrumental.[16] Then again, the phenomena of physics, chemistry or biology, especially when their need is obvious, can often be studied more easily than men's instincts or passions.[17] Lastly, the very numbers in which they are being produced seems to inhibit their own realization that they are the 'General Staff of our productive systems' who shape 'the very organization of the economy and of society'. For, as R. K. Merton has shown, the principle of the 'division of scientific labour', with its concomitant, the multiplication of professional groups, tends to foster an ethical sense of limited responsibilities, whilst the ever larger scale of their employment in ever larger scale industrial bureaucracies increases a hierarchy within themselves as opposed to enhancing their own collective position in society.[18]

Nor would they seem to have the desire to do so:

Fifty years ago an engineer could have a perfectly good conscience when he bent over his job, fully satisfied that he was a benefactor of humanity [said a distinguished professor of electrical engineering in Britain].

He can still have his good conscience if he happens to be a Russian, an Indian or a Chinese. But in Western industrial countries at the present time such myopic self satisfaction amounts to blindness.[19]

The conservatism of these technocrats, experts and engineers has led Molnar to describe them as 'second zone intellectuals'. Far from questioning or criticizing the values of their society they seem to concentrate on preserving or adjusting to them.[20]

This trend has long been visible. 'When capital enlists science into her service,' said Andrew Ure 130 years ago, 'the refractory hand of labour will always be taught docility.'[21] And Labour has not forgotten, for nearly a century later, in 1911 Samuel Gompers warned members of the American Federation of Labour that 'science would thus get the most out of you before you are sent to the junkpile'.[22] Nor have the fabulists, who have for long conjured up passionless, remorseless technical genii like the senseless broom evoked by Goethe's *Sorcerer's Apprentice*, the bottle-bound genie liberated by the fisherman in the *Arabian Nights*, the monkey's paw of W. W. Jacobs or the musical banks of Butler's *Erewhon*. Even when Rossum endowed his universal robots with feeling he could not stop them from murdering him.

Contemporary observation of the U.S.A. and the U.S.S.R. seems to reinforce this. Though in the U.S.S.R. 25 per cent of the Supreme Soviet have a scientific training, as opposed to 3 per cent in comparable power echelons in the U.S.A., yet attitudes seem to be the same in both countries.

Amongst the Russian *apparatchiks*, one acute observer searched 'in vain'

> for that undisciplined love of theorising, that receptivity to new ideas, that intellectual sweep, that was so characteristic of the old Russian intelligentsia. . . . Their competence is usually of a technical nature, it is limited to the utilitarian aspects of the subject, and narrowly confined. . . . As of now it is difficult to discern among Soviet professional personnel (among whom one should include professors), those spiritual and intellectual qualities which are essential if the group is to serve Russian Society in its never-ending contest with the State.[23]

whilst in America two others observed,

> It is clear that the role of the intellectual has diminished. His criticisms and questionings have been largely ignored. Instead . . . we have a picture of a stable society and of a population conservatlve in its basic beliefs and attitudes almost to the point of complacency. Instead of *spawning* resentment, leisure has *dampened* it.[24]

This dislike of novelty, incapacity to see results in perspective, and lack of flexibility at the margins of expertise led Harold Laski to conclude that experts often failed to recognize that 'conclusions to which men assent are far better than conclusions to which they are bidden, without persuasion, to decline at their peril'. To him 'any political system in which a wide initiative belongs to the expert is bound to develop the vices of bureaucracy'.[25] Bertrand Russell agreed that the unavoidable feature of a scientific society was the subordination of individuals to organizations in that it increased the extent to which an individual became a cog. He argued that 'ways must be found of preventing him from being a *mere* cog'.[26]

(3)

The present organization of science offers some striking ecclesiastical analogues: with its high priests (the theoretical physicists), monastic orders (research teams), secular clergy (engineers) and universal tongue (mathematics). Nor is its theology dissimilar: the belief in the redemption of man by knowledge, the mortification of the flesh through work in the laboratory and rejection of external trappings for freedom to work.[27]

The mendicant order of science are the sociologists, who share the obvious nostalgia of Comte, their spiritual father, for what Elton Mayo calls 'the simple religious feeling of medieval times'. Sometimes, like Mayo, they seem to hope that factories might offer an institutional embodiment of 'the medieval idea of the co-operation of all'.[28] 'The need for an organized spiritual power' was also appreciated by Karl Mannheim.[29] Others like A. A. Berle, think that the modern corporation is 'the conscience-carrier' of American society, and that it is working towards 'The City of God'.[30]

Even more striking analogues, conforming 'to the typical pattern of the Judaeo-Christian prophetism', can be found in Communist thought. Raymond Aron finds:

> The Classless Society . . . comparable to the dreams of the millenium. The misery of the proletariat proves its vocation and the Communist Party becomes the church which is opposed by the bourgeois pagans who stop their ears against the good tidings and by the Socialist Jews who have failed to recognise the Revolution which they themselves have been heralding for years.[31]

The Communist vision of material efficiency, the Fascist idea of organized *élites* and the democratic faith in the importance of the individual need supplementing, according to Teilhard de Chardin, by a larger and more satisfying goal: the Human Front. For Teilhard, a Jesuit priest, saw in the world only two groups—those who believed in progress and were prepared to suffer for it and those who disbelieved in progress or were afraid of it. Whilst in exile in China from 1939 to 1941 he defined this Human Front (in his *Phénomène humain*) as being brought about by 'the organization of research, the concentration of research upon the subject of man, and the conjunction of science and religion'. He discerned a thinking envelope of interacting components forming the contemporary habitat of thought which he called the nöosphere. This, he thought, was generating powerful psycho-social pressures favouring his ideas. Such Christian universalism has provoked a controversy described as 'hardly paralleled since the pontifical heresy-huntings of the fifth century'. That the chief 'heresy-hunter' in Teilhard's case was P. B. Medawar, a Nobel Prize winner, indicates how much the 'philosophy of science' had become the theology of the secular age.[32]

Even in a secular age, knowledge monopolized tends to become arcane, elevating its holders into a priesthood. To counteract this, there is a great need for its widest diffusion. Unless this is done, argues Dr. Bibby 'society will become effectively controlled by a scientific hierarchy which could be as pernicious as every other all powerful priesthood'.[33]

Other maps of heavens or hells are prolifically, if not pontifically, sketched by those imaginative cartographers: the science-fiction writers. And behind the best of these one catches the feeling that:

> Somehow the religious attitude of life must be restored and yet the only body of doctrine available to the Western World is the one which the great mass of people are obviously less and less willing to accept.[34]

Or, as George Orwell said in another place:

> One cannot have any worthwhile picture of the future unless one realises how much we have lost by the decay of Christianity.[35]

One can even identify a line of patristic writers of this twentieth-century secular sacerdocy, among them Henry Adams. For his prophecy that 'the very future of thought and therefore of history lies in the hands of physicists', has been nowhere more strikingly demonstrated than in his own country. For having reduced the molecule, the atom and the electron to costless servitude, they have had to organize that subjection.[36] This organization, to Henry Adams, made for Socialism. Like Marx (of whom he wrote, 'I never struck a book which taught me so much, and with which I disagreed so radically in conclusion'),[37] Adams detected an end in the historical process. 'We have reached the point', he wrote, 'where further cheapness can only be reached by a social system growing rapidly more and more socialistic.'[38] A year later he wrote, 'The only possible political party must stand on a well defined platform of State Socialism. Nothing else can reflect the social movement.'

This process of levelling down—of growing laterally instead of vertically—is one which has been going on since the starfish first crawled—if they do crawl—and is near completion. We have now only to cut off the heads of a very few more poppies, and our dear friends the socialists will alone remain. I am glad to see every country hurrying the process . . . Society . . . is a formless lump of globular lumps. This is, I believe, what the Socialists say, and I think they are about right.[39]

(4)

Since Adams's time 'an island of socialism in a free enterprise economy',[40] has developed from the exploitation of atomic energy. A retiring president (a general) has warned his countrymen that public policy 'could become the captive of a scientific-technological élite'.[41] This élite has been fostered by the armed forces, in America, as elsewhere. 'Concern over successes in military aspects of science', wrote two other American observers, 'has reinforced a tendency, already observable as society and production methods have become more complex, to seek out the expert for guidance.'[42] Though once 'seated in the economy', technocrats are increasingly part of the military order; in 1955 94 per cent of the 2-billion dollar budget was for military technology.[43] In the U.S.S.R. the military were, even before Stalin, so powerful that when Mekhonoshin was asked by Lenin to report on it he replied, 'This machine cannot be remodelled. This is more likely to change us than be changed by us.'[44]

The alliance of the army and the experts is visible in non-Western countries too. Here the army is usually modern: a quality described by Edward Shils as 'dynamic, concerned with people, democratic and equalitarian, scientific, economically advanced, sovereign and influential.'[45] Also in many of these countries the army, as the patron-consumer of technology, is often the only channel of social mobility. Since field officers realize the need of road building as well as road blocking, they can, and do, initiate national socialist revolutions.[46] China's example[47] has been follosed by Egypt (1952),[48] 13 of the 20 South American states (by 1954), Pakistan,[49] Burma, Thailand, Iraq and the Sudan (in 1958), Turkey (in 1960), Korea (in 1961) and Burma (in 1962).[50] The Egyptian revolution began when Colonel Nasser asked 'if the army does not do this job, who will?'[51] which has its Western echo in de Gaulle's (1958) opinion that politics was 'too serious a matter to be left to the politicians',[52] or in Brooke Adams's prophecy that 'the time is rapidly approaching when we shall be reorganized by soldiers'.[53] Nearly a quarter of a century later, his fellow-American, James Burnham after examining the technocrats in *The Managerial Revolution*, confessed that he did not 'give enough attention to this phase of the revolution'. He rectified his error three years later by saying:

> This time the soldiers are here to stay. Never again, in our time or our children's, will the army dry up into a small puddle on the fringe of social pond. The armed forces will henceforth be not merely quantitatively large. They will also become a major arena for the contests of the ambitious and powerful, will supply a considerable section of the ruling class of the future, and will exert a great, perhaps sometimes the decisive, influence on the social equilibrium.[54]

(5)

Between them, the army and the experts have fostered operationalism. By enabling scientists to qualify and quantify the performance as well as the design of weapons, the army allowed them to ascertain their real purpose, and, by further questions, to influence operations to fulfil that purpose. So tactics were inexorably subordinated to weapons, instead of vice versa.

The inexorability of the process has been visible ever since Uncle Toby and Corporal Trim conducted their imaginary campaigns in *Tristram Shandy*. War games got ever more serious as they involved ever more people, and the 'total wars' of this century led to staff officers being recruited from industry. As played by them these games became exercises in economic analysis, whereby players 'are taught carefully to consider *all* their resources. The player who comes to the game with a passionate interest in one of his several missions to the exclusion of several others will soon find that a clever opponent has him pinned.'[55] Probabilities and the clash of interest were now scientifically studied, and attempts were made to abstract a number of the problems into a mathematical system. Here John Von Neumann and Oskar Morgenstern clarified the issues involved with their book *The Theory of Games and Economic Behaviour* (1944).[56]

To apply mathematical method to problems of behaviour, new mathematics had to be invoked,[57] and more important, traditional military and political outlooks had to be revised.

> It is inevitable [said Sir Solly Zuckerman] that there will be increasingly less freedom for decision at those political and military levels where the responsibility for policy, in fact, rests . . . it is for that reason that an increasing burden falls on the scientist, and—using the term loosely—the operational research worker.[58]

The algebra of logic had already been evoked to cope with the classification and digestion of rapidly accumulating scientific information. The electrical engineer Claude Shannon had discovered in 1938 that some electrical circuits could be used in such calculations.[59] Going on to work in the Bell Telephone Laboratories he showed how telephone relays could help. So the coding and storage of information proceeded with help from the electrical engineers. Thus, too, the centuries-old concepts of a universal symbolism and a calculus of reasoning as held by Leibnitz came into their own. 'If I were to choose a patron Saint,' said Norbert Wiener, the formulator of cybernetics, 'I should have to choose Leibnitz.'[60]

Cybernetics, from the Greek word for steersman, was a

logical development from operational research. In its formulation Norbert Wiener was building by the philosophic tradition of Harvard, as articulated by Royce, no less than the physiological insights of his friend Arturo Rosenblueth. It emphasized the need for what Wiener called 'a good deal of planning and a good deal of struggle'. He envisaged difficulties with organized labour whose members were 'totally unprepared to enter into the larger political, technical, sociological and economic questions which concern the very existence of labour'.[61]

Such complex problems inhibit definite devices, theories and methods. As J. C. R. Lickleider remarked:

> The problem is no longer to design a pulley or a gear. It is to find a mission worthy of a million men, to plan a flow of metal and ideas and of flexibility and change, to build adaptive means, to forestall obsolescence till the maiden flight is flown . . . Modern technology is as much politics and sociology as physics and chemistry. It is even more economics and psychology . . . The central problems are problems of organised complexity.[62]

Projects like thermo-nuclear power, space travel and ballistic-missile warfare and counter-warfare, have exposed man's imperfect reaction to his world. Technology has extended his senses to enable him to come to terms with novelty, to become aware of it, to find out more about it, to try to apply it and finally to adopt it. This adoption demands new social organizations, new hierarchies, new values, new forms of training and above all, new echelons of expertise.

Today these echelons of expertise are multiplying. More of the workforce is engaged in designing and developing the machines to supplant their fellows. More technicians are needed to repair them. As scientists make new discoveries, more engineers are needed to design new processes, more administrative staff are needed to facilitate the flow of materials to and from the places where they are manufactured, more planners are needed for transport for highways, for housing and for health. And, to keep all this in touch, more communications engineers are needed.[63]

(6)

The operational revolution is international. The *Wall Street Journal* of 16 April 1958 carried an article with the revealing title 'Handle with Care—Scientists in Industry Often Baffle the Bosses, Force Policy Changes', whilst *Business Week* carried others like 'Where does the Lab end and the Plant Start?' (24 December 1958), or 'Splurge of Research is Piling up New Problems for Management' (24 January 1959). By November 1962, cybernetics, computers and control-systems were to be introduced on a large scale in Russian industry, research, design, planning, accounting, statistics and management. Later, Krushchev told a plenary committee of the Soviet Communist Party on 21 February 1964:

> We have no right to be idealists, day dreamers, divorced from life ignoring human experience. . . . The last thing I want . . . is to ignore the achievements of foreign science and practice.

In this foreign science and practice, actions were modified by knowledge of the results. This is a significant abandonment of the party line which posits that results are known anyway.[64]

The convergent trends of these technate states—greater control in the U.S.A., greater decentralization in the U.S.S.R.— conform to a pattern presented by four acute observers of industrialism and industrial man. They write:

> The complexity of the fully developed industrial society requires in the name of efficiency and initiative, a degree of decentralisation of control, particularly in the consumer goods and service trade industries, but it also requires a large measure of central control by the state and the conduct of many operators by large scale organisations.[65]

Earlier internationalist implications of operational groups can be cited too. Consider the difficulties of electric power which, before the first congress of electricians met in Paris in 1881 to set them, had no standards. Now the ohm and the volt and the watt are universally adopted, and as further redefined by the International Electro-technical Commission (established in 1906), were 'the indispensable preliminary to the massive development of electrical engineering in the twentieth century'.[66]

Their method, that of collaboration and co-operation, has always been the theme of scientific life. As Lavoisier remarked:

> most of the work still to be done in science and the useful arts is mainly that which needs the collaboration and co-operation of many

scientists . . . This is why it is necessary for scientists and technologists to meet periodically in common assemblies and that these
meetings should cover even branches of knowledge that seem to
have the best relation and connection with one another.[67]

These 'common assemblies' have multiplied rapidly in the
century and three-quarters after Lavoisier's death, accelerating
the interchange of technical knowledge.[68] Epidemics necessitated the convention of international health conferences:[69] well
organized internationally from 1851 onwards. To provide them
with statistical techniques, L. A. J. Quetelet worked on the
statistical identifications of (average) human, physical and intellectual qualities, and he too convened an international statistical
conference on the subject in 1853. 'Resourceful' men like
General J. J. Baeyer, president of the central bureau of European surveys at Berlin (a German counterpart of J. W. Powell's
bureau), convened some geodesists at Berlin in 1862, just as
Kekulé had convened chemists at Karlsruhe two years earlier.
Their fellow-countryman William Ostwald, to facilitate international discourse, promoted a new language called IDO[70]
('offspring'), and by 1899 the International Association
of Academies had taken shape, embracing scientific societies
in all capitals from Berlin to Toyko and on to Washington.
Other organizations, like the positivist Alliance Scientifique
Universalle offered world-wide identity cards for entry to the
libraries and archive repositories of the five continents, while the
Catholic Association for the Advancement of Science[71] reflected
the internationalist trend. Indeed, no less than 3,000 international gatherings took place between 1840 and 1914.[72] The
increasing need to take international action to solve problems
affecting all nations led to the foundation of an International
Office of Public Health in 1907. This coped with not only Asiatic
cholera, but with plague and yellow fever as well. Further
problems posed by earthquakes, over fishing in the sea and the
mapping of the world called other bodies into life like the
International Association of Seismology (1903), and International Fisheries' Council, and an International Committee for
the Map of the World (1909) (which aimed at putting the
world on 2,400 sheets to a scale of 16 miles to the inch).

Lacing nations ever more closely, communications engineers
spun nets whose safety was assured first by the Telegraphic

Union (formed in 1865), supplemented by the Radiotelegraphic Union (from 1906) and the International Postal Union (established in 1874).[73]

The horrors of war elicited the Geneva Red Cross (1864) and the St. Petersburg Convention on explosives in war (1868); the harsh necessities of farming, the International Institute of Agriculture, founded by a Polish-American, David Lubin, in association with the King of Italy, which has, thanks to the Rockefeller Foundation conducted the first international census of crops.

Thirty or more public bodies of this kind were set up before 1919, as well as 500 private international organizations[74] all endorsing the need for collective administration to avoid mutual inconvenience. After 1919 the International Research Council grew from the International Association of Academies, nourished by special unions for Astronomy, Geology, Geophysics and Pure and Allied Chemistry. Subsequent unions for Radio Science (1921), Biological Sciences (1923), Pure and Applied Physics (1923) and Geography (1923) were accompanied by the adhesion of Germany, Austria, Hungary and Bulgaria in 1926. Five years later it became the International Council of Scientific Unions (I.C.S.U.).

(7)

Three of these international organizations, the International Labour Organization, the International Telecommunication Union and the Universal Postal Convention, were absorbed as agencies by the United Nations Organization,[75] which then went on to found nine others.

Two were to provide capital for projects, the International Bank for Reconstruction and Development, formed in 1947, with a capital of 18,000 million dollars to help governments; and the International Finance Corporation, formed in 1957 with a capital of 100 million dollars to discharge a similar role with regard to private individuals. Three others were to facilitate communications: the International Civil Aviation Organization, the Inter-Governmental Maritime Consultative Organization and the World Meteorological Organization.

Another two were to cope with the energy resources and the food, health and education of the exploding world population:

The Food and Agriculture Organization (F.A.O.) and the World Health Organization (W.H.O.). F.A.O. furnishes specialists in nutrition, animal husbandry, fisheries, forestry and the conservation of food to backward areas, forecasts production, distribution and consumption throughout the world and takes measures to ensure the conservation of timber. W.H.O., through its legislative assembly of 87 member nations and an executive council at Geneva, has virtually eliminated yaws in certain tropical regions, is keeping leprosy at bay, checking tuberculosis and malaria and sustaining vigorous offensives against venereal diseases, influenza and poliomyelitis. By founding public clinics, organizing seminars and discussions, keeping a chain of centres to report on outbreaks, W.H.O. is doing work which would make a seventeenth-century Utopist rub his eyes.

Since the minimum conditions for these agencies' success is world literacy (a hollow phrase since in 1946 more than 1,000 million people in the world could neither read nor write), an Educational, Scientific and Cultural Organization, U.N.E.S.C.O., was set up in that year. Aptly enough Sir Julian Huxley was its first secretary.[76]

These 11 agencies have made over a quarter of the land surface of the world productive. Basic training centres have been established for Latin America (in Mexico), and the Arab states (Egypt), science clearing-houses have been organized in Montevideo, Cairo, New Delhi, Djakarta, Istanbul and Manila. 'Shock brigades' of teachers and experts have been sent to various areas. Attacks on the arid zones of the world, especially the much-publicized *Men against the Desert* scheme, illustrate how far-reaching its operations have been. Moreover, the International Oceanic Organization, launched to secure food supplies for a rapidly increasing world population, has dredged up information about the deep-sea creatures which would have taken years of individual or State research to obtain.[77]

(8)

But if science was making all these regions productive, politicians could make it unproductive—at a blow. Continued detonation of atomic bombs led to the convention of an international conference on the peaceful uses of atomic energy out of which came the International Atomic Energy Agency. The

I.A.E.A. encourages research on atomic energy for peaceful uses throughout the world, fosters exchange programmes and training schemes and acts as a bank of fissionable materials. It maintains its own laboratory at Seibersdorf in Austria and its headquarters in Vienna. Closely allied with it, the Scientific Committee on the Effects of Atomic Radiation, established in 1955, reports directly to the United Nations and works with W.H.O. and F.A.O. on the hazards to food and water. At a second conference in 1957 so much information was given in the 2,000 papers presented that it was said that probably at no time in human history has so large an amount of significant technological information been shared by so many nations.[78]

An even more ambitious international operation was launched in 1957–8, involving 60 nations in a study of the earth and the sun. Known as the International Geophysical Year (I.G.Y.) it nourished yet further world-wide exchange of data through a network of centres. To cope with the diverse problems posed yet further international organizations were formed, C.O.S.P.A.R., or the International Committee for Space Research, began to hold international symposia in January 1960 and April 1961. S.C.O.R. (the Special Committee on Oceanic Research) began to plumb the food and energy resources of the Indian Ocean. S.C.A.R. (the Special Committee for Antarctic Research) has literally frozen territorial claims in the Antarctic for 34 years so that 12 nations can maintain a network of stations there. A fourth, C.I.G. (the Comité International de Geophysique), on which all of the 5 interested international unions are represented (Geodesey, Geophysics, Astronomy, Scientific Radio and Physics), is making plans for, amongst other things, a World Magnetic Survey in 1964–6.[79]

Such geodetic-structured plenary assemblies, information dispersers and agencies of mutual help epitomize a new ecumenicism. Even the Anglocentric British Commonwealth should now, argue its friends, be regrouped to work through continental regions: Africa, south-east Asia and the West.[80]

(9)

Nations, to Ortega y Gasset, were 'mere past accumulating all round Europe, weighing it down, imprisoning it'; and nationalism 'nothing but a mania, a pretext to escape from the necessity of inventing something new'.[81] Ortega also sounded the contemporary note, 'everything that today is done in public and in private—even in one's inner conscience—is provisional, the only exception being certain portions of certain sciences'.[82]

This 'provisional' nature of public and private action has been more closely defined by Karl Mannheim as a 'state of fruitful uncertainty'. 'No previous age had the conviction of our period,' he wrote, 'namely that *we have no truth.*' All ages prior to our time had their truths, even the sceptics. This is the 'operational attitude', or the 'tendency to question and seek rather than to affirm', 'the uniquely modern propensity to reach behind and beyond appearances and to explode any fixed frame of reference which relies on ultimates'. Linked to this Mannheim finds a 'tendency to outrun the time, to take one's stand beyond and ahead of each situation, and to anticipate alternatives before they become acute'.[83] Or, as A. N. Whitehead puts it, 'We must expect, therefore, that the future will disclose dangers. It is the business of the future to be dangerous; and it is among the merits of science that it equips the future for its duties.'[84]

About that future many in the West are pessimistic, especially about the role of science in social change. The collapse of the umbrella of Christian culture has led, says one, 'to a tendency towards a despair of any good coming from political or social change, and a fear that all human values will be lost in the rapid break up of existing patterns of power and responsibility.'[85] Yet another laments the possibility of 'an epidemic of mysticism'. According to Karl Popper, 'this is certainly possible, for since some intellectuals *do* react to scientific progress (or to the demands of an open society), by withdrawing into mysticism, everyone *might* react in this way'.[86] The feeling that this was already happening provoked Kurt Mendelsohn to the 'sad reflection' that 'the East should have succeeded where we seem to have failed'. He considers that in the West, technology—the harnessing of atomic energy and the transmutation of the elements—has 'been met in the West with nothing better than apathy or even revulsion', whereas 'the Chinese and Russians take these same things as exciting new developments, destined to enrich the life of human society'.[87]

Not for nothing have the political theorists been lamenting the decay of their craft. One of them attributed it to 'the belief in the power of science to solve all problems, and, more particularly, all political problems which confront men in the modern age'. Though he championed the right of science to determine politics, Hans J. Morgenthau could only do so by invoking scientists like Eddington, Heisenberg, Sullivan and James Jeans to buttress his argument, thereby revealing that his craft was more involved in the politics of science rather than the science of politics.[88]

So too the doyen of American political scientists might assert that 'despite their spectacular successes, science and technology have been singularly without effect on the fundamental structure of world politics'. But he also was compelled to ask whether or not 'a turning point in the relation of science to power has finally come'. He suggested 'the potentialities of man's newly accessible astral environment will provide a new set of goals . . . that traditional differences will rapidly become obsolete'.[89]

He might well be right.

(10)

'There hardly seems any escape from the internationally planned economy', concluded Marston Bates after considering the increasing complexity of organization needed to serve the increasing number of people, and the increasing specialization needed for the exploitation, utilization and distribution of resources. The alternatives, as far as he could see were either in war or 'a totalitarian sort of world organisation for human society'.[90]

Such an organization might well be, as Grenville Clark and Louis B. Sohn have suggested, a World Development Authority under a revised United Nations Charter. This World Development Authority would be sustained from a United Nations budget equivalent to 3 per cent of the estimated gross world product in any year. Out of this budget the United Nations would, of course, also sustain a heavily armed police force and judicial system.[91]

Indeed, W. H. Ferry considers that 'the theory adequate to our present condition would be that of a wealthy internationalized and technologized democracy, in which all the strands making up the general welfare are irretrievably tangled . . . It would shun the economic determinism to which Americans today are almost as devoted as the Russians'.[92] The value system of such a society has been described by Talcott Parsons as one of 'instrumental activism'. This

> involves an attitude of active mastery toward the empirical situation external to the society, a situation which includes both physical and psychological nature and other societies. This attitude favors increasing the level of adaptive flexibility primarily through increase of knowledge and economic production.[93]

This 'increase of knowledge' is a social portent. In America it is growing at twice the rate of the present economy, and its production, distribution and consumption make up 29 per cent of the gross national product.[94] 'Certainly never in history', wrote Clark Kerr, 'has knowledge been so central to the conduct of an entire society'.[95]

Its centrality has so affected social policy that Don K. Price now considers that

> The development of public policy and of the methods of administration owe less in the long run to the processes of conflict among political parties and social or economic pressure groups than to the more objective processes of research and discussion among professional groups.[96]

This is not new. Years ago, A. N. Whitehead indicated the importance of professional and scholarly groups in contributing to sum total of abstract knowledge, as well as to the advance of technology,[97] whilst Dr. Joseph Needham stressed that nature presents itself to us as a continuous rise in level of organization.[98]

But one should not carry this too far. 'The really shocking scientific prophecy of the present day', wrote C. H. Waddington, 'is the prediction that scientists will come to exert an enormous influence of this kind in the grand questions of social policy'.[99] Waddington insists that the kind of apprehensive anticipation of technocracy as evidenced in Huxley's *Brave New World* or Forster's *When the Machine Stops* is the product of men whose systems of thought are conditioned and motivated by a non-scientific training. He continues, 'I am optimist enough to expect that the gradually increasing prestige of the scientific method of study will force all those concerned with public affairs to make some attempt to live up to its standards. If one could be confident . . . that all men were ready to believe that the knowledge and understanding on which alone action can be securely based needs to be so wide and profound that it demands the co-operative endeavours of many minds—then we should be on our way towards a Utopia which a scientist could recognise as akin to his own professional world'.[100]

These 'co-operative efforts of many minds' still operate in 'invisible colleges'. The institutional strength of science merely serves to sustain them, and to fill up the world with science. Contemplating this recently, Derek de Solla Price was reminded of 'a handicap race in which the first starters are the slowest runners'. For the later a country starts, he said, the faster it seems to expand. Thus, he pointed out, 'Britain's expansion from the first few scientists to the order of hundreds of thousands took 300 years, that of the United States took 150, Japan about 60, and the U.S.S.R. about 30. China and the next new nations will be even quicker.' He continued

> It would seem that during this next generation we shall stand at the finishing post as all the runners come home much at the same time, and rather rapidly we shall emerge into a new situation where at least most of the population masses of the world have some considerable quota of science."[101]

As foregoing pages indicate, this is no understatement.

Notes

PREFACE

[1] E. M. Forster, 'The New Disorder', *Horizon*, IV (1941), 379–80.

[2] Karl Marx, *A Contribution to the Critique of Political Economy* (1904), 11–12. But Marx continues p. 12, 'With the change of the economic foundations the entire immense super structure is more or less rapidly transformed. In considering such transformations the distinction should always be made between the material transformation of the economic conditions of production *which can be determined with the precision of natural science*, and the legal, political, religious, aesthetic or philosophic —in short, ideological forms in which men become conscious of this conflict and fight it out.'

[3] P. A. Schillp, 'The Formal Problems of Scheler's Sociology of Knowledge', *The Philosophical Review*, XXXVI (1927), 101–20; Howard Becker and H. O. Dahlke, *Max Scheler's Sociology of Knowledge Philosophy and Phenomenological Research* (1942), 310–22.

[4] R. K. Merton, 'Karl Mannheim and the Sociology of Knowledge', *Journal of Liberal Religion* (1941), 125–47.

[5] Carl Becker, *The Heavenly City of the Eighteenth Century Philosophers* (New Haven, 1932), 18–19.

[6] ibid., 19.

PART I

1: GARDEN ECONOMIES

[1] 'Joao Huyghen von Linschoten, administrator de casa do Arcebispo de Goa e espiao da Holanda (1583–1587)', *Occidente*, LVIII (1960), 123–30; Me de Jong, ibid., LXV (1963), 79–96.

[2] Botanic gardens evolved from herb gardens, so necessary to medieval mortals whose enormous diets of meat needed seasoning. Since they also needed sedatives (from opium), purgatives (from colcynth) and castor oil (from croton), the gardens were often a semi-public responsibility. The papal physician, Simon of Genoa, laid out one in Rome in 1288, another existed at Hamburg in 1316, yet another at Salerno in 1340, and another at Marburg in 1500. The son of the founder of the last-named garden wrote the most important German herbal of the sixteenth century, *The Historia Plantarum* (1561). Members of the trading communities of Genoa and Venice seem to have really transformed the herb into the botanic garden. That established at Padua in 1525 by Gaspar de Gabrieli was the first private one of its kind, and that at Pisa some twenty years later, the first public one. In these gardens botany began to flourish as a science. Pisa had as its successive directors Ghini and Caesalpini, whilst the great lay university of Padua, sustained by the republic of Venice, obtained a garden where lectures on simples were delivered by Francis Bonafide, and by 1563 had a chair of botany. Everyone went to study in the Padua garden for it was kept well stocked by the Republic of

Venice, which sent collectors to its islands in Levant, to Egypt and even to India for plants. Here Lluca Ghini, author of *A Comparison between the Old Thought and the New* (1537), devised herbaria—dried plants on paper—as a teaching device. Ghini taught Germans like Valerius Cordus and Englishmen like John Falconer and William Turner. *Maister Falconer's Book* (1547) was the earliest English record of a herbarium of dried plants, whilst William Turner proved to be a restless radical of a type destined to become familiar. J. H. Randall, jun., *The School of Padua and the Emergence of Modern Science* (Padua, 1961), T. A. and M. S. Sprague, 'The Herbal of Valerius Cordus', *Journal of the Linnaean Society*, LII (1938–45), 1–113. Leonard Fuchs (1501–66). A. P. de Candolle, 'Notice abregee de l'histoire et l'administration des jardins botaniques', *Dict. de Sci. Nat.* (1822), 165–81; G. W. Johnson, *A History of English Gardening* (London, 1828); J. C. Loudon, *An Encyclopaedia of Gardening* (ed. Mrs. Loudon, 1850) Anton Kerner von Marilaun, *Die botanische Garten, ihre Aufgabe in der Vergangenheit, Gegenwart und Zukunft* (Innsbruck, 1870); F. Phillip, *Los jardinos botanicos* (Santiago, Chile, 1878); N. L. Britton, 'Botanical Gardens', *New York Botanic Garden Bulletin* (1897, 62–77; J. H. Marden, 'Functions of a botanic garden', *Royal Society of New South Wales Journal and Proceedings*, XLIII (1912), 1–73; Alicia Amherst, *A History of Gardening in England* (London, 1896); A. W. Hill, 'The History and Functions of Botanic Gardens', *Annals of the Missouri Botanical Gardens*, vol. II (St. Louis, 1915), 185–241; C. Stuart Gager, 'Botanic Gardens of the World: Materials for a History', *Brooklyn Botanic Garden Record*, XXVII (1938), p. 283, for a discussion as to which was first; Edith Grey Wheelwright, *The Physic Garden* (1939); Miles Hadfield, *Gardening in Britain* (1960).

[3] Gervase Huxley, *Talking of Tea* (1956), 11–12.

[4] Miles Hadfield, *Gardening in Britain* (1960), 58; J. C. T. Uphof, *The Contributions of Holland to the Sciences* (n.d.); W. Blunt, *Tulipomania* (1950); John J. Murray, 'The Cultural Impact of the Flemish Low Countries on Sixteenth and Seventeenth Century England', *American Historical Review*, LXII (1956–7), 837–54.

[5] F. W. Gibbs, 'Boerhaave and the Botanists', *Annals of Science*, XIII (1957), 47–61.

[6] *Memorialia Herman Boerhaave, optimi medici* (Haarlem, 1939), 33; R. W. Innes Smith, *English speaking students of Medicine at Leyden* (1932), and Douglas Guthrie, 'The Influence of the Leyden School upon Scottish Medicine', *Medical History*, iii (1959), 108–21.

[7] That this was so largely due to the Abbé Nollet (1700–70), a French physician who had visited both Holland and England some years earlier and for whom a chair of experimental physics was created at the College of Navarre.

[8] In 1728 Albrecht von Haller 'found no better method than the study of Botany which would oblige me to take exercise. I was short-sighted and suffered from haemorrhoids, and I hoped by means of movement to cure myself of these infirmities', G. R. de Beer, 'Haller's *Historia Stirpium*' *Annals of Science*, IX (1953), 1–46.

[9] T. Bileroth, *The Medical Sciences and German Universities* (New York, 1924). Van Swieten called two other Leyden-trained physicians, De Haen and Jacquin to help him establish surgical clinics in the town and schools for rural surgeons.

[10] *Kew Bull. Misc. Inf.* (1913), 243–52. Six members of the Russian Academy of Sciences, 7 professors, 30 doctors and 30 aristocrats all received their education here; N. Hans 'Russian students at Leyden in the Eighteenth Century', *Slavonic Review*, XXXV (1956), 551–62. See also W. Horsley Gantt, *Russian Medicine* (New York, 1937), 51–54.

[11] Bond's brother Thomas collaborated with Benjamin Franklin to found the

Pennsylvania Hospital in 1752; both assisted John Morgan in 1765 to establish the first medical school in North America. Joseph L. Miller, *Joyfull Newes out of the New-Found World*, 'The First American Materia Medica'. *Mayo Foundation Lectures on the History of Medicine 1926–1932* (Philadelphia, 1933), 253–96, I. Bernard Cohen, 'The New World as a Source of Science for Europe', *Actes du IXe Congrés International d'Histoire des Sciences* (Barcelona, (1959), 98. The Spanish curtain extended not only to the products but to knowledge about them too. The 16 huge folios of drawings compiled by Francisco Hernandez in his Mexican wanderings did not see the light till 100 years later, whilst Oviedo's *General History of the Indies* did not appear in his lifetime.

12 French beans, carrots, spinach and cabbage only began to be cultivated at the end of the sixteenth century. E. S. Rohde, *A Garden of Herbs* (1926), 3. 'Fifty years ago this art of gardening began to creep into England, into Sandwich and Surrey, Fulham and other places. Some old men in Surrey, where it flourisheth very much at present, report that they knew the first gardeners that came into these parts to plant cabbages colleflowers and to sow turneps and carrots and parsnips, and raith-rape peas, all of which at that time were great rarities; we having few or none in England but what came from Holland and Flanders.' Samuel Hartlib, *The Compleat Husbandman* (1659).

13 Sebastian del Cano, who took over from Magellan, killed in 1521.

14 R. N. Salamon, *The History and Social Influence of the Potato* (Cambridge, 1949), 77–79, 437.

15 R. T. Gunther, *Oxford Gardens* (1912) and *Early British Botanists* (1922). Mea Allen, *The Tradescants, Their Plants, Gardens and Museums 1570–1662* (1964), 119–20.

16 Kenneth Dewhurst, *John Locke (1632–1704)* (London, 1963); Sir D'Arcy Power, 'The Oxford Physick Garden', *Annals of Medical History*, II, 109–25.

17 I. B. Balfour, 'History of the Royal Botanic Garden Edinburgh', *Notes on the Royal Botanical Garden Edinburgh* (1904), IV, v–viii; 'A Sketch of the Professors of Botany in Edinburgh from 1670 until 1887', in F. W. Oliver (ed.), *Makers of British Botany* (Cambridge, 1913), 280–301.

18 R. H. Jeffers, 'Edward Morgan and the Westminster Physick Gardens', *Proc. Linnaean Society*, CLXIV (1953), 102–32.

19 John J. Murray, 'The Cultural Impact of the Flemish Low Countries on Sixteenth and Seventeenth Century England', *American Historical Review*, LXII (1956–7), 837–54.

20 Daniel Defoe, *A Tour Through England and Wales* (Everyman edition), 166–7.

21 C. E. Raven, *John Ray, Naturalist* (Cambridge, 1942), 452.

22 *A General Treatise of Husbandry and Gardening* (1724), II, 167–8.

23 Spring (1728), 28.

24 *Vide* supplement to vol. v (1779) of his 44-volume *Histoire Naturelle*.

25 J. S. Wilkie, 'The Idea of Evolution in the Writings of Buffon', *Annals of Science*, XXII (1956), 48–62, 212–27. Buffon was the first to attempt an empirical approach to the idea of organic evolution, subjecting it to the test of application to a wide range of data, much of which he had himself brought together for the first time. Jean Leroz (ed.), *Les Botanistes français en Amérique du Nord avant 1850* (Colloques Internationaux du Centre de la Recherche Scientifique LXII, Paris, 1956), Paris: Centre National de la Recherche Scientifique, 1957.

26 Quoted by Harcourt Brown, 'Buffon and the Royal Society of London', in M. F. Ashley Montague (ed.), *Studies and Essays on the History of Science and Learning Offered in homage to George Sarton* (New York, 1946), 141–65.

27 Agnes Arber, 'The Botanical Philosophy of Guy de la Brosse', *Isis* (1913), i,

359–69. Bouvard seems to have been a tartar for his *Histoirae hodiernae medicinae veritatis* (*c.* 1635) contained strong criticisms of the medical practice of his day.

[28] G. Bonno, 'Hans Sloane et les relations intellectuelles franco-anglaises au 18e siècle', *Romanic Review*, XXXIV (1943), 40–49.

[29] H. Field and R. H. Semple, *Memoirs of the Botanic Garden at Chelsea* (1878); E. St. John Brooks, *Sir Hans Sloane* (1954). Sloane was also responsible for reviving the *Philosophical Transactions* of the Royal Society of which he was secretary for 19 years and president for another 14. His own collection of plants and objects of virtue, gathered from all corners of the globe, were considered so valuable that the State purchased them in 1754 and housed them in what is now the British Museum. See also F. D. Drewitt, *Romance of the Apothecaries Garden at Chelsea* (1924); R. Ferbur, *Twelve Months of Flowers* (1720).

[30] W. R. Dawson (ed.), *The Banks Letters* (1958), 56. Banks was given French botanical news by P. M. A. Broussonet (1761–1807), who in return asked Banks to support his candidature for a demonstratorship at the Jardin. Banks acknowledged that 'the French respect for science and scientists never abated even during the most terrible part of the revolution'.

The first organized immigration into South Island, New Zealand, was promoted by French merchants of Nantes and Bordeaux who sent out a contingent of 65 settlers to Akaroa in New Zealand. Among them was de Belligny, who applied the training he acquired at the Jardin des Plantes in Paris to establish French farms across the Bay where he experimented with potatoes and other vegetables. T. L. Buick, *The French at Akaroa, An Adventure in Colonisation* (Wellington, 1928).

[31] Ernst Ekman, 'Gothic Patriotism and Olaf Rudbeck', *Journal of Modern History*, XXXIV (1962), 52–63.

[32] B. D. Jackson, *Linnaeus* (London, 1923), gives (pp. 380–3) a list of his principal pupils.

[33] One cannot resist the story of William Linnaeus Gardner (nephew of Lord Gardner), who whilst serving with the Indian Army was captured, disguised himself as a grass-cutter and escaped to found an Indian regiment called Gardner's Horse.

[34] His *General View of the Writings of Linnaeus* (1781) ran to a second edition in 1785.

[35] L. Bultingaire, 'Les peintres du jardin du Roy au XVIIIe siècle', Archives du Museum, Ser. 6. 3 (1928), 19–36; 'L'Art au jardin des Plantes', ibid., Ser. 10. 12 (1935), 667–78.

[36] Wilfrid Blunt, *The Art of Botanical Illustrations* (1950), 113–16. Unfortunately he went to Sweden where in 1747 he was beheaded for 'plotting against the king'.

[37] W. R. Dawson (ed.), *The Banks Letters* (1958), 856.

[38] Others a little less notable were Zürich (1950), Bologna (1568), Leipzig (1579), Montpellier (1598), Heidelberg (n.d.), Giessen (1608), Strasbourg (1620), Jena (1679), Berlin (1679), Amsterdam (1682), Petrograd (1713) and Vienna (1754). More than 1,500 other botanic gardens were flourishing by the end of the eighteenth century.

[39] W. R. Dawson, *The Banks Letters* (1958), 322–5.

[40] J. Jean Hecht, *The Domestic Servant Class in Eighteenth Century England* (1956), 48.

[41] E. G. Wheelwright, *The Physic Garden* (London, 1939), 143.

2: THE BEAT OF THE IMAGINATION

[1] *The Works of Francis Bacon*, ed. J. Spedding, R. L. Ellis and D. D. Heath (1870–2), i, p. 144.

[2] Sir T. Clifford Allbut, 'Palissy, Bacon and the revival of Natural Science',

Proc. Brit. Acad. (1914), VI, pp. 233 ff., suggests that Bacon was influenced by Bernard Palissy a French glassworker and potter who secured the patronage of the bigoted Catholic Catherine de Medici by offering in 1564, *La Recepte véritable par laquelle tous les hommes de la France pourrant apprendre a multiplier et augménèr leurs thrésors*. So impressed was Catherine de Medici by his skill that, although she was a strong Catholic, she allowed him to lecture in Paris. His lectures were generalized prescriptions for the study of geology, chemistry, minerology and other aspects of the natural history of the earth. They have been described as 'the first of their kind in Paris and perhaps in the world'. George Sarton, *Six Wings: Men of Science in the Renaissance* (London, 1958), 167.

³ ibid., vol. 1, p. 1, cxix. See M. E. Prior, 'Bacon's Man of Science', *J.H.I.*, 1954, 15, pp. 348–70.

⁴ F. H. Anderson, *The Philosophy of Francis Bacon* (Chicago, 1948); Benjamin Farringdon, *Francis Bacon: Philosopher of Industrial Science* (1951); R. C. Cochrane, 'Francis Bacon and the Rise of Mechanical Arts in Eighteenth Century England', *A. of S.*, XII (1956), pp. 137–56. 'If I were asked to describe Bacon as briefly as I could,' wrote Leigh Hunt *(Table Talk*, 1851, p. 88), 'I should say he was the liberator of the hands of knowledge.'

⁵ He is credited with the introduction of the Angora cat and eiderdown quilts and was the first to verify by experiment Harvey's discovery of the circulation of blood. G. T. H. Wright, *Nicholas Fabri de Peiresc* (Roxburghe Club Publications, 1926); Pierre Humbert, *Un Amateur: Peiresc* (Paris, 1933); Seymour L. Chapin, 'The Astronomical activities of Nicholas Claude Fabri de Peiresc', *Isis*, XLVIII (1957), 13–29.

⁶ G. Tiere, *Cornelius Drebbel* (Amsterdam, 1932).

⁷ J. S. Spink, *French Free-Thought from Gassendi to Voltaire* (London, 1960).

⁸ L. M. Richardson, 'The Conferences of T. Renaudot, an episode in the Quarrel of the Ancients and Moderns', *Modern Language Notes*, May 1952, 312.

⁹ Mme Paul Tannery, *Correspondence du Père Marin Mersenne, Religieux* (Paris, 1933–46); Robert Lenoble, *Mersenne ou la Naissance du Mécanisme* (Paris, 1943).

¹⁰ G. Bigordan, 'L'Académie de Montmor', *Comptes rendus de l'Académie des Sciences* (1917), 164, 217–18.

¹¹ The last-named included F. Salviati, a disciple of Galileo who appears as a character in Galileo's *Dialogue Concerning Two Chief World Systems* (1632) and the *Discourses on Two Sciences* (1638).

¹² M. Maylender, *Storia delle Accademie d'Italia* (Bologna, 1926–7); R. Caverni, *Storia del methodo sperimentale in Italia* (Florence, 1891).

¹³ A. E. Bell, *Christian Huygens* (1947).

¹⁴ A. J. George, 'A Seventeenth Century Amateur of Science: Jean Chapelain', *A. of S.* (1938), 217–36, iii.

¹⁵ A. J. George, 'The Genesis of the Académie des Sciences', *A. of S.* (1938), 111, pp. 372–407.

¹⁶ H. C. Bolton, *The Follies of Science at the Court of Rudolph II* (Milwaukee, 1904), The wonder houses of German princelings were remarkable. Albrecht V (1550–79) of Bavaria, had an egg which an abbot had found within another egg, manna which fell from heaven in a famine, a stuffed elephant, a hydra and a basilisk. The Tradescants in Britain amassed such a good collection that, when bought by Elias Ashmole (1617–92) in 1659, it filled 12 carts. It became the nucleus of the Ashmolean Museum at Oxford University in 1682. J. W. Schlosser, *Kunstkabinette und Wunder Kammern der Spätrenaissance* (Leipzig, 1908).

¹⁷ In his anxiety to discover the nature of primitive speech he is said to have

reared several infants in complete silence to find what words they spoke of their own volition. The children died. If another story is to be believed, he fed two men, bade one of them rest and the other take exercise, and then cut both of them open to see whether exercise facilitated digestion. He built artificial incubating ovens, initiated the systematic breeding of animals, established a vivarium and himself wrote a book on falconry. His scientific familiar, Michael Scot, an active translator of Arabian astronomical and zoological works, came from Toledo to Sicily to serve him. One of Frederick's correspondents at Pisa, Fibonacci, introduced the system of Arab numerals we use today, and provided him with mathematics problems. He also instituted an anatomical school at Salerno (where a guild or universitas of doctors was growing) and made decrees in 1231 and 1240 regulating the granting of degrees by the masters whose university had suffered from being sacked. He also founded at Naples in 1244 the first utilitarian State university, as a nursery for State officials. This set yet another precedent as the first conscious and deliberate attempt of an emperor to dominate the minds of men. Other universities at Padua (1222) and Sienna (1240) developed in sympathy, and by 1275 the dissection of humans had begun at Bologna. Pupils of Bologna carried these ideas to France, and by 1405 the practice of public dissections had spread to Vienna. Yet only in Italy could surgery really develop, since the Church's prohibition of clerks shedding blood was outweighed by the secular need—in Bologna at any rate—for post-mortem examinations for determining the cause of death. Ernst Kantorowicz, *Frederick the Second 1194–1250* (London, 1931), 135; P. O. Kristeller, 'The School of Salerno: its development and contribution to the history of learning', *Bull. Hist. Med.*, XVII (1945), 138–94.

[18] These tables were an essential adjunct of any navigation. Three hundred years earlier, Alphonso the Wise, King of Leon and Castile (d. 1284) had commissioned Hassan, a Jew, to revise the 200-year-old Toledan Tables. The revisions gave detailed instructions for the making of astrolabes and quadrants and were the best of their kind for 300 years. He gave a copy of them to his grandson, King Denis of Portugal (1261–1325) who founded the University of Lisbon in 1290. Portugal now applied this astronomical knowledge under King John I (who married an English princess) and his son, Duarte (1391–1438). King John's other son, Prince Henry the Navigator (1394–1460) strengthened the University of Lisbon with a chair of astronomy and mathematics and built an observation post in the Sagres peninsula at Cape St. Vincent, enlisting Jafuda Cresques from Majorca, a Catalan cosmographer, to synthesize on maps the knowledge obtained there. Armed with these maps, Portguese ships ventured to Madeira (1420), the Azores (1437) and the Cape Verde Islands (1456). From such voyages further information was pooled and codified enabling nautical astrolabes with new tables of declination for the equatorial sun to be devised. One member of the Sagres team actually went on an experimental voyage to Guinea in 1482. By 1487 Bartholomew Diaz turned the Cape of Good Hope and 11 years later reached India. But fearing foreign rivalry, the Portuguese kept this knowledge to themselves. Indeed it has been suggested that this was one of the reasons why Columbus was so much behind the high standards of the Portuguese navigation of his age. On the other hand it has also been suggested that Columbus was a secret agent in the service of the King of Portugal, sent to distract the rival King of Spain from the eastward passage to India by 'discovering' a large land on the western route.

Other knowledge grew from this continuous application and improvement of navigation. Tides were studied by Duarte Pachus, maps and charts posed the problem of magnetic deviation, the mathematics of navigation stimulated Pedro Nunes to invent a *nonius*, an early Vernier scale. And Nunes was a great friend of John Dee. J. B. Trend, *Portugal* (1957), 134; F. L. Ganshof, *The European Inheri-*

tance (1954), iii, xvi, 480; J. Cortesas, 'The Mystery of Columbus', *The Contemporary Review*, March 1937, and *Hist. de America*, III (Barcelona, 1947), 504–6; E. G. R. Taylor, *The English Debt to Portuguese Nautical Science in the Middle Ages* (1938); D. W. Water, *The Art of Navigation in England in Elizabethan and Early Stuart Times* (London, 1958), 104.

[19] Wilhelm Begemann, *Die Fruchtbringende Gesellschaft und Johann Valentin Andrea* (Berlin, 1911), 25. The King of Denmark built Tycho Brahe an observatory of redbrick and sandstone 14 miles north of Copenhagen and 9 miles south of Elsinore on the island of Hveen. Uraniborg, or the Castle of the Heavens, began operations in December 1576, and continued regularly night by night for the next 20 years. Its laboratory and library became a mecca for students, who arrived in such numbers that Tycho Brahe had to build a second observatory south-east of Uraniborg, known as Stjerneborg (Castle of the Stars), with instruments placed underground. From the manorial rents and ecclesiastical preferments provided by his royal patron, he sent some of these students on astronomical expeditions, arranged for the keeping of meteorological diaries, and undertook chemical research (or 'terrestial astronomy'). Indeed Tycho's laboratory was the source of several remedies in the Danish *Pharmacopoeia*. He also established a printing press. He trained 40 astronomers here over a period of nearly 20 years. At the same time he compiled a catalogue of 777 fixed stars, and conducted a lengthy correspondence with the Landgrave of Hesse at Cassel on astronomical matters. When the King of Denmark died, Tycho's son-in-law and disciple Franz Tengnagel sounded Galileo with a view to Tycho making observations in the Mediterranean area. Tycho, however, went to Prague at the invitation of Rudolf II and installed his smaller instruments in Benatky Castle. Again he wrote to Galileo in person, but seems to have had no reply.

[20] Nicholas Hans, 'The Rosicrucians of the Seventeenth Century', *Adult Education*, vol. VII (1935), 229; F. E. Held, *Christianopolis* (London, 1916), 203; Martha Ornstein, *The Role of Scientific Studies in the Seventeenth Century* (Chicago, 1928), 168. One of Jungius's English correspondents was Sir Charles Cavendish who maintained contacts with scientists in France too. Cavendish was a friend of Thomas Hobbes. He was described by John Aubrey as collecting 'with no small chardge, as many mathematicall bookes as filled a hoggeshead, which he intended to have printed; which if he had lived to have donne the growth of mathematicall learning had been 30 years or more forwarder than 'tis'. When Cavendish died 'of the scurvey, contracted by hard study', his collection was unfortunately sold 'to the past-board makers for wast-paper'.

[21] Harcourt Brown, *Scientific Organisations in Seventeenth Century France* (1620–80) (Baltimore, 1934), suggests (p. 29) that Renaudot's Office of Address was probably the 'stimulus which produced the Office of Intelligence set up in London' in 1638 by Captain Robert Innes under letters patent from Charles I. He is, however, 'almost certain that Renaudot's activity in Paris was partly responsible for Samuel Hartlib's transformation of the Comenian scheme for a pansophic College into a project for a self-supporting and utilitarian Office of Address for Communications'.

[22] Dorothy Stimson, 'Dr. Wilkins and the Royal Society', *J.M.H.* (1931), iii, p. 545.

[23] *Festschrift zu Gustav Schmollers 70* (Leipzig, 1908), 65–99.

[24] Harcourt Brown, op. cit., 163.

[25] B. T. Morgan, *Histoire du Journal des Scavans, 1665–1700* (Paris, 1929).

3 : ACADEMIC HONEYCOMBS

[1] Leibnitz was also deeply affected by Erhard Weigel of the University of Jena

who had such a passion for *realia* as opposed to metaphysical speculations that the philosophical faculty of the University of Jena expelled him, not before, however, he introduced G. W. Leibnitz to the study of mathematics. Like his teacher Weigel, Leibnitz corresponded with the foreign scientists and after subsequent visits to Paris (the first at the age of 23), began to draft numerous schemes for a German society to forward all the sciences.

2 This began when the State physician of Schweinfurt, Lorenz Bausch, proposed in 1651 to three others the establishment of an academy to advance medicine through observation, and to publish their findings. They went their quiet way for several years as the *Academia Naturae Curiosorum* until the State physician of Breslau joined them to expand their name and scope as the *Academia Leopoldino-Carolina Naturae Curiosorum*. Under P. J. Sachs von Lewenhaimb their position was still further enhanced by a number of privileges and the title of Imperial Leopoldine Academy. They issued one of the earliest medical publications: the *Miscellanea Curiosa . . . Medico-Physicorum Germanorum*, for which they obtained full copyright privileges.

To mask their identity members were given pseudonyms. Since the symbol of the society was the ship 'Argo', Bausch, as the founder was called 'Jason I'. Sachs von Lewenhaimb, for ensuring that the society's light shone before the world, was 'Phosphorus I'. G. W. Wedel (1645–1721) for unspecified but identifiable medical services to various German electors became 'Hercules I' in 1672. G. C. Kirchmaier (1637–1700) on election in 1677 became 'Phosphorus II' for his account of the fluorescence or phosphorescence of fluorspar.

Unlike the English or the French academies, the Leopoldines digested and spread others' discoveries rather than maintained an atmosphere where they could make their own.

Perhaps the apogee of its influence was exerted when Friedrich Hoffmann (1660–1742) and G. E. Stahl (1660–1734) became members. Stahl, a 'sour-faced metaphysician' was invested with the title of 'Olympiodorus' in 1700, three years after the publication of his famous *Zymotechnica* which pointed the way to the twin blind alleys of Phlogiston and Vitalism. Hoffmann disagreed, maintaining (as befitted a friend of Robert Boyle), more mechanistic ideas, though still in a German way, insisting that a mysterious ether-like fluid acted through the nervous system giving it 'tonus' when health prevailed. As the first Professor of Medicine at the newly founded University of Halle, Hoffmann drafted its statutes in 1693.

Two of the professors of the University of Altdorf were also members of the Leopoldine Academy, contributing to its *Ephemerides*. One was Christopher Sturm, Professor of Mathematics and Physics, a former attender at the Cimento's gatherings in Florence and a friend of Halley and Haak. Sturm formed yet another group in 1673, the *Collegium Curiosum sive Experimentale*, centred round physics. Composed mainly of his own students it published two accounts of their experiments— in 1676 and 1683. The first volume began with an account of a diving bell, and continued with accounts of the camera obscura, pumps and telescopes. Sturm planned another society to institute a world-wide survey of magnetic deviations, but died before it could materialize. The other was Johann Moritz Hoffman (1653–1727) who had become the first Professor of Chemistry in 1682, building a laboratory for courses. His *Laboratorum novum chemicum apertum medicinae cultoribus* (1683) was a spirited advocacy of laboratory work as a part of medical training. In 1721 he became Director of the Leopoldine Academy. The first real evaluation of what the academy had effected was attempted by M. B. Valentini (1657–1729) of Giessen in 1705. Valentini was an authority on medical jurisprudence, whose cool reflective mind, recognized by the title of 'Thessalus I' had been sharpened by contacts with Boyle, Sydenham, du Hamel, du Verney and Tournefort. In 1708 he published a synoptic account of the papers written for the academy. Grouped under various heads like animal, vegetable and mineral, this synopsis gives an admirable picture of the work done during the first half of the academy's existence. Soon after he became the Director of the *Ephemerides* he was elected to the Italian Society of Recuperati (1689), to the Royal Society of London (1717) and was made Count Palatine. He was also Professor of Physics at Giessen.

3 Ruth Lydia Saw, *Leibnitz* (Penguin Books, 1945); Ernest Cassirer, *The Philosophy of the Enlightenment* (trans. F. C. A. Koelln and J. P. Pettegrove, Princeton, 1951).

4 Leonard M. Marsak, 'Fontenelle in defence of Science', *J.H.I.*, XX (1959), 111–22.

5 F. Klemm, *A History of Western Technology* (1959), 244.

6 M. Lanson showed that the Encyclopaedia probably had a Masonic origin, *Revue d'Histoire Littéraire* (1912), 293–317; D. H. Gordon and N. L. Torrey, *The Censoring of Diderot's Encyclopédie and the Re-established text* (1947); Jean Thomas, *L'humanisme de Diderot* (1938); Joseph Le Gras, *Diderot et l'Encyclopédie* (1942); Arthur M. Wilson, *Diderot, The Testing Years 1713–1759* (1957).

7 Bernard Fäy, 'Learned Societies in Europe and America in the Eighteenth Century', *American Historical Review*, XXXVII (1931–2).

8 Jean Sarrailh, *L'Espagne éclairée de la second moitié du XVIIIe siècle* (Paris, 1954), 223–85.

9 G. Delpy, *L'Espagne et l'Esprit Européen: L'Oeuvre de Feijoo* (Paris, 1936).

10 Its nuclear member was Tommaso Cornelio, who had spent some time with Torricelli (publishing his work), and was Professor of Mathematics at the University of Naples.

Faced with the suppression of a book by one of their members, and a controversy over infected marsh land, the Investiganti had to form themselves into an academy to secure patronal protection against the medical fraternity. Amongst those whom they entertained were Magliotti (secretary of the Cimento), Sir John Finch (the Professor of Anatomy at Pisa), Francis Willughby and John Ray (both English naturalists of distinction). G. A. Borelli repeated his experiments on animal motion before them, and his book *De vi percussionis* was published with the help of the Marquis of Arena.

They met on the Wednesday afternoon sessions, with about 60 people present, though the regular members numbered only 14. Ray was impressed at such a 'knot of ingenious persons . . . of that latitude and freedom of judgement in so remote a part of Europe', and of their knowledge of the works of Galileo, Descartes, Gassendi, Harvey and Francis Bacon.

Max H. Fisch, 'The Academy of the Investigators', *Science, Medicine and History: Essays on the Evolution of Scientific Thought and Medical Practice*, collected and edited by E. Ashworth Underwood (Oxford, 1953), pp. 521–63.

11 A. Harnack, *Geschichte der Koniglich Preussichen Academie der Wissenschaften zu Berlin* (Berlin, 1900); Erik Amburger, *Die Mitglieder der Deutschen Akademie Der Wissenschaften Zu Berlin 1700–1950* (Berlin, 1950), p. 12; J. G. Hagen, *Index Operum Leonardi Euler* (Berlin, 1896).

12 A. Harnack, op. cit. (Berlin, 1910), 1–94.

13 ibid., pp. 300–2.

14 Peter Gay, *Voltaire's Politics, the Poet as Realist* (Princeton, 1959), 170.

15 Max Spindler (ed.), *Electorolis Academiae Scientiarum Boicae Primordia* (Munich, 1959); Ludwig Hammermayer, *Grüdungs-und Frühgeschichte der Bayerischen Akademie der Wissenschaften* (Munich, 1959). Its guiding spirit was J. G. Lori (1723–86).

16 Adam Ferguson, *History of Civil Society* (1767).

¹⁷ D. A. Kronick, *History of Scientific Periodicals* (New York, 1962), 127.

¹⁸ Karl Mannheim, *Essays on the Sociology of Culture* (1956), 102.

¹⁹ Fäy, op. cit.

²⁰ Henry Woolf, *The Transit of Venus: A Study of Eighteenth Century Science* (Princeton, 1959).

²¹ Louis Amiable, *Une Loge Masonnique, La Proix Les Neuf Soeurs* (Paris, 1897); N. Hans, 'UNESCO of the Eighteenth Century: La Loge des Neuf Soeurs and its venerable master, Benjamin Franklin', *Am. Phil. Society*, vol. XCVII, 513–24.

²² Gavin de Beer, *The Sciences were never at War* (London, 1960), IX, who gives many case-histories.

4: GLANDS OF THE PLANTOCRACY

¹ George R. Potter, 'The Significance to the History of English Natural Science of John Hill's *Review of the Work of the Royal Society*', *University of California Publications in English*, XIV (1943), 157–80.

² T. G. Hill, 'John Hill 1716–1775', in F. W. Oliver (ed.), *Makers of British Botany* (1913), 92–93.

³ J. A. Lovat-Fraser, *John Stuart, Earl of Bute* (1912). He also helped William Curtis (1746–99), Demonstrator at the Chelsea Garden from 1772–7, who established in 1787 the *Botanical Magazine* to satisfy the now widely diffused hunger for botanical knowledge.

⁴ Mark Catesby, preface to *Hortis Europae Americanus* (1767); J. R. Butler, 'America . . . a hunting ground for Eighteenth Century Naturalists', *Bibliog. Society of America, Papers*, XXXIII (1938), 6–7.

⁵ American colonies had gradually been developing botanic gardens of their own. Following that established near Philadelphia by German pietists in 1694, another was laid out on the Schuykill River in 1728 by John Bartram (1699–1777), the man who set himself to satiate the hunger which Europeans had for American plants. Visited by Peter Kalm, the envoy of Linnaeus, in 1728, it slowly became known, and Bartram was appointed botanist to King George III. W. M. and M. S. G. Smallwood, *Natural History and the American Mind* (1941), 150–5.

⁶ Francis Harper, *The Travels of William Bartram* (New Haven, 1958), indicates its influence on Coleridge and Carlyle.

⁷ John Bartram's friend and fellow-Philadelphian James Logan decided to test the thesis of M. Geoffroy that corn kernels could be formed without silks or pollen. So in his backyard on Second Street Philadelphia in 1727 he planted four hills of corn. In one he cut off all the tassels just as they were beginning to appear. On another he covered the ear shoots with muslin before the silks came out. On the third and fourth he took away the various portions of silks leaving the tassels. In the autumn he found no kernels on any of the ears which had the tassels removed, no corn on the ears covered with muslin. He thus proved the female function of the silks and the ovules to which they led. He told his friend Peter Collinson, a great London importer of plants who secured its publication in the *Philosophical Transactions* of 1736. Three years later it was published in Latin at Leyden. Logan's was the first of a number of experiments with corn which were later in the hands of Beal, Reid, Krug and Hershey, to produce hybrid corn. Henry A. Wallace and William L. Brown, *Corn and its Early Fathers* (Lansing, 1956).

⁸ R. Hingston Fox, *Dr. John Fothergill and his Friends* (1919), 166. Fox also gives plants introduced by Collinson (174 ff.) and Fothergill (203 ff.).

⁹ ibid., 174

¹⁰ He obtained the seeds from Sir Richard Jebb, who probably brought them

from France. When he found that they would grow he secured the translation of a French treatise on its cultivation by the Abbé de Commerel, added a preface, and published it as *An Account of the Culture and Use of the Mangold Wurzel or Root of Scarcity* (1787). This ran to four editions in a year. See G. E. Fussell, *More Old English Farming Books* (1950), 129–30; Nichols, *Literary Anecdotes*, IX, 40, *Memorials of Lettsom*, i, 106: iii, 117.

[11] He was the subject of the famous rhyme.

> When patients used to come to I
> It was 'I physics and I sweats 'em'
> When after that they choose to die,
> It did not grieve—I Lettsom.

See *Notes and Queries*, CXCI (1906), 210.

[12] A Linnaean botanic garden, established on Long Island by William Prince, was also the scene of the earliest American experiments in breeding new varieties of fruit trees, whilst that of Humphrey Marshall at Marshallton in Pennsylvania, founded in 1773, cultivated both exotic and native plants. A botanic garden was established at New Haven in 1784 with help from M. M. Mich-Guillaume and St. Jean de Crèvecoeur, whilst at Charleston, South Carolina, Andre Michaux had a garden of some 111 acres. The American Philosophical Society passed an order in 1784 that a botanic garden be planted in Philadelphia. One of Bartram's friends, Dr. Alexander Garden (after whom Linnaeus called the gardenia), corresponded with most of the European figures of his day, and returned to England in 1783 to become a pioneer teacher of chemistry with Dr. Accum. Garden sent the first electric eels to Europe with accounts of how persons joining hands received an electric shock by having contact with them.

[13] T. J. Wedtenbaker, *The Golden Age of Colonial Culture* (New York, 1942), 145. Smallwood, op it., 151.

[14] Derek Hudson and K. W. Luckhurst, *The Royal Society of Arts 1754–1954* (1954), 166.

[15] L. J. Ragatz, *The Fall of the Planter Class in the British Caribbean 1763–1833* (New York, 1928), 73.

[16] Lord Olivier, *Jamaica* (1936).

[17] Bryan Edwards, *The History, Civil and Commercial, of the British Colonies in the West Indies* (1793), vol. 1, p. 197, described it as 'perhaps the most magnificent establishment of its kind in existence', and in the appendix gave a catalogue of plants in it. For both men's correspondence with Sir Joseph Banks see Warren R. Dawson, *The Banks Letters* (1958).

[18] L. Guilding, *An Account of the Botanic Garden in the Island of St. Vincent from its First Establishment until the Present Time* (Glasgow, 1825); William Harris, 'History of the Introduction of the Economic Plants of Jamaica', *Bulletin of the Department of Agriculture* (Kingston, Jamaica, 1910), 181 ff. (1911), 284 ff.

[19] J. H. Parry and P. M. Sherlock, *A Short History of the West Indies* (1956), 149. A visit to Jamaica as a boy of 13 ignited in Nathaniel Ward (1791–1868) a passion for botany which he subsequently attempted to assuage by collecting plants in the intervals of practising medicine in London. In 1829 he invented his famous cases for their transmission, which enabled even more massive botanical offensives to be launched in other parts of the world.

[20] J. C. Beaglehole (ed.), *'The Endeavour' Journal of Joseph Banks 1768–1771* (1962), i, 99.

[21] H. C. Cameron, *Sir Joseph Banks* (1952), 120.

As the contemporary jingle went:

> While you, great George, for Knowledge hunt
> And sharp conductors change for blunt,

> Franklin a wiser course pursues
> And all your thunder useless views
> By keeping to the point.

Franklin, now in France, confessed on 14 October 1777 that:

> Disputes are apt to sour one's temper and improve one's mind. I have no private interest in the reception of my inventions by the World, having never made, nor proposed to make, the least profit by any of them. The King's changing his *pointed* conductors for *blunt* ones is therefore a matter of small importance to me. If I had a wish about it, it would be that he had rejected them altogether as ineffectual. For it is only since he thought himself safe from the thunder of Heaven that he dared to use his own thunder in destroying his innocent subjects.

[22] C. R. Weld, *History of the Royal Society* (1848), 101–2.

[23] Peter Pindar, *Peter's Prophecy, or the President and Poet* (1789).

[24] James Grahame, *The History of the United States of America, from the Plantation of the British Colonies till their Revolt and Declaration of Independence* (London, 1836), ii, 555.

America was also a cheap prison, a repository for criminals too dangerous and troublesome to remain in Britain. This 'torrent of vicious and profligate example directed by the parent state among the laborious classes of her colonial subjects' evoked strong protests from Maryland as early as 1676, while Pennsylvania imposed a duty of £5 on every convict so imported.

An order in Council was issued to prevent these practices as far back as 1686, but this and subsequent attempts could not provide a substitute for the labour of these convicts, for which planters craved so much that they were prepared to wink at past delinquencies and would even purchase bondsmen from enterprising captains who had kidnapped them at home.

Benjamin Franklin, as agent for Pennsylvania, craftily suggested to the British House of Commons that the practice be yet further extended. The plantations, he argued, should be enabled to transport their felons to Scotland and 'every English ship arriving in our ports with goods for sale, should be obliged to give bond . . . that she will carry to Britain one felon for every fifty tons of her burthen', B. Franklin, *Essays* (1819–21), 98–101.

[25] *Commons Journals*, XXVIII, 311. His proposal was amplified and elaborated four years later by James Matra and Admiral Sir George Young.

[26] W. J. Bean, *The Royal Botanic Gardens Kew, Historical and Descriptive* (1908); W. R. Dawson, *The Banks Letters* (1958). For the rest of this chapter known as 'B.L.'

[27] *B.L.*, 34.

[28] *B.L.*, 171.

[29] *B.L.*, 398.

[30] *B.L.*, 486: 'He is to pay special attention to plants producing fibre.'

[31] His *Travels in the Interior of Brazil* (1846) gives an account of his years there from 1836 to 1840.

[32] Tennent, quoted by J. C. Willis, Director of the Royal Botanic Gardens, *Ceylon in Agriculture in the Tropics* (Cambridge, 1909), 181. For a vivid account of the consequences of the blight see the novel *The Bitter Berry* (1957), by Christine Wilson.

[33] *B.L.*, 289.

[34] *B.L.*, 293.

[35] *B.L.*, 884. In the same year Lord Cornwallis the Governor General sent a 'botanical dispatch' containing a schedule of plants for Calcutta and places where they could be obtained. *B.L.*, 283.

NOTES

[36] *B.L.*, 291–2.

[37] *B.L.*, 510–14.

[38] *B.L.*, 513.

[39] *B.L.*, 715.

[40] W. H. Lang, 'William Griffith 1810–1845', in F. W. Oliver (ed.), *Makers of British Botany* (Cambridge, 1913), 183.

[41] Sir Joseph Hooker, *Himalayan Journals* (1854), i, 3–4.

[42] The personnel of these gardens played a wider role in British scientific life. J. F. Royle on leaving Saharanpur, became Professor of Materia Medica at King's College, London. Hugh Falconer's interest in fossils led, amongst other things, to the discovery that English caves once housed elephants and rhinoceri, thereby preparing opinion for the *Origin of Species*.

[43] Sir Clements R. Markham gave a brief autobiographical account of his part in the enterprise in the exchange of products between the New and Old Worlds, in *The Geographical Teacher*, v (1909–10), 6–18.

[44] G. Watt, *Dictionary of the Economic Products of India* (1889), ii, 79: vi, 429; T. Eden, *Tea* (1958), 2.

[45] Desmond King-Hele, *Erasmus Darwin* (1963), 172.

[46] Robert E. Schofield, *The Lunar Society of Birmingham* (Oxford, 1963), 206.

[47] De Witt Bowden, *Industrial Society in England Towards the End of the Eighteenth Century* (New York, 1925).

[48] The convivial nature of these groups goes back to the coffee-houses, which proliferated after the Restoration, and which John Houghton (d. 1705) considered had 'improved useful knowledge' as much as the universities. From exciting conversations like those of Robert Hooke, who, at Garaway's taught 'quaker to make cantilever', discussed clock-making with Tompion, or experimented with Shortgrave, his assistant, clubs formed. With John Hoskins, another F. R. S. Hooke was at Joe's Coffee House on 11 December 1675 where, he said 'we began New Clubb with John Aubrey'. Six months later he 'contrived new Decimal Society', this time with Robert Boyle, Christopher Wren, Nehemiah Grew, Theodore Haak and others. On 15 July 1676, the club discussed 'Logarithmotechnia, "an Arithmetick Engine" and music'. A third venture, which he launched with Aubrey in this year, was a 'Rosicrucian Club' to study alchemy, but it came to nothing. At the 'Grecian', Sir William Petty, inventor of the catamaran or double-hulled boat, also attended a club (and another at the 'Turk's Head', Westminster, where an amateur parliament was sustained). It was from the Grecian that Steele proposed to date his articles in the *Tatler*.

This universal thirst led Sir Hans Sloane's servant, James Salter, in 1695, to open a coffee-house in Cheyne Walk, Chelsea with 'Ten Thousand Gimcracks, round the Room on the ceiling'. At the Marine Coffee House, in Birchin Lane, the London Assurance Company took shape and remained till 1748. Here too, John Harris, F.R.S. (1667–1719) lectured on mathematics from 1698 to 1704, when his *Lexicon Technicum, or a Universal English Dictionary of the Arts and Sciences*, was published—the first of a long line of English encyclopaedias. At the Rainbow Coffee House in 1735 a Society for the Encouragement of Learning 'was established with the general aim of promoting the Arts and Sciences'. Earlier the Botanical Society was formed in 1721 by Johann Jacob Dillen or Dillenius (1681–1747), the Sherardian Professor of Botany at Oxford, and John Martyn (1699–1768). An Aurelian Society similarly took shape in the 'Swan Tavern', in the Cornhill, in 1745, till a fire, three years later, destroyed it. In its resurrected form it used to meet at the York Coffee House, in St. James's Street, and from this was formed the Linnaean Society in 1788.

The Royal Society itself transacted much business in a coffee-house. Its president, Martin Folkes (1690–1754) was such a *habitué* of Rawthmell's in Henrietta Street, Covent Garden, that, according to one Fellow, he chose the council and officers out of 'his junto of Sychophants' that used to meet him there every night.

Rawthmell's also incubated a more ambitious venture some thirteen years later on 22 March 1754, when a group of Fellows of the Royal Society decided to subsidize inventions by prizes in much the same way as horse-breeding was fostered by competition at the Northampton horse fair. They were anxious to find substitutes for cobalt and madder, both dyes used in the cloth trade, both imported, and both difficult to obtain. Meeting again at Rawthmell's on 29 March, they decided to make their meetings more formal, and arranged to forgather regularly at a circulating library in Crane Court, Fleet Street. From this grew the Society for the Encouragement of Arts, Manufacturers, and Commerce, perhaps better known today as the Royal Society of Arts.

These coffee-houses acted as clearing-houses for new discoveries in science. At 'Buttons', in Russell Street, Covent Garden, of which Martin Folkes was also a member, there was a post-box where intelligence of all kinds was deposited for Addison's paper, the *Guardian*. Fashioned like a lion's head, it stood on the western side of the coffee-house, 'holding its paws under the chin, on a box which contains everything that he swallows'. As Addison remarked, it was 'a proper emblem of knowledge and actions, being all head and paws'. This 'lion post-box' was later moved to the 'Bedford'. This was even more directly concerned with science. Here John Stirling, F.R.S., and later J. T. Desaguliers, F.R.S. (1683–1744), lectured on experimental philosophy. Stirling was a friend of Nicholas Bernouilli and Isaac Newton and later went on to become a mine manager in Lanarkshire. Desaguliers, once a demonstrator at the Royal Society, discoursed at large over the Great Piazza at Covent Garden to, amongst others, the Fieldings, Hogarth, Woodward, Lloyd and Goldsmith.

Joshua Ward (1685–1761) so aptly caught by Hogarth in the 'Harlot's Progress', made such good use of the scraps of gossip and information he picked up in coffee-houses that in 1736 he was able to manufacture sulphuric acid at Twickenham by the bell process, thus reducing the price of this valuable commodity some sixteenfold. But the local inhabitants were so offended by the smell of burning brimstone and nitre that they forced him to remove his plant to Richmond. By 1749 he had patented his process, and by 1758, when the French metallurgist and 'industrial spy' Gabriel Jars began visiting England, he noticed that Ward was employing Welsh women, probably so that the secret of his work would not be divulged.

A more respectable chemist, Dr. Morris, had an 'elaboratory' at Robert's Coffee House in the Great Piazza, Covent Garden, where a number of crucibles were tested in 1757. By 1782 a Chemical Society was meeting at the Chapter Coffee House in London.

E. F. Robinson, *The Early History of Coffee Houses in England* (1893); Aytoun Ellis, *The Penny Universities: A History of the Coffee Houses* (1956); G. H. Turnbull, 'Peter Staehl, the First Public Teacher of Chemistry at Oxford', *Annals of Science* IX (1953), 265. M. 'Espinasse, *Robert Hooke* (1956); A. T. Gage, *A History of the Linnean Society of London* (1938); Stuart Piggott, *William Stukeley* (Oxford, 1950); Derek Hudson and K. W. Luckhurst, *The Royal Society of Arts 1754–1954* (London, 1954); Karl Mannheim, *Essays on the Sociology of Culture*, (1956), 136 ff.

49 E. Robinson, 'The Derby Philosophical Society', *Annals of Science*, IC (1953).

50 B. D. B. Benas, *Transactions of the Historic Society of Lancashire and Cheshire*,

C. Supplement (1950), 9; H. A. Omerod, *The Liverpool Royal Institution* (1953).
51 R. A. Smith, *Memoirs of the Lit. and Phil. Soc. of Manchester*, 3rd series, IX (1883), 29; F. Nicholson, ibid., 8, LXVIII (1923–4); C. L. Barnes, *The Manchester Literary and Philosophical Society* (Manchester, 1938).
52 E. K. Clarke, *The History of 100 years of Leeds Philosophical and Literary Society* (Leeds, 1924).
53 A Temple Patterson, *Radical Leicester 1750–1850* (1954).
54 R. Spence Watson, *The History of the Literary and Philosophical Society of Newcastle upon Tyne 1793–1896* (1897).
55 *Journal of the Royal Horticultural Society*, LXX (1954), fig. 123.
56 He told Banks that 'the friends of Forsyth . . . looked on me as a potential enemy', *B.L.*, 500.
57 F. W. Oliver (ed.), *Makers of British Botany* (Cambridge, 1913), 166.
58 *Botanical Register*, XIII (1828), 1118.
59 Musk, as a fixative for scents, originally came from the male musk deer of the Himalayas and the high mountains of western China.
60 For an explanation see Frank Kingdon-Ward, *Pilgrimage for Plants* (1960) 146–56.
61 A. G. Harvey, *Douglas of the Fir* (Cambridge, Mass., 1947).
62 In addition to his *Report upon the Tea Plantations of the N.W. Provinces of India* (1851) and *Two Visits to the Tea Countries of China and the British Plantations in the Himalayas* (1853), he published *Yeddo and Peking* (1863).
63 *Rural Rides* (1893) (i), 35.
64 E. W. Bovill, *English Country Life 1780–1830* (Oxford, 1962), 116–17.
65 W. B. Turrill, *The Royal Botanic Garden, Kew* (1959), 23–24.
66 *Report made to the Committee appointed by the Treasury in 1938 to inquire into the management of the Royal Gardens by Dr. Lindley in conjunction with Messrs. Parton and Wilson 1838*, pp. 1840 (292), XXIX, 259.
67 Richard Herr, *The Eighteenth Century Revolution in Spain* (Princeton, 1958), 44; John Tate Lanning, *The Eighteenth Century Enlightenment in the University of San Carlos in Guatamela* (Ithaca, 1956), 318; *B.L.*, 777. See also pp. 641 and 567 with Casimiro Gomez Ortega, F.R.S. (1740–1818) and Joao Jacento Magellan, F.R.S. (1722–90).
68 Victor Wolfgang von Hagen, *South America called them, explorations of the great naturalists. La Condamine, Humboldt, Darwin, Spruce* (New York, 1945); Alexander von Humboldt journeyed together with Aime Bonpland (1773–1858), who after 1815 returned to America; V. W. von Hagen, 'The immortal botanist (Jose Celestine Mutis)', *J. N. York Bot. Gdn.* (1948), 177–84, 210–18.
69 Quoted in Salvador de Madariaga, *The Rise of the Spanish American Empire* (London, 1947), 225–6; Rey Pastor, *La Ciencia y la Tecnica en el Descubrimiento de America* (Buenos Aires, 1942).
70 A. Brunel, *Biographie d'Aime Bonpland* (Paris, 1872).
71 Jean Anker, 'An Eighteenth Century project for the propagation of Botanical Knowledge', *Centaurus*, III (1954), 296–304.
72 S. Garside, 'Baron Jacquin and the Schonbrunn Gardens', *J. South Africa Bot.* (1942), 201–4.
73 *B.L.*, 418.
74 ibid., 265.
75 Constantia Maxwell, *Dublin under the Georges 1714–1830* (1946), 173. It was taken over by the science and art department. In 1901 it was transferred to the newly formed Department of Agricultural and Technical Institution.
76 R. Michea, *Les travaux scientifiques de Goethe* (Paris, 1943); Agnes Arber, 'Goethe's Botany', *Chronica Botanica X* (Waltham, 1946); Sir Charles Sherrington,

Goethe on Nature and Science (Cambridge, 1949); Hans Burgin, *Der Minister Goethe* (Weimar, 1953).

[77] W. H. Bruford, *Culture and Society in Classical Weimar 1775–1806* (Cambridge, 1962), 380.

[78] Sir Stamford Raffles, F.R.S. who repaired the Penang garden laid out by the East India Company in 1800, to break the Dutch monopoly of spices. H. N. Ridley, 'The Abolition of the Botanic Gardens of Penang', *Agricultural Bulletin Straits and Federated Malay States IX* (1910), 97.

[79] Hooper was recommended as gardener to Lord Amherst's Embassy to China in 1812. Under Dr. Clarke Abel, botanist to the expedition, he was to collect seeds for Kew, noting the locality of each kind. Warren R. Dawson, *The Banks Letters*, 423.

[80] Jaime Jaramillo-Arango, 'A Critical Review of Basic Facts in the History of Cinchona', *Journal of the Linnean Society of London*, LII (1956–62), 272–312.

PART II

5: FROM PHYSIOCRACY TO PHYSICISM

[1] André J. Bourde, *The Influence of England on the French Agronomes 1750–1789* (Cambridge, 1953), 10–27.

[2] Auguste Oncken (ed.), *Oeuvres Économiques et Philosophiques de F. Quesnay* (Paris, 1888), 330, 333; Thomas P. Neill, 'Quesnay and Physiocracy', *Journal of the History of Ideas*, IX (1948), 164, and John A. Mourant, 'Mr Neill and Physiocracy', *Journal of the History of Ideas*, X (1949), 113.

[3] Warren J. Samuels, 'The Physiocratic Theory of Economic Policy', *Quarterly Journal of Economics*, LXXVI (1962), 152, 156.

[4] Jean Paul Contant, *L'Enseignement de la Chimie au Jardin royal des Plantes de Paris* (Cahors, 1952); E. T. Hamy, 'William Davisson', *Nouvelles Archives*, Series 3, X (Paris Museum d'histoire naturelle, 1898), 1–38, *D.N.B.*; J. R. Partington, *A History of Chemistry* (1962), iii, 5–7.

[5] E. S. de Beer, *The Diary of John Evelyn* (Oxford, 1955), iii, 336, iii, 9; Le Fevre's *Traicte de la Chymie* (1660), a two-volume summary of his teaching was translated into German and into English three times (in 1662, 1664 and 1670). His English laboratory contained the Cabinet of Drugs which had belonged to the wife of Oliver Cromwell; R. T. Gunter, *Early Science in Oxford* (1923), i, 29.

[6] Lynn Thorndyke, *A History of Magic and Experimental Science* (New York, 1959), VIII, 146–53. Partington, op. cit., 28–41.

[7] Henry Guerlac, 'A note on Lavoisier's scientific education', *Isis* (1956), XLVII, pp. 221–226, suggests that Lavoisier actually worked with Rouelle at his house and apothecary's shop on the corner of the rue Jacob and the rue des Anges in the St. Germain quarter.

[8] L. J. M. Coleby, *The Chemical Studies of P. J. Macquer* (1938); Ernest Cassirer, *The Philosophy of the Enlightenment* (1951).

[9] But even this did not exhaust its capacity to sustain fundamental science. For 100 years after this happened Henry Becquerel, who occupied the same post as his father had done before him in the Museum, discovered in 1896 that uranium minerals could produce radiation which could pass through solid materials and could affect photographic prints.

[10] J. R. Partington, *History of Chemistry*, iii (1962), 516, 557.

[11] This school was established in 1749 to supply engineers for the Corps des Ingénieurs des Ponts et Chaussées, themselves established by Jacques III Gabriel

(1667–1742) thirty years before. Students wore grey uniforms with grey and silver facings, symbolizing their para-military status. They were the brainchildren of D. C. Trudaine (1703–69), and their first director, J. R. Perronet, was a pioneer of production engineering; his nephew, L. M. H. Navier (1785–1836), a pioneer of modern structural analysis.

Though small—there were only 20 pupils at the school of whom 10 graduated each year as lieutenants in engineering—the École des Ponts et Chaussées set a second precent: 70 per cent of the pupils' fees were paid by the State. The investment was a rich one, for N. J. Cugnot (1725–1804) invented the first steam-propelled truck, while Gaspard Monge (1764–1818) the great descriptive geometer, were both students here. Monge's geometry, though originally intended for use in military engineering, became the basis of the methods by which mechanical engineers work. Without it, said E. T. Bell (*Men of Mathematics* (1939), 212), 'the wholesale spawning of machinery in the nineteenth century would probably have been impossible'. Monge in turn taught Lazare Carnot (1749–1827)—'le grand Carnot'—the statesman, general and 'organiser of victory' who directed the armies of Revolutionary France from 1793 to 1795.

The horse and cow were also too important to miss the benefits which organised training of their service personnel could bring, and so the École Vétérinaire was founded at Lyons in 1761 by Claud Bourgelat (1712–92). This was so successful that five years later two others were founded at Limoges and Alfort. The Government gave grants to all of them. Under the directorship of the Abbé J. B. Rozier, the École Vétérinaire produced some remarkable people: Daubenton, Vicq d'Azyr, Fourcroy, Gilbert and Brussonet. J. B. Rozier trained men from other countries too, like Denmark and Sweden. Hernquist founded a similar school at Scara in 1772. Stellinger was made a director of another at Hanover in 1773 and Abilgaard founded a third at Copenhagen in 1773. The care for horses and animals fostered by these institutions was further disseminated by other foundations at Dresden (1794), Vienna (1776), Budapest (1786), Berlin and Munich (1790), Milan (1791), Madrid (1793) and Brussels (1832).

[12] A. Fourcy, *Histoire de l'École Polytechnique* (Paris, 1828); G. Pinel, *Histoire de l'École Polytechnique* (Paris, 1887); F. Schabel, *Die Anfänge des technischen hochschulwesens* (Stuttgart, 1925); L. de Launay, *Un grand français, Monge, Fondateur de l'école Polytechnique* (Paris, 1933).

[13] R. Taton, 'The French Revolution and the Progress of Science', *Centaurus*, iii (1953), pp. 73 ff.; F. B. Artz, 'L'Enseignement technique en l'époque révolutionnaire', *Revue Historique*, CXCVI (1946), p. 257; L. Pearce Williams, 'Science, Education and the French Revolution', *Isis*, XLIV (1953).

[14] F. A. Hayek, 'The Counter-Revolution of Science', *Economica* (London, 1941), vii, 15 ff., 119 ff., 281 ff., gives an excellent bibliography.

[15] Hayek, op. cit., 138; Adeline Daumard, 'Les Élèves de l'École Polytechnique de 1815 à 1848', *Revue d'histoire moderne et contemporaine* (1958).

[16] Vicesimus Knox, *Works* (1924), 277–383.

[17] Napoleon's *coup d'état* on 9 November 1799 led to the academic freedom of the École Polytechnique being curtailed and the students channelled on graduation into public service. In 1804 it became a military academy with sergeants, barracks and military discipline congealing the warm optimism of the original foundation. The same spirit extended to the *écoles centrales* where the dictum of J. A. Chaptal was rigorously applied that 'The principal goal of education ought to be to give everyone the knowledge necessary for them to fulfil the functions of society to which he is called.' Even lower down in the *lycées*, only 8 of the total of 44 had any courses going in physics, chemistry, or natural history and 10 taught mathematics beyond intermediate algebra.

The strings of centralization were pulled even more tightly when Napoleon established on 17 March 1808 the Imperial University at Paris. This had branches in Aix, Dijon, Caen, Lyons, Strasbourg and Toulouse by 1809 and Besançon, Grenoble, Metz, Montpellier, Rennes, Brussels, Liége, Genoa, Turin and Leyden by 1812. Science wilted under such constriction: in the subsequent 6 years the Faculty of Science granted only 40 licences and 10 doctorates. L. P. Williams, 'Science, Education and Napoloen I', *Isis*, XLVIII (1956), 369–86.

[18] Luce Langevin, 'The Introduction of the Metric System', *Impact of Science on society*, XI (Paris, 1961), 77–95.

[19] W. A. Smeaton, *Fourcroy, Chemist and Revolutionary 1755–1809* (1962).

[20] W. A. Smeaton, 'The Early Years of the Lycée and the Lycée des Artes', *Annals of Science*, XI (1955), 257 ff., 309 ff.; 'The Early History of Laboratory Instruction in Chemistry at the École Polytechnique and Elsewhere', *Annals of Science*, X (1954), 224.

[21] D. I. Duveen, 'Augustin Francois Silvestre and the Société Philomathique', *Annals of Science*, X (1954), 339–41.

[22] *Oeuvres IV*, 179, quoted E. S. Mason, 'St.-Simonism and the Rationalisation of Industry', *Quarterly Journal of Economics*, XLV (1930–1), 650.

[23] G. G. Iggers, *The Cult of Authority: The Political Philosophy of the Saint Simon* (The Hague, 1958); F. E. Manuel, *The New World of Henry St. Simon* (Cambridge, 1956).

[24] D. O. Evans, *Social Romanticism in France 1830–1848* (Oxford, 1951), 25–26. This has a very good critical bibliography.

[25] E. M. Butler, *The Saint-Simonian Religion in Germany* (Cambridge, 1926).

[26] D. B. Cofer, *St. Simonism and the Radicalism of Thomas Carlyle* (London, 1931).

[27] John Stuart Mill, *Autobiography*, 166; I. W. Mueller, *John Stuart Mill and French Thought* (Urbana, 1956).

[28] The influence of St. Simon on Comte has been contested by Henri Gouhier, *La Jeunesse d'August Comte*, 3 vols. (Paris, 1933–41); For the spread of Comte's ideas in England and the United States see J. E. McGee, *A Crusade for Humanity, The History of Organised Positivism in England* (1931); R. L. Hawkins, *Auguste Comte and the United States (1816–1857)* (Cambridge, Mass., 1936); *August Comte and the United States 1853–1861* (Cambridge, Mass., 1938).

[29] Auguste Comte, *Appeal to Conservatives* (1855), translated by T. C. Dinkin and Richard Congreve (London, 1889), 122.

[30] ibid., 133.

[31] ibid., 43.

[32] ibid., 115–16.

[33] ibid., 117.

[34] Comte's own worship of Clothilde de Vaux does not explain this heavy emphasis on the Worship of the Virgin. He was basically anti-Communist. He has been described as 'by temperament a theologian' and his *Système de Politique Positive* as the culmination of French social thought and philosophical history. Frank E. Manuel, *The Prophets of Paris* (Cambridge, Mass., 1962), 275.

[35] *Appeal to Conservatives*, 120–1.

[36] ibid., 149–52.

[37] ibid., 149

[38] ibid, 145–6.

[39] Alexandre Zevaes, 'De l'origine du mot socialisme', *Revue politique et parliamentaire*, CCVI (1952), 142.

[40] Charles Madge, *Society in the Mind: Elements of Social Eidos* (1964), 51.

[41] ibid., 131–2.

6: MATERIALISTS AND MONISTS

1 Heinrich Bechtel, *Wirtschaftsgeschichte Deutschlands im 19. und 20. Jahrhundert* (Munich, 1956); W. O. Henderson, *The State and the Industrial Revolution in Prussia* (Liverpool, 1958), 96–118.

2 R. H. Thomas, *Liberalism, Nationalism and the German Intellectuals 1822–1847* (Cambridge, 1952).

3 See the excellent new biography, by a physicist, L. Kellner, *Alexander von Humboldt* (1963).

4 Rondo E. Cameron, *France and the Economic Development of Europe* (Princeton, New Jersey, 1961). Rudolph Virchow, 'The founding of the Berlin University and the transition from the Philosophic to the Scientific Age', *Annual Report of the Board of Regents of the Smithsonian Institution* (Washington, 1896), 685 ff.

5 *Report of the Commissioner of Education for the Year 1898–9* (Washington, 1900), i, 230 ff.

6 John Read, *Humour and Humanism in Chemistry* (London, 1947), 233 ff.

7 Quoted by H. G. Good, 'On the Early History of Liebig's Laboratory', *Journal of Chemical Education*, XIII (1936), 557–62.

8 ibid.

9 H. M. Leicester in *Journal of Chemical Education*, XVII (1940), 303 ff.

10 L. F. Haber, *The Chemical Industry during the Nineteenth Century* (Oxford, 1958), 71.

11 O. J. Walker, 'August Kekulé and the Benzene Problem', *Annals of Science*, IV (1939), 34.

12 Philipp Lenard, *Great Men of Science* (trans. H. S. Hatfield) (London, 1933), pp. 263–70. For an overall picture of the political troubles into which Weber was drawn in 1848 see L. B. Namier, '1848: The Revolution of the Intellectuals', *Proceedings of the British Academy*, XXX (1944), 161–282.

Incidentally, Weber's elder brother E. H. Weber (1795–1878) of Leipzig, made measurements of another kind: the differential response of touching different parts of the skin, and helped lay the foundations of what Fechner was in 1860 to call 'psychophysics' This too used a laboratory which was first organized by Wilhelm Wundt (1832–1920) who, under the influence of Helmholtz (whose assistant he had been), turned his attention to psychology. Wundt's psychological laboratory—the first in the world—did more than anything else to establish psychology as a serious subject for scientific instruction. Herman Ebbinghaus (1850–1909), influenced by Fechner, wrote the first really effective textbook on the subject.

13 This was first published as an appendix in the 1888 edition of Engels' *Ludwig Feuerbach* (English Edition, 1934). Engels originally published a series of articles reviewing a book on Feuerbach by Starcke in *Die Neue Zeit* in 1886.

14 Engels, *Ludwig Feuerbach;* quoted in *A Handbook of Marxism* (London, 1935), 220.

15 ibid., 222.

16 F. Fischer, *Das Studium Der Technischen Chemie an Den Universitäten und Technischen Hochschulen Deutschlands* (Braunschweig, 1897).

17 Philip Frank, *Einstein, His Life and Times* (New York, 1953), 18–21. G. Guggenkuhl, *Geschichte der Eigenössischen Technische Hochschule* (1955). For a picture of life there see John Read, *History of Chemistry*, 265 ff.

18 S. P. Timoshenko, *History of Strength of Materials* (London, 1953), 133 ff. Karlsruhe also nursed K. Culmann (1821–81), whose incorporation of much of the best American and British techniques in German bridge building earned him the

chair of the theory of structures at the Zürich polytechnic, and Friedrich Engesser (1848–1931) the notable railway engineer. Indeed its distinction was such that August Föppl (1854–1924) moved here from Stuttgart to study under O. Mohr (1835–1918). Keeping step with these advances were the mathematicians. Siegfried H. Aronhold (1819–84), who also taught at the Technische Hochschule in Berlin, worked on algebraic invariants. These in the hands of Alfred Clebsch (1833–72) of Karlsruhe, and later of Giessen and Göttingen carried forward in algebra the work of the English mathematicians Cayley and Sylvester. Following them came Paul Gordan (1837–1912) of the University of Erlangen. Nor should A. F. Mobius (1790–1868) be forgotten. In the Leipzig observatory he became one of the founders of modern topology. Some of these German mathematicians were experimental physicists too. Julius Plucker of Bonn worked on electrical conduction in gases, spectroscopy and crystal magnetism. One of Plucker's pupils, Felix Klein (1845–1929), was to become in 1875 the Professor of Mathematics at the Munich Technische Hochschule, where he pressed for the inclusion of more mathematics in the engineering curriculum. Klein's real service, however, was his teaching of a number of American students. He not only attracted them, but was himself attracted by American methods. In 1898, 12 years after resuming the chair at Göttingen, he persuaded German industrialists to establish a number of research institutions there under the Göttinger Vereinigung zur Förderung der Angewandten Physik und Mathematik. Not the least of Klein's activity was his work on the gyroscope.

[19] ibid., p. 349.

[20] E. Berl, 'Fritz Haber', *Journal of Chemical Education*, XIV (1937), 203–7.

[21] The first German industrial engineering laboratory was established at Munich in 1871 under Johann Bauschinger (1833–93). Others were established at the Berlin Polytechnic (1871) under A. Martens, at Vienna (1873) under K. Jenny, at Zürich (1879) under Ludwig von Tetmajer and at Stuttgart (1879) under C. Bach.

[22] C. Matschoss, *Great Engineers* (trans. H. S. Hatfield) (London, 1939), 300.

[23] *First Report of the Royal Commission on Technical Instruction* (1882), pp. 208–9.

[24] Josef Becker, *Von der Bauakademie zur Technischen Universität* (1949); Franz Schnabal, *Die Anfänge des Technischen Hochschulwesens* (1955).

[25] J. J. Beer, *The Emergence of the German Dye Industry* (Urbana, 1959).

[26] R. E. Oesper, 'Alwyn Mittasch', *Journal of Chemical Education* (1948), 531–2. See also 'A. Mittasch and W. Frankenburger', in *Journal of Chemical Education* (1929), VI, 2098 ff.

[27] J. J. Beer, 'Coal Tar Dye Manufacture and the Origins of the Modern Industrial Research Laboratory', *Isis*, XLIX (1958), 123, 131, and *The Emergence of the German Dye Industry* (Urbana, 1959).

[28] L. Konigsberger, *Hermann von Helmholtz* (1906).

[29] J. Stark, *Forschung and Prüfung. 50 Jahre physicalisch-technische Reichsanstalt* (Leipzig, 1937).

[30] *The British Association for the Advancement of Science*, p. 549. (Cardiff, 1891).

[31] Max Planck, *Scientific Autobiography and other papers* (trans. F. Gaynor) (London, 1950), 15, 24.

[32] Max Planck, *25 Jahre Kaiser Wilhelm-Gesellschaft zur Förderung der Wissenschaften*, 3 vols. (Berlin, 1936); F. Glum, *The Kaiser-Wilhelm Gesellschaft for the Promotion of Science* (1930).

[33] In 1949 the Deutsche Forschungstat was established for assisting the various academies of sciences. By 1951 there was created the *Deutsche Forschungsgemein-*

schaft—an association of all the academies, universities and the *Max Planck Gesellschaft*; supported by local authorities and industry and in turn supporting expeditions and foreign journeys and researches. Their co-operation in rebuilding the shattered fabric of the German industrial complex has been such that D.S.I.R. was 'impressed' by the work achieved in a mere decade. That one-quarter of the 127,000 students were in technical universities says much for the perseverance of a tradition in the scientific life of a state. *A Brief Review of Science and Technology in Western Germany* (H.M.S.O., 1955).

34 F. Engels, *Herr Eugen Dühring's Revolution in Science* (*'Anti-Dühring'*) (1878).

35 Erik Nordenskiold, *The History of Biology* (translated by L. B. Eyre) (New York, 1928), 5, gives a good account of this struggle.

36 At the Institute for Infectious Diseases founded by Robert Koch (1843–1910), discoverer of the organisms of some 11 diseases including anthrax and tuberculosis, chemistry was made a normal part of medical training, instead of being only a Ph.D. course. His pupil Paul Ehrlich (1854–1915) found that by staining cells with acid, basic or natural dyes, he could track a synthetic chemical substance which would act on organisms without damaging them. His 606th attempt to find such a substance to cure syphilis produced Salvarsan (606) and, later on, Neosalvarsan (909).

In 1896 Ehrlich became Director of a small State Institute for Investigation and Control in Berlin and 3 years later at a larger Institute for Experimental Therapy at Frankfurt-am-Main, where for 16 years he did most of his work. Ludwig Benda at the Casella chemical works at Frankfurt (later part of I. G. Farben) helped him with pharmaceuticals. From here Dr. Shiga took his techniques to Japan. The Georg Speyer Haus founded in 1909 for chemotherapy by a wealthy admirer of Ehrlich's, was yet another centre in Frankfurt for his work.

37 F. E. Wall, 'Wilhelm Ostwald', *Journal of Chemical Education* XXV (1948), 2 ff. Ostwald influenced, through A. A. Boyes (1866–1936), the chemical department of the California Institute of Technology as well as the establishment of the Rice Institute of Texas.

7: EMERGENT OPERATIONALISM IN ENGLAND

1 T. Carlile, *An Address to Men of Science* (1821), quoted by Brian Simon, *Studies in the History of Education 1780–1870* (1960), 200–4.

2 L. Pearce Williams, 'The Royal Society and the founding of the British Association for the Advancement of Science'. *Notes and Records of the Royal Society*, XVI (1961), 221–33. See also note 12.

3 O. J. R. Howarth, *The British Association* (1931), 260–2.

4 L. Pearce Williams, op. cit.

5 I. Todhunter, *William Whewell D.D.* (1876), ii, 293.

6 For further details see C. E. Raven, *Natural Religion and Christian Theology* (Cambridge, 1953), 174; Charles Colston Gillispie, *Geology and Genesis* (1951).

7 Sir J. S. Flett, *The First Hundred Years of the Geological Survey of Great Britain* (1937), 78.

8 Andrew Ure, *Philosophy of Manufactures* (1835). See exegesis of this in Karl Marx, *Capital*, and L. Mumford, *Technics and Civilisation* (1934), 173, 270.

9 Admiration of French Revolutionary principles had led James Anderson, Professor of Natural Philosophy at the University of Glasgow, to send a new kind of gun to the Constituent Assembly which they hung in their hall under the inscription 'The Gift of Science to Liberty'. The assembly also adopted his suggestion

to use fireballoons of paper varnished with boiled oil, to disseminate their propaganda in Germany. On his death, he left what his biographer has called 'the most valuable collection of scientific apparatus in Britain, or perhaps Europe' together with a library of some 2,000 volumes, to Glasgow, 'for the good of Mankind and the Improvement of Science'.

The most significant aspect of Anderson's bequest was for a functional council to manage his new institution; to be composed of 9 representatives from each of 9 classes: tradesmen, agriculturists, artists, manufacturers, 'mediciners', lawyers, divines, natural philosophers and his own kinsmen. The professoriate (36 in number), were not to be 'Drones, or Triflers, Drunkards of negligent of their Duty in any manner of way'.

Taking shape in part of the grammar school, the Andersonian Institution (now the University of Strathclyde) appointed Thomas Garnett, M.D., to lecture in 1796. Garnett's courses (one on the Arts and Manufactures connected with Natural Philosophy and Chemistry, a popular course on experimental philosophy, and a popular course in modern discoveries and their application) drew bumper audiences —100, 528 and 344 respectively attended them. After four years he left for a similar institution recently founded in London and his successor, Dr. George Birkbeck, who also drew large audiences, also left after four years to be succeeded by Dr. Andrew Ure, a chemist and encyclopaedist. Like Garnett and Birkbeck, Ure also migrated to London after teaching at Glasgow for 24 years.

Thomas Kelly, *George Birkbeck, Pioneer of Adult Education* (Liverpool, 1957), 236, and James Mure, *John Anderson, Pioneer of Technical Education* (Glasgow, 1950), 12, 23, 49.

[10] A. Audigane, 'Du mouvement intellectual parmi les populations ouvrières', *Revue des Deux Mondes*, X (1851), 860–93.

[11] M. Tylecote, *The Mechanics' Institutes of Lancashire and Yorkshire before 1851* (Manchester, 1957), 36–39.

[12] J. L. Pritchard, *Sir George Cayley 1773–1857: The Inventor of the Aeroplane* (1961), 126.

[13] B. V. Bowden, *Faster than Thought. A Symposium on Digital Computing Machines* (1953), 7–18; also P. and E. Morrison, *Charles Babbage and his Calculating Engines* (1961); Maboth Moseley, *Irascible Genius* (1964).

[14] 'The Society of Civil Engineers', *Transactions of the Newcomen Society*, XVII (1938), 51–71.

[15] I. Todhunter, *William Whewell D.D.* (1876), ii, 204.

[16] *Philosophy of the Inductive Sciences* (1840), i, 113.

[17] I. Todhunter, op. cit., i, 219.

[18] I. Todhunter, op. cit., ii, 217. He told Murchison on 15 July 1835: 'I saw Lord Auckland on the subject yesterday, and want to set my man to work before I leave London.'

[19] ibid., 239.

[20] ibid., ii, 277.

[21] ibid., ii, 357.

[22] *Report of the British Association . . . for 1849*, XIX. Lord Wrottesley was a founder of the Royal Astronomical Society in 1820, of which he became secretary (1831–41) and president (1841–3). He was elected F.R.S. in 1841 and P.R.S. 1854–7. According to Howarth his death in 1867 'was the death blow of the Parliamentary Committee of the Association. The weakness of the scheme for a parliamentary committee, unless under a chairman of strong personality and predisposed towards using that quality to keep the committee active, lay probably in the necessarily frequent changes in its personnel, in addition to the preoccupation

of its members with other claims upon their time.' *The British Association* (1931), 227–8.

23 W. H. G. Armytage, 'James Heywood's resolution: Prelude and Finale', *Universities Review*, XXIII (1950), 139–83.

24 He urged the British Association to prepare a report on the Polytechnic in Paris. See *Annual Reports* (1841), 96–98; (1842), 93, 94, 96; (1848), 86.

25 See J. A. Caski, *Life and Letters of Matthew Fontaine Maury* (Richmond, 1928). He was Superintendent of the Department of Charts and Instruments and his chart of the sea-bottom between England and the U.S.A. showed the practicality of the submarine cable. Lord Wrottesley gave a full and appreciative account of his work in the House of Lords on 26 April 1853.

26 *Hansard*, 10 June 1856. He originally announced that he would move for a commission. *Hansard*, 6 August 1855.

27 *Hansard*, 10 June 1856.

28 O. J. R. Haworth, *The British Association for the Advancement of Science 1831–1931* (1931), 260–2.

29 R. H. Shoen, 'Prince Albert and the Application of Statistics to Problems of Government', *Osiris*, v (1939), 216–318.

30 Yvonne French, *The Great Exhibition* (1951); Wemyss Reid, *Memoirs and Correspondence of Lord Playfair* (1899), 312.

31 *Report of the British Association . . . at Glasgow* (1955), l–li.

32 D. S. L. Cardwell, *The Organisation of Science in England* (1957), 66 ff. He considers that it was the multiplication of the facilities for training scientists that whetted the appetite for employing them.

33 George Haines IV, *German Influence upon English Education and Science 1800–1866* (Connecticut College Monographs No. 6. New London, 1957).

34 H. B. Charlton, *Portrait of a University* (Manchester, 1951), 54: 'It was largely though Roscoe . . . the experimental science became the motive force by which the British idea of a university was revolutionized.'

35 G. A. Foote, 'The Place of Science in the British Reform Movement', *Isis*, XLII (1951), 192 ff., 3.

36 A. H. Huth, *A. T. Buckle* (1880), ii, 142; Giles St. Aubyn, *A Victorian Eminence* (1958), 32.

37 W. M. Simon, *The Growth of Organised Positivism in Europe* (Ithaca, 1963), 174.

38 ibid., 88.

39 Herbert Spencer, *Education* (1861), chapter 2.

8: THE LAWS AND THE PROPHETS

1 Tom Burns and G. M. Stalker, *The Management of Innovation* (1961), 27.

2 Sir Henry Lyons, *The Royal Society 1660–1940* (Cambridge, 1944), 275.

3 Thomas S. Kuhn, 'The Function of Dogma in Scientific Research' in A. C. Crombie (ed.), *Scientific Change* (1961), 347–69.

4 B. Willey, *Darwin and Butler* (1960), 15–16.

5 Marston Bates and Philip S. Humphrey, *The Darwin Reader* (1957), 103, 55.

6 L. Huxley (ed.), *The Life and Letters of J. D. Hooker* (1918), 525–6; Gertrude Himmelfarb, *Darwin and the Darwinian Revolution* (1959), 239.

7 H. Festing Jones (ed.), *The Notebooks of Samuel Butler* (1912), 339. He also wrote: 'I tore open the wounds of my Redeemer as he hung upon the Cross in *The Fair Haven* and people rather liked it. But when I attacked Mr. Darwin they were up in a moment.' A. T. Bartholemew, *Further Extracts from the Notebooks of Samuel Butler* (1934), 183.

8 M. L. Cazamian, *Le Roman et les idées en Angleterre: L'influence de la science 1860–1890* (Paris, 1923); Leo J. Henken, *Darwinism in the English Novel 1860–1910* (New York, 1963).

9 Karl Marx and Friedrich Engels, *Correspondence 1846–1895* (1934), 125; E. H. Carr, *Karl Marx. A Study in Fanaticism* (1934).

10 Herbert Spencer, *Man versus the State* (1885), chapter I is entitled 'The Coming Slavery'.

11 Karl Pearson, *Darwinism, Medical Progress and Eugenics* (1912), 2: 'The right to live does not connote the right of each man to reproduce his kind . . . As we lessen the stringency of natural selection, and more and more of the weaklings and the unfit survive, we must increase the standard, mental and physical, of parentage.' So too Darwin's son, in Major Leonard Darwin, *Problems in Eugenics* (1912), 5: 'If we tell the breeders of cattle that their knowledge of the laws of heredity is so imperfect that it is useless for them either to attempt to or to avoid breeding from their worst stocks or to try only to breed from their best stocks, why, they would simply laugh at us; and the number of those who now see matters as regards mankind in the same light is steadfastly increasing.'

12 C. B. Davenport, *Heredity in Relation to Eugenics* (1912).

13 J. Arthur Thompson, in *Darwin and Modern Science* (1909), 15.

14 *The Education of Henry Adams* (1919), 225–6.

15 *Kapital* (Moscow, 1949), 1, 387; quoted S. G. Shapovalenko, *Polytechnica Education in the U.S.S.R.* (Unesco, 1963), 73.

16 Crane Brinton, *The Shaping of the Modern Mind* (Mentor Park, 1957), 207.

17 Samuel Butler, *Erewhon* (Signet Classics, 1961).

18 D. S. L. Cardwell, *The Organisation of Science in England* (London, 1957), 149. But he argues that it was the production of scientists in England which created an appetite for them in industry.

19 A. Wood, *The Cavendish Laboratory* (1946).

20 J. Scott-Russell, *Systematic Technical Education for the English People* (London, 1869). Since the Liberals were slow to take this up he began to intrigue for a new functional constitution. As he saw it, a 'Council of Workmen' and a 'Council of Legislation' could establish an 8-hour day, county councils and publicly maintained recreation grounds, would nationalize public undertakings (like railways) and pass a homestead law. He secured the furtive adhesion of some prominent Conservatives and some Trades Unionists. Unfortunately one of them blurted out details of the scheme at Leeds on 6 October 1871, and 'so electrified the old party managers', that they 'began to feel that the end of the world was at hand'. Even Mr. Gladstone abandoned his customary Delphic style to assure his constituents at Blackheath that: 'Those who promise to the dwellers in towns that every one of them shall have a house and garden in free air, with ample space; those who tell you that there shall be markets for selling at wholesale prices retail quantities—I won't say they are imposters, because I have no doubt they are sincere—but I will say they are quacks.'
The *Observer*, 17 October 1871; *The Economist*, 18 November 1871.

21 *Suggestions on Academical Organisation* (1868); see also V. H. H. Green, *Oxford Common Room* (1957), 239–61.

22 Matthew Arnold, *Higher Schools and Universities in Germany* (1874).

23 G. M. Young, *Victorian England* (1937), 164–5.

24 W. H. G. Armytage, *Civic Universities* (1955).

25 L. F. Haber, *The Chemical Industry in the Nineteenth Century* (Oxford, 1958).

26 E. Garcke, *The Progress of Electrical Enterprise* (1907); Rollo Appleyard, *History of the Institution of Electrical Engineers 1871–1931* (1931); Ferranti and

Ince, *Life and Letters of Sebastian Ziani de Ferranti* (1934); R. H. Parsons, *Early Days of the Power Station Industry* (1939); K. R. Swan, *Sir Joseph Swan* (1946); J. D. Scott, *Siemens Brothers 1858–1958.*

[27] J. P. Brown, *Some Aspects of the Early Development of the Electric Lighting Industry 1882–1919* (M. A. Thesis, Sheffield, 1964), 438, quoting Ayrton's obituary in *Nature* (1908).

[28] Vargas Eyre, *Henry Edward Armstrong (1841–1937)* (1958), 67–163.

[29] Further research in the biographies of these men will reveal others.

[30] At Winnington H. E. Cocksedge asked the Board for a free hand to investigate low and high temperatures, high vacuums and high pressures. Work was continued on lines initiated by F. A. Freeth, and by 1933 the first specimen of polythene was obtained by R. O. Gibson. Not until 1935 did M. W. Perrin and W. D. R. Manney make it again and not until 1938 was a ton of it made for trials. These were satisfactory and so I.C.I. built a plant at Wallerscote which provided material for radar. After the Second World War the production of polythene became part of the £40 million plant at Wilton.

[31] S. H. Longrigg, *Oil in the Middle East. Its Discovery and Development* (1954); Henry Longhurst, *Adventure in Oil* (1959).

[32] Frederic Stanley Kipping, *Obituary Notices of Fellows of the Royal Society*, VII (1950–1), 183, 219.

[33] Charles Wilson, *The History of Unilever. A Study in Economic Growth and Social Change* (1954), i, 37–38.

[34] A fine study of the role of the B.M.A. in politics can be found in Harry Eckstein, *Pressure Group Politics* (1960), 46. See also E. M. Little, *The British Medical Association* (1932), 79–80.

[35] L. F. Haber, *The Chemical Industry During the Nineteenth Century* (Oxford, 1958), 209.

[36] Rollo Appleyard, *History of the Institution of Electrical Engineers 1871–1931.*

[37] Karl Pearson, *National Life from the Standpoint of Science* (1905), 54, 56; Karl Pearson, *The Grammar of Science* (1900).

[38] Sir Francis Galton, *Essays in Eugenics* (1909), 42.

[39] Karl Pearson, 'The Moral Basis of Socialism' (1887); *The Ethic of Free Thought* (1901), 325.

[40] ibid., 305. See also Ernest Haeckel, *Freedom in Science and Teaching* (1892), 89–90; Herbert Spencer, *Man versus the State* (1892), 65–72; F. W. Headley, *Darwin and Modern Socialism* (1909), 308–9; Benjamin Kidd, *Social Evolution* (1894).

[41] Bernard Bergonzi, *The Early H. G. Wells. A Study of the Scientific Romances* (Manchester, 1961), 112–61. By 1918 Wells himself had become the prophet of another Utopia for Victor Rousseau, *The Apostle of the Cylinder* (1918).

[42] ibid., 69.

[43] H. G. Wells, *Anticipations* (1902), 167.

[44] Bernard Shaw, *Man and Superman* (Penguin edition, 1946), 94.

[45] *The Revolutionist's Handbook*, 227.

[46] ibid., 265, 266.

[47] ibid., 272.

[48] Bernard Semmel, *Imperialism and Social Reform. English Social-Imperial Thought 1895–1914* (1960), 51, 75–77. It was not the only such group to have been formed. Forty years earlier what John Fiske, the American historian, called 'the most powerful and influential scientific coterie in England', was founded by T. H. Huxley in 1864. This was the X Club, which lasted for 20 years as a caucus for science. Though the 10th member never materialized, the ever-present 9 were

all powerful in their respective spheres: Herbert Spencer as a publicist, William Spottiswoode the mathematician and Royal Printer, Edward Frankland as a chemist, T. A. Hirst as a physicist, Sir John Lubbock as a banker, John Tyndall of the Royal Institution, Sir Joseph Hooker as Director of Kew and George Busk as a zoologist. Dining before meetings of the Royal Society, it seemed to signalize that Babbage's battle had indeed been won and that the professionals were now in command of that venerable institution: Cyril Bibby, *T. H. Huxley* (1959), 248. Nor was it the first group to indicate the progress of the German pacemaker—see George Haines (1958), 'German Influence upon Scientific Instruction in England 1867–1887', *Victorian Studies*, I (Bloomington, Indiana 1957), p. 230; *German Influence upon English Education and Science 1800–1866* (New London, Connecticut).

49 H. F. Heath and A. L. Hetherington, *Industrial Research and Development in the United Kingdom* (London, 1946); *Final Report* (1918), C09035, 21–22.

50 Sir Harry Melville, *The Department of Scientific and Industrial Research* (1962); *Report of the Committee of the Privy Council for Scientific and Industrial Research 1915–16*, Cd8336; *1916–17*, Cd8718.

51 PEP, *Advisory Committees in British Government* (1960), 3–4. Strictly speaking, the Inland Revenue established a laboratory in 1843 to examine adulterable goods like spirits and tobacco, and the War Department established another in 1854: both earlier examples of science called in to help government. For more details see A. Chaston Chapman, *The Growth of the Profession of Chemistry during the past half-century* (London, Institute of Chemistry, 1927).

52 'This', remarks Sir Henry Lyons, 'seems to have been one of the earliest international organisations which have been established in increasing numbers in order to initiate and foster international co-operation in many branches of science.' *The Royal Society 1660–1940* (Cambridge, 1944), 293.

53 S. P. Thompson, 'Le but et l'oeuvre de la Commission Électrotechnique Internationale', *La Vie Internationale* (Brussels, 1914), V, 5–26.

54 *Proc. Roy. Soc.*, 98 A (1921), XLVII. Amongst other posts he held were Scientific Adviser to Trinity House (from 1896), and Chief Examiner (1901).

55 Early in 1915 it established its own journal, even though, thanks to Lockyer, it had always been able to rely on *Nature*. Following an editorial on 21 October 1915, on 'Science in National Affairs', *Nature* expressed every week an opinion upon current affairs in which scientific methods and services were involved. These editorials were written by the assistant editor, Richard Gregory, 'to promote a more sympathetic attitude towards those who were engaged in the pursuit of scientific truth'. Such State aid as there was to science before the First World War was described in *Nature* editorial as 'a sham supplemented by a few doles'.

56 Cecil J. Schneer, *The Search for Order* (1960), 201–2, 259–63.

57 ibid., 346.

58 J. Balfour, *Decadence* (1908).

PART III

9: IMPROVISED EUROPEANS

1 *Oeuvres*, XVIII, 63–68, quoted *Henri, Comte de Saint-Simon (1760–1825)*, edited and translated by F. M. H. Markham (Oxford, 1952), 70.

2 Michel Chevalier (1806–79) was a graduate of the École Polytechnique and a mining engineer of some distinction. He was released from prison to go to the United States to study their techniques of communication. On his return his report, *Lettres Sur L'Amérique du Nord* (1836), made him famous. Alexander von Hum-

boldt described it as a treatise on the civilization of the peoples of the West. He subsequently became a moving figure in the Commercial Treaty with Britain, initiated on the British side by Richard Cobden, another admirer of America.

3 Mortimer Cromwell, *Philosophical Transactions* (London, 1741), cited R. S. Bates, *Scientific Societies in the United States* (New York, 1958), p. 2; F. E. Brasch, *The Newtonian Epoch in the American Colonies* (1940), and 'The Royal Society of London and its influence upon Scientific Thought in the American Colonies', *Scientific Monthly*, XXXIII (1931), 337–55, 448–9; Michael Kraus, 'Scientific Relations between Europe and America in the Eighteenth Century', *Scientific Monthly*, LV (1942), 259–72.

4 R. E. Schofield, *The Lunar Society* (Oxford, 1964).

5 Galen C. Ewing, 'The Early Teaching of Science in the College of William and Mary in Virginia', *Journal of Chemical Education*, XV (1958), 3–13.

6 I. B. Cohen (*Franklin and Newton* (Philadelphia, 1956), 207–9.

7 George Gregory, editor of the *New Annual Register* was the author of *The Economy of Nature* which attracted Joseph Henry to a scientific career; T. Coulson, *Joseph Henry. His Life and Work* (Princeton, 1950), 14.

8 E. S. Dana and others, *A Century of Science in America, with Especial Reference to the American Journal of Science* (New Haven, 1918); R. C. Loehr, 'The Influence of English Agriculture on American Agriculture 1775–1825', *Agricultural History*, XI (1937), 3–16.

9 Durand Echeverria, *Mirage in the West. A History of the French Image of American Society to 1815* (1957); Gilbert Chinard, *L'Amérique et la rêve exotique dans la littérature au XVIIe et XVIIIe siècle* (1913); A. H. Hirsch, 'French influence on American Agriculture in the Colonial Period', *Agricultural History*, IV (1930), 1–10; Léonie Villard, *La France et les États-Unis: Échanges et Rencontres 1524–1800* (Lyon, 1952).

10 W. M. and M. C. Smallwood, 145. *Natural History and the American Mind* (New York, 1941).

11 R. S. Bates, *Scientific Societies in the United States* (New York, 1958), 51.

12 H. M. Jones, *America and French Culture 1750–1848* (Chapel Hill, 1927).

13 V. C. Miller, *Joel Barlow, Revolutionist* (Hamburg, 1932); T. A. Zuider, *The Early Days of Joel Barlow* (1934); C. B. Todd, *Life and Letters of Joel Barlow* (New York, 1886), 82. In America his house 'Kalorama' housed the biggest and most valuable library in the country, and was the port of call of everyone of note: Fulton, the pioneer of steamboats, is said to have constructed a model of the *Clermont* there and to have first tested its powers on the waters of nearby Rock Creek.

14 Belknap papers. *Massachusetts Historical Society Collections 5*, Series II, 255.

15 Knight, *A Documentary History of Education in the South before 1860* (1949), ii, 86; H. B. Adams, *Thomas Jefferson, the University of Virginia* (Washington, 1888), 45-50.

16 Roy T. Honeywell, *The Educational Work of Thomas Jefferson* (Cambridge, Mass., 1931), 110–11.

17 Richard Rathburn, 'The Columbian Institute for the Promotion of Arts and Sciences', *Smithsonian Bulletin*, 101 (1917).

18 G. B. Goode, *The Smithsonian Institution, 1846–1896* (Washington, 1897).

19 E. T. Martin, *Thomas Jefferson: Scientist* (New York, 1952); C. A. Browne, *Thomas Jefferson and the Scientific Trends of his Times* (1943); J. G. Greene, 'Science and the Public in the Age of Jefferson', *Isis*, XLIX (1958), 12–25.

20 John Crane and J. F. Kieley, *United States Naval Academy: The First Hundred Years* (New York, 1945); William Baumer, *West Point, Moulder of Men* (New York, 1942).

[21] Sidney Forman, *West Point* (New York, 1950); R. E. Dupuy, *Men of West Point* (New York, 1951).

[22] Palmer C. Ricketts, *History of the Rensselaer Polytechnic Institute* (1930); Ethel McAllister, *Amos Eaton* (Philadelphia, 1941).

[23] Forest G. Hill, 'Formative Relations of American Enterprise, Government and Science', *Political Science Quarterly*, LXXV (1960), 419.

[24] J. Kip Finch, *A History of the School of Engineering, Columbia University* (New York, 1954), p. 58.

[25] H. A. Pochmann, *German Culture in America: Philosophical and Cultural Influences 1600–1900* (Madison, 1957), 45, 515.

[26] Orie W. Long, *Literary Pioneers: Early American Explorers of European Culture* (Cambridge, Mass., 1935), and Charles F. Thwing, *The American and German University* (New York, 1928).

[27] For a brief historical sketch see F. R. Moulton in *Science*, CVIII (1948), 217–18.

[28] Bates, op. cit., 239–40; Carl Wittke, *Refugees of Revolution* (Philadelphia, 1952).

[29] For the influence of Göttingen, Halle, Berlin and Leipzig see B. A. Hinsdale in *Report of the U.S. Commissioner of Education*, i (1897–8), 610–13, and for a partisan account Albert B. Faust, *The German Element in the United States* (New York, 1909).

[30] For further studies see: Merle M. Odgers, *Alexander Dullas Bache. Scientist and Educator 1806–1867*; F. W. True, *A History of the First Half-Century of the National Academy of Sciences* (Washington, 1913); Nathan Reingold, 'Science in the Civil War', *Isis*, XLIX (1949), 307–18.

[31] E. W. Gilbert, *The Exploration of Western America 1500–1550* (Cambridge, 1933).

[32] Donald G. Tewkesbury, *Founding of Colleges and Universities before the Civil War* (New York, 1932).

[33] Harrison Hale, 'Early Chemical Laboratories West of the Mississippi', *Journal of Chemical Education*, XIV (1937), 62–65.

[34] J. S. Nohsinger, *Correspondence Schools, Lyceums and Chantauquas* (1926). One of the most popular scientific lecturers on the Lyceum circuits was a half-blind enthusiast, E. L. Youmans (1821–87). The chemistry of familiar objects stimulated him to produce a variety of lively textbooks and a collection of papers called *The Culture Demanded by Modern Life* (1867). To compass the increasing sweep of scientific discovery, he initiated the famous International Scientific Series, and the famous *Popular Science Monthly* (1872) which as the *Scientific Monthly* still brings the results of scientific investigations to a non-scientific public. H. G. Good, *Sci. Monthly*, March 1924; C. M. Haar, *Journal of the History of Ideas*, IX (1948), 193–213. 'He did more than anyone else to prepare the way in America for the great scientific awakening which first became visible after the publication of the *Origin of Species*', wrote John Fiske in 1894. For generalized surveys see also: W. M. Smallwood and M. C. Smallwood, *Natural History and the American Mind* (New York, 1941); Dirk Struik, *Yankee Science in the Making* (Boston, 1948); Theodore Hornberger, *Scientific Thought in the American College 1638–1800* (Austin, 1945); I. B. Cohen, *Some Early Tools of American Science* (Cambridge, 1950); Louis W. McKeehan, *Yale Science, The First Hundred Years (1701–1801)*; J. F. Fulton and E. H. Thomson, *Benjamin Silliman* (New York, 1947); Courtney R. Hall, *Samuel Latham Mitchell* (New York, 1934); E. T. Martin, *Thomas Jefferson: Scientist* (New York, 1952); Whitfield J. Bell, jun., *Early American Science. Needs and Opportunities for Study* (Williamsburg, 1935); Wyndham Mills, 'Early American Chemistry Societies', *Chymia* (1950), III, 95–113.

[35] Merle Curti, *Probing our Past* (1955), 214.

[36] G. A. Sala, *My Diary in America in the Midst of War* ii (1856), 396.

10: THE ZAPADNIKI

[1] William Richardson, *Anecdotes of the Russian Empire* (1784).

[2] Lady Elizabeth Craven, *A Journey through Crimea to Constantinople* (1789).

[3] P. I. Lyashchenki, *History of the National Economy of Russia* (trans. L. M. Herman) (New York, 1949), 424; Inna Lubimenko, 'Les Étrangers en Russie avant Pierre le Grand', *Revue des études slaves*, iii (1923), iv (1924).

[4] Alexander Lipske, 'The Foundation of the Russian Academy of Sciences', *Isis*, XLIV (1953), 349; G. A. Knjaev and A. V. Kolzov, *A Short Outline of the History of the Academy of Sciences of the U.S.S.R.* (Moscow, 1957).

[5] B. N. Menshutkin, *Russia's Lomonosov: Chemist, Courtier, Physicist* (Princeton, 1952); B. N. Menschutkin, 'A Russian Physical Chemist of the Eighteenth Century', *J.C.E.*, IV (1927), 1079–87; L. Langevin, 'Lomonosov and the Science of his Day', *Impact of Science on Society*, XIII (1963), 93–94, 119.

[6] Allen McConnell, 'Helvetius' Russian Pupils', *Journal of the History of Ideas*, XXIV (1963), 373–86; N. Verdiaev, *The Russian Idea* (trans. R. French) (London, 1937); L. G. Crocker, *An Age of Crisis, Man and World in Eighteenth-Century French Thought* (Baltimore, 1959).

[7] A. N. Radischev, *A Journey from St. Petersburg to Moscow* (trans. Leo Wiener) (Cambridge, Mass., 1958), 264.

[8] Emile Haumant, *La Culture francaise en Russie* (1910); J. Mathorez, *Les Étrangères en France sous l'ancien régime* (Paris, 1919–21); Dimitri S. von Mohrenschildt, *Russia in the Intellectual Life of Eighteenth Century France* (1936); Albert Lortholary, *Les 'philosophes' du XVIIIe siècle et la Russie* (1951).

[9] N. Hans, *The Russian Tradition in Education* (1963), 16–18.

[10] W. Kirchnev, 'Samuel Bentham and Siberia', *Slavonic and East European Review*, XXXVI (1958), 471–80; M. S. Anderson, 'Some British Influences on Russian Intellectual Life and Society in the 18th Century', *Slavonic and East European Review*, XXXIX (1960), 148–63; W. O. Henderson, *The Industrial Revolution on the Continent, Germany, France, Russia 1800–1914* (London, 1961).

[11] W. H. Gantt, *Russian Medicine* (1937). Nothing has been said about Masonic influence, visible in 1772 when Ivan Yelagin became Grand Master, or about Russian students in England and Scotland. Simon Desnitski and Ivan Tretyakov, graduates of Moscow, were in Glasgow in 1761. Both returned to become professors in Russia.

[12] William Coxe, *Travels in Poland, Russia and Sweden* (5th edition, 1802), iii, 134; Peter Putnam, *Seven Britons in Imperial Russia* (Princeton, 1952), considers him along with John Perry, engineer to the Tsar (1698–1712), Jonas Hanway, merchant of the Russia Company (1743–50), William Richardson, student of slavery (1768–72), Sir James Harris, British Ambassador (1777–83) and Robert Ker Porter, Court Painter (1805–7).

[13] A similar parallel can be seen between the work of V. V. Petrov, who discovered the electric arc in 1805, and that of Humphry Davy three years earlier.

[14] The person who introduced the writings of Darwin (and Marx) to Russia was N. K. Mikhailovsky (1842–1904), a mining engineer—the only radical to live *and* publish in Russia, which shows what a guarantee of safety the *technical* intelligentsia enjoyed. J. H. Billington, *Mikhailovsky and Russian Populism* (Oxford, 1958).

[15] A. H. Huth, *H. T. Buckle* (1880), 142; Giles St. Aubyn, *A Victorian Eminence* (1958), 32.

[16] D. Mackenzie Wallace, *Russia* (1877), 1, 167–8.

[17] Quoted in Richard Kindersley, *The First Russian Revisionists* (Oxford, 1962), 6.

[18] Rondo E. Cameron, *France and the Economic Development of Europe, 1800–1914* (Princeton, 1962); S. P. Timoshenko, *History of Strength of Material* (New York, 1953).

[19] *Économie sociale des intérets du commerce, de l'industrie, de l'agriculture et de la civilisation en général* (1836); G. Maray, *Constantin Pecqueur fondateur du collectivisme d'État (1801–87)* (Paris, 1934).

[20] In his paper *Le Salut du Peuple*, 10 April 1850, quoted D. O. Evans, op. cit., 66.

[21] T. Dobzhansky, in E. J. Simmons (ed.), *Continuity and Change in Russian and Soviet Thought* (Cambridge, Mass., 1955), 338–9.

[22] A. Tarsaidze, 'The Air Blitz of 1812', *The Russian Review*, ii (New York, 1942), 89–101.

[23] Nicholas Halasz, *Nobel* (New York, 1959).

[24] H. M. Leicester, *J.C.E.*, XVII (1940), 203; *J.C.E.*, XXIV (1947), 438–43. In 1861 Butlerov introduced the structural theory of organic compounds. His pupils included A. M. Zaytsev, S. N. Reformotsky and Ye Ye Wagner. It continued under A. Y. Arbuzov (1877–?) who graduated at Kazan in 1900 and became Dean in 1924 of the Department of Physics and Mathematics. His son Boris graduated from the Kazan Institute of Agriculture and Forestry in 1926 and became Professor of the Kazan Institute of Chemical Technology (1935) and at the university in 1938.

[25] Richard Kindersley, *The First Russian Revisionists* (Oxford, 1963), 9.

[26] ibid., 34. M. I. Tugan-Baranovsky began as a natural scientist in the Faculty of Physics and Mathematics at the University of Kharkov; Sergey N. Bulgakov, in 1871, bound himself at Moscow like a convict to his barrow . . . to devote himself to a science which was 'alien' to him (i.e. Political Economy) and Nikolay Berdyaev studied both natural science and law at the University of Kiev.

[27] Martin Malia, *Alexander Herzen and the Birth of Russian Socialism 1812–1855* (Oxford, 1961), 61 ff.

[28] P. P. Kohler, *The Journals of the Marquis de Custine* (New York, 1951), 85.

[29] K. Galkin, *The Training of Scientists in the Soviet Union* (Moscow, 1959), 10.

[30] David Hecht, *Russian Radicals look to America 1825–1894* (Cambridge, Mass., 1947), 25.

[31] A. S. Lappo-Danilevsky, in J. D. Duff (ed.), *Russian Realities and Problems* (Cambridge, 1917).

[32] Nicholas V. Riasanovsky, 'Russia and Asia: Two Nineteenth Century Russian Views', *University of California Slavic Studies* (Berkeley, 1960), 170–81.

[33] Roger Dow, 'Prostor; A geopolitical Study of Russia and the U.S.A.', *Russian Review*, i (1941), 6–19.

[34] D. M. Wallace, *Russia* (1877) 111, 375.

[35] 'American Democracy was born of no theorist's Dream . . . it is stark and strong and full of life out of the American forest and it gained new strength each time it touched a new frontier.' So F. J. Turner wrote in 1914, but when his essay was reprinted in 1920 he omitted the words 'stark and strong and full of life'. For an examination of this see Henry Nash Smith, *Virgin Land. The American West as Symbol and Myth* (Cambridge, Mass., 1950), 153–196; Lee Benson, *Turner and Beard, American Historical Writing Reconsidered* (Glencoe, 1960), 2–91, suggests that this theory was European in origin.

[36] For an illuminating comparison of its literary legacy with that of transportation see E. S. Bates, *Soviet Asia, Progress and Problems* (London, 1942), 41. Siberia was more humane than the Georgia chain gangs of the time.

[37] Donald W. Treadgold, *The Great Siberian Migration: Government and Peasant in Resettlement from Emancipation to the First World War* (Princeton, 1957), 42ff.

[38] Geroid T. Robinson, *Russia Under the Old Regime* (1932), 251.

[39] H. De Windt, *Siberia as it is* (London, 1892), 344.

[40] Tredgold, op. cit.

[41] Charles Vevier (ed.), P. McD. Collins, *Siberian Journey Down the Amur to the Pacific (1856–1857)* (Madison, 1962).

[42] Charles Vevier. 'The Collins Overland Line', *Pacific Historical Review* XXVIII (1957).

[43] J. R. Robinson, *A Kentuckian at the Court of the Tsars, the Ministry of Cassius Marcellus Clay in Russia 1861, 1862 and 1863–9* (Berea College, Kentucky, 1935), *The Life of Cassius Marcellus Clay* (Cincinnati, 1886), 445–6.

[44] G. F. Kennan, *Siberia or the Exile System* (1891) (ed. G. F. Kennan) (Chicago, 1958), XVI.

[45] *Autobiography of Mark Twain* (ed. Charles Nedier) (1959), 272.

[46] A. B. Paine, *Mark Twain's Notebook* (1935).

[47] Louis J. Budd, *Mark Twain: Social Philosopher* (Bloomington, 1962), 140–1.

[48] *The American Claimant* (author's National edition), p. 15. Mark Twain was a ready supporter of Russian Revolutionary organization. Sergius Stepniak came to see him at Hartford about the Society of American Friends of Russian Freedom. When the Russo-Japanese War broke out, Mark Twain wrote an article in favour of rioting, and when Maxim Gorki came to lecture he supported him. Gorki, however, embarrassed his American well-wishers by travelling about with a mistress.

[49] W. C. Ford, *Letters of Henry Adams 1858–1891* (Boston, 1930), 511.

[50] America was, in time, to profit from the Russian interest in electricity, for in 1875 P. H. Yablochkov (1847–94) devised his famous arc lamp by using parallel carbons, following it up by improved dynamos and motors, by flying machines and by an experimental generator that did not involve the combustion of fuel. Edison's carbon-filament lamp was matched by that of A. N. Lodykin (1840–1923) which was based on a vacuum tube and used successfully in St. Petersburg in 1873. Two years later it was perfected by Florensov and Didrechson and demonstrated in Paris and Berlin. In 1876 it was used during the construction of the Alexandrovsky Bridge over the Neva. It was later acquired (together with Lodykin's patent on molybdenum and tungsten filaments) by the General Electric Company. Later Boris Rosing, a pioneer of ultra-short-wave radio, published a method of electrical image reproduction using electronic methods of scanning, and his pupil, V. K. Zworykin, was after the revolution of 1917, to play such an important part in the development of the American electronics industry.

A. Zvorkine, 'Inventions and Scientific Ideas in Russia', in G. S. Metraux and Francis Crouset, *The Nineteenth Century World* (Mentor Books, 1963), 274.

[51] A. Tarsaidze, 'American Pioneers in Russian Railroad Building', *Russian Review*, ix, 286–95.

[52] E. Dvoichenko-Markov, 'Americans in the Crimean War', *Russian Review* xiii (1954), 137–62; G. A. Vernadsky, 'Reforms under the Czar Nicholas I: French and American Influences', *Review of Politics*, IX (1947), 47–64.

[53] James H. Billington, 'The Intelligentsia and the Religion of Humanity', *American Historical Review*, LXV (1959–60), 807.

[54] J. R. Robertson, *A Kentuckian at the Court of the Tsars* (Berea College, 1935), 246–7.

[55] V. N. Ipatieff, 'Modern Science in Russia', *Russian Review*, ii (1943), 68–80.

11: SCIENCE AND THE AMERICAN FRONTIER

[1] Worthington C. Ford, *A Cycle of Adams Letters 1861–1865* (Boston, 1920), 135, 196.

[2] A. Hunter Dupree, *Science in the Federal Government*. (Cambridge, Mass., 1957), 141.

[3] E. D. Eddy, *Colleges for our Land and Time* (New York, 1937), 31.

[4] A. D. White, *A History of the Warfare of Science with Theology in Christendom* (1896), ii, 393.

[5] ibid., i, 415.

[6] Quoted by Bernard Crick, *The American Science of Politics* (1959), 45, who adds (p. 45): 'Spencerism could thus be used as a synthesis of low Protestantism and of a high rationalist Scientism.' Richard Hofstadter, *Social Darwinism and American Thought* (Philadelphia, 1944), 21; Stow Parsons, *Evolutionary Thought in America* (New Haven, 1950).

[7] As incubators of trained men and women in quantity, these colleges set world precedents. By 1955 over a third (39·4 per cent) of all doctorates were obtained by them. The proportion of scientific doctorates awarded in lang-grant colleges was even higher—over 50 per cent of the biological, 43·6 per cent of those awarded in physical and 40·3 per cent in the mathematical sciences. Eddy, op. cit., 221.

[8] V. Branford, *Interpretations and Forecasts* (1914), 333–6.

[9] P. Mairet, *Pioneer of Sociology. The Life and Letters of Patrick Geddes* (1957), 61; Eddy, *Colleges for our Land and Time* (1957), 6–7.

[10] J. D. Hicks, *The Populist Revolt* (Minneapolis, 1931); W. P. Webb, *The Great Plains* (New York, 1931), 353–6, 419–27; H. H. Durham, *Government Handout: A Study of the Administration of Public Land* (1941), 66–69.

[11] H. S. Smith, *Virgin Land. The American West as Symbol and Myth* (1950), 198–9; William Culp Darrah, *Powell of the Colorado* (Princeton, 1951), 268, comments on the 'inevitable socialism' of such opinions of Powell's as 'Modern civilised Society is based on property—the unit being the individual. The social unit will eventually be a business corporation, and there will be a hierarchy of corporations, the highest of which will embrace all the rest and constitute the government. The basis of society will then cease to be property, and will become industry.'

[12] Clement Wood, *The Sociology of Lester F. Ward* (1930). He imported many terms into sociology like 'organicists', 'sympodial development', 'creative synthesis', 'gynaeocracy', 'social telesis'. See also Samuel Chugerman, *Lester F. Ward: The American Aristotle* (Durham, N.C., 1939).

[13] Lester F. Ward, *Dynamic Sociology* (New York, 1883), i, 698.

[14] 'In Wisconsin the University is as close to the intelligent farmer as his pig pen or his tool-house; the University laboratories are part of the alert manufacturer's plant; to the worker, the University is drawing nearer than the school around the corner and is as much his as his union is his or his favourite saloon. Creeping into the minds of students with pure seed, into the debates of youth with pure facts, into the opinions of voters with impersonal, expert knowledge, the State University is coming to be part of the citizen's own mind, just as the State is becoming a part of his will. And that's what this whole story means: the University of Wisconsin is a highly conscious lobe of the common community's mind of the State of the people of Wisconsin.' Lincoln Steffens, 'Sending a State to College', *The American Magazine*, LXVII (1909), 364.

[15] Elizabeth Dilling, *The Roosevelt Red Record and its Background* (Chicago, 1936).

[16] William H. Hay, 'Paul Carus: A Case-Study of Philosophy on the Frontier', *Journal of the History of Ideas*, XVII (1956), 498–510.

[17] Engels wrote his pamphlet against him for the Leipzig *Vorwarts*. It was subsequently published in English, with prefaces by Engels, in 1878, 1885 and 1894.

[18] R. B. Perry, *The Thought and Character of William James* (Oxford, 1936), ii, 288.

[19] R. B. Perry, *The Letters of William James* (Oxford).

[20] ibid.

[21] ibid., ii, 245–6.

[22] Mussolini said *(Sunday Times*, 11 April 1926), 'William James taught me than an action should be judged rather by its results than by its doctrinary basis.'

[23] Richard Gerber, *Utopian Fantasy* (London, 1955), 51, 55; Vernon L. Parrington, *American Dreams, A Study of American Utopias* (Providence, R. .1 1947). It is significant that A. E. Morgan, whom we shall meet in connection with the T.V.A., wrote a study of Edward Bellamy in 1944 and noticed (p. 240–1) that a mathematics professor at the University of North Dakota, John Macnie, published *The Diothas, or a Far Look Ahead* (1883), another forecast of radio, television, automobiles and various technical developments.

[24] Sir Michael Sadler, *International Review of Missions* (1921), 454–5, Bernard Crick, *The American Science of Politics* (1959).

[25] Bernard Barber, *Science and the Social Order* (Glencoe, 1952), 114; Fritz Machlup, *The Production and Distribution of Knowledge in the United States* (Princeton, 1962), 51–144.

[26] C. V. Kidd, *American Universities and Federal Research* (Cambridge, Mass., 1959).

[27] J. Frederic Dewhurst and associates, *America's Needs and Resources* (New York, 1955).

[28] Abraham Flexner, *Daniel Coit Gilman* (1946); Hugh Hawkins, *Pioneer: A History of the Johns Hopkins University 1874–1889* (Cornell, 1960); E. C. Kirkland, *Dream and Thought in the Business Community* (Ithica, New York, 1956).

[29] Donald Fleming, *William H. Welch and the Rise of Modern Medicine* (Boston, 1954).

[30] Helen Wright, *The Great Palomar Telescope* (London, 1953).

[31] To provide an outlet for a series of articles by Herbert Spencer, originally commissioned for *Galaxy*, Edward N. Youmans started the *Popular Science Monthly* in 1872. It successfully carried forward the promise of its title till 1915 when the title was sold, and the journal became the *Scientific Monthly*. Frank Luther Mott, *A History of American Magazines 1865–1885* (Cambridge, Mass., 1957), 495–9.

[32] Courtney R. Hall, 'The Lessons of the War Between the States', in F. Martin-Ibanez (ed.), *A History of American Medicine* (New York, 1959).

[33] T. Swann Harding, *Two Blades of Grass. A History of Scientific Development in the U.S. Department of Agriculture* (Norman, Oklahoma, 1947).

[34] A. Hunter Duprée, *Science in the Federal Government* (Harvard, 1957), 183.

[35] The British scientific journal *Nature* carried a report by A. D. Little (12 March 1914, vol. XCIII, p. 45), which said: 'There is devoted to American agriculture a far greater amount of scientific research and effort than is at the service of any other business in the world.' The Bureau was later to foster soil erosion programmes under the Bankhead-Jones Act of 1935, and sustained laboratories (endowed by the Agricultural Adjustment Act of 1938), where surpluses might be utilized. Of these laboratories, New Orleans (Louisiana), Albany (California), Wyndmoor (Pennsylvania), Beltsville (in Maryland) and Peoria

(Illinois)—the last is perhaps the best known. For here was developed during the Second World War, the mass-manufacture of penicillin.

[36] As a great-grandson of the second President, grandson of the sixth and son of the American Ambassador to Britain during the American Civil War, Henry Adams knew the corners in the corridors of power. At his Washington house on H. Street, many conversations, nominations and suggestions were empitomized in a casual phrase and a dropped hint. For Adams learned early.

[37] His biographer wrote, 'Not since the exploration of Siberia a hundred years earlier, under orders from Catherine the Great, had any government undertaken such an ambitious enquiry into its domain.' Ernest Samuels, *Henry Adams, the Middle Years* (Cambridge, 1958), 34.

[38] David H. Dickason, 'Henry Adams and Clarence King, the Record of a Friendship', *New England Quarterly*, XVII (1944), 229–54.

[39] Thurmon Walker, *Clarence King* (1958), 312–27.

[40] M. de Wolfe Howe (ed.), *Holmes-Laski Letters* (Oxford, 1953), ii, 103. *Holmes to Laski 1 March 1928*. The Adams enzyme was a long-lived agent in the intellectual ferment associated with America. Even before the United States took shape, Thomas Hutchinson wrote in 1771 to one of his friends, 'We have not been so quiet here these five years . . . if it were not for two or three Adamses, we should do well enough.' Carl Becker, 'The Education of Henry Adams', *The American Historical Review*, XXIV (1919), 422.

[41] *The Education of Henry Adams*, 380.

[42] W. C. Ford, *Letters of Henry Adams (1892–1918)* (1938), 301.

[43] ibid., 315.

[44] Harold D. Cater (ed.), *Henry Adams and His Friends* (Boston, 1947), 649 f.; William H. Jordy, *Henry Adams, Scientific Historian* (New Haven, 1952), 251.

[45] Jordy, op. cit., 251.

[46] *Education*, 421–2; Max. I. Bagin, 'William James and Henry Adams', *New England Quarterly*, X (1937), 712–42; Herbert L. Creek, 'The Medievalism of Henry Adams', *South Atlantic Quarterly*, XXIV (1925), 86–97; John Lydenberg, 'Henry Adams and Lincoln Steffens', *South Atlantic Quarterly*, XLVIII (1949), 42–64; R. H. Gabriel, 'Frederick Jackson Turner versus Henry Adams', *The Course of American Democratic Thought* (New York, 1940), 251–7.

[47] *Letters to a Niece and Prayer to the Virgin of Chartres* (Boston, 1920), 129–30.

[48] C. A. Beard, introduction to Brooks Adams, *The Law of Civilisation and Decay* (Vintage Books, 1949), XLVI. Writing to his brother Brooks in 1894 he asked, 'Were we on the edge of a new and lost great centralisation, or of a first great movement of disintegration?' His conclusion was 'one so-called civilisation has shown its movement, even at the centre, arrested. Its next effort may succeed, but it is more likely to be one of disintegration with Russia as the eccentric on one side and America on the other . . . In either case the next great conclusive movement is likely to take at least one full generation.' William James, too, was writing in 1910: 'I devoutly believe in the reign of peace and in the gradual advent of some form of socialist equilibrium.' R. B. Perry, *The Thought and Character of William James* (Oxford, 1936), ii, 289.

[49] Arthur F. Beringause, *Brooks Adams; a biography* (New York, 1955) sees him as influencing Theodore Roosevelt.

[50] Charles Forcey, *The Crossroads of Liberalism: Croly, Lippman and the Progressive Era 1900–1925* (New York, 1961), 15–16. His father was David Croly the educated editor first of the New York *World*, then of the *Daily Graphic*. His mother, Jane, was also a journalist, and a generous espouser of new causes, like the eugenics experiments at Oneida.

51 *The Promise of American Life* (1909), 79.

52 ibid., 436.

53 C. Forcey, op. cit., 38–39.

54 ibid.

55 M. Caullery, *Universities and Scientific Life in the United States* (New York, 1922).

12: THE RISE OF THE RUSSIAN INTELLIGENTSIA

1 Albert A. Woldman, *Lincoln and the Russians* (New York, 1952); John Hope Franklin, *The Emancipation Proclamation* (Edinburgh, 1963).

2 Frank A. Golder, 'The Russian Fleet and the American Civil War', *American Historical Review*, XX (1914–15), 801–4; 'The American Civil War through the eyes of a Russian Diplomat', ibid., XXVI (1920–1); A. E. Adamov, 'Russia and the United States at the time of the Civil War', *Journal of Modern History*, II (1930), 586–611; E. S. Pomeroy, 'The Visit of the Russian Fleet in 1863', *New York State Historical Association*, XXIV (1943), 512–17; Benjamin F. Gilbert, 'Welcome to the Czar's Fleet', *California Historical Society Quarterly* (San Francisco, March 1947), 13–19; Oscar Lewis, *The War in the Far West (1861–1865)* (New York, 1961), 219–26; A. R. Tyrner-Tyriaeur, *Lincoln and the Emperors* (London, 1962).

3 Gideon Welles, *Diary* (1911), 443.

4 ibid., 147.

5 R. F. Leslie, *Reform and Insurrection in Russian Poland 1856–1865* (London, 1963).

6 John Quincy Adams II was a great-grandson of the second President, and grandson of the sixth President of the United States and son of the then U.S. Ambassador to Britain. He spoke perhaps with even greater authority since his namesake and grandfather, John Quincy Adams, had been the U.S. Minister to Russia during the years 1812–14 when Britain went to war with the United States and the Emperor of Russia tried to mediate. John Quincy Adams I, in fact, had subsequently virtually scripted the doctrine attributed to President Monroe that the 'American continents are henceforth not to be considered as subjects for future colonisation by any European power'. The Monroe Doctrine was in essence analogous to Slavophilism, just as Pan-Americanism was to Pan-Slavism.

John Quincy Adams II's brother, Henry, we shall meet elsewhere in this book.

7 *A Complimentary Banquet given by Boston to Rear-Admiral Lessoffsky* (Boston, 1864), 49. Social thought in America and Russia had up to the Russian Fleet's arrival, been polarized by the problem of slavery. The case against it in America had been forcefully put by Harriet Beecher Stowe in *Uncle Tom's Cabin* (1852). In the same year Turgenev's *Sportsman's Sketches* helped crystallize a similar feeling in Russia (helped perhaps by a Russian translation of *Uncle Tom's Cabin* which appeared within a year). The misconceptions in both these books were the subject of fairly authoritative exposure: in Harriet Beecher Stowe by Albert J. Beveridge, in working on his life of Lincoln, and in Turgenev by Count Tolstoy in *War and Peace*; Roger Dow, 'Seichas: A comparison of Pre-reform Russia and the Anti-Bellum South', *Russian Review*, vii (1947), 3–15. Other analogies between Russia and America could be and were drawn. Some are fanciful, like that between the Pugachev's Revolt and the Boston Tea Party; others less so, like the roles of the Stroganovs and the Astors, both great merchants and fur traders. The aptest is the Russian southern lunge to the Black Sea and the American purchase of Louisiana: one gave Russia control of the Dnieper with an outlook on Turkey, the other gave the U.S.A. New Orleans with a view to Mexico. Thus Charles Boynton in his

study of the *Russian Empire* (Cincinnati, 1856), 108–9, could prophesy that 'Turkey will vanish at last in the same manner that Mexico will vanish before the steady advance of the U.S.A.'

⁸ D. M. Wallace, *Russia* (1877), 127, 492. See also his advice in *MacMillan's Magazine* (June 1876), and Baron von Haxthausen, *The Russian Empire, its people, institutions and resources* (trans. Robert Farie) (London, 1856), ii, 229 f. 'The Commune developed from the family and is still considered in law to form a family. If a stranger comes to reside in a village he is adopted. Every member has an equal claim upon the joint and undivided communal property, the distribution of the produce rests with the fathers, the "white-heads" or *starosta* (elders). A member cannot possess private property in the land.'

⁹ D. Mackenzie Wallace, who was in Russia from 1870 to 1875 remarked, 'as to a thoroughly democratic character there can be no possible doubt' (p. 572). Indeed it possessed the power of ordering transportation to Siberia, on which Wallace commented: 'This summary, informal move of procedure seems to the peasants very satisfactory. They are at a loss to understand how a notorious culprit is allowed to "buy an advocate to defend him, and are insensible to the bought advocate's eloquence". Indeed they regarded it as equivalent to bribing a judge.'

¹⁰ W. H. Gantt, *Russian Medicine* (London, 1937), 72.

¹¹ A. P. Mendel, *Dilemmas of Progress in Tsarist Russia: Legal Marxism and Legal Populism* (Cambridge, 1961), 91.

¹² Albert J. Beveridge, *The Russian Advance* (1904), 323.

¹³ ibid., 328.

¹⁴ ibid., 332. See also P. Vinogradoff, *Self-Government in Russia* (1915), 157–70. Vinogradoff was a great Russian historian who subsequently took a chair at Oxford.

¹⁵ Eugene Schuyler was at the time a young law student at Columbia University, who had already obtained his Ph.D. at Yale. He was so enchanted by the Russians that when he joined the staff of *The Nation* two years later his first article was 'On the Progress of Russia in Asia'. In this he stressed that Tashkent was the lock, and the development of the Syr-Darya area was the key.

The U.S.A., said Schuyler, 'has of all countries, the least to fear from the aggrandisement of its mighty neighbour and is absolutely free from the jealousy of competition'.

A year later Schuyler became the Consul in Moscow—a post he held for nine years. This article was written whilst he was in Russia: M. M. Coleman, 'Eugene Schuyler: Diplomat Extraordinary from the United States to Russia 1862–1876'. *Russian Review*, viii (1948), 33–47.

¹⁶ Strangely neglected by R. L. Hawkins, in *Auguste Comte and the United States* (Cambridge, Mass., 1936) and *Positivism in the United States 1853–1861* (Cambridge, 1938), but adequately treated by Donald Fleming, *John William Draper and the Religion of Science* (Philadelphia, 1950).

¹⁷ A. H. Huth, *H. T. Buckle* (1880), 152. He also said (p. 142), 'I want my book to get among the Mechanics' Institutes and the *people. . . .* These are they whom I am now beginning to touch and whom I wish to move!' Giles St. Aubyn, *A Victorian Eminence* (1958), 32; D. Mackenzie Wallace, *Russia* (1877), 1, 167–8 observed: 'During the first year of my residence in Russia, I rarely had a serious conversation without hearing Buckle's name mentioned; my friends almost always assumed that he had succeeded in creating a genuine science of history on the inductive method. In vain I pointed out that Buckle had merely thrown out some hints in an introductory chapter as to how such a science ought to be constructed and that he himself had made no serious attempt to use the method which he commenced. My objections had little, or no effect, the belief was too deep rooted

to be so eradicated. In books, periodicals, newspapers and professional lectures, the name of Buckle was constantly cited—often violently dragged in without the slightest reason—and cheap translations of his work were sold in enormous quantities.'

18 Charles C. Livermore, 'Henry C. Carey and his Social System', *Political Science Quarterly* (1890), 553–82; David Hecht, *Russian Radicals Look to America 1825–1894* (Cambridge, Mass., 1947), 87, described Carey as Chernyskevsky's 'political mentor'. Schipoff, a leading Moscow merchant, hailed Carey as a link between the two countries—see J. F. Loubat, *Narrative of the Mission to Russia in 1866 of the Hon. Gustavus Vasa Fox. From the Journal and Notes of Boubat*, ed. John D. Champlin, jun. (New York, 1873), 250–3. Unfortunately Carey is indifferently served by his two biographers, A. D. Kaplan, *Henry Charles Carey. A Study in American Economic Thought* (Baltimore, 1931) and Arnold W. Green, *Henry Charles Carey. Nineteenth-Century Sociologist* (Philadelphia, 1951). There is an essay on him in R. L. Bruckberger, *Image of America* (trans. G. G. Paulding and Virgilia Peterson) (London, 1960), 149–77.

In 1861 C. B. Clarke of Queens' College, Cambridge, printed a private denunciation of H. C. Carey's *Political Economy* (3 vols., Philadelphia, 1838), describing it as 'so barrenly unsuggestive as to be worthless reading, even for the purpose of becoming acquainted with the arguments of adversaries', and objecting to it being placed on the list of recommended books for the Moral Sciences Tripos at Cambridge. A copy of his objection is in the Goldsmith's Library of the University of London. His first objection is to Carey's statement that 'Labour is the sole cause of value'.

19 To Weydemeyer, 5 March 1852.

20 Earl Browder, 'Socialism in America', in St. Anthony's Papers Number 9. *International Communism*, ed. David Footman (London, 1960), 92–93. See also his *Marx and America* (1959).

21 Nicholas Berdyaev, *The Origin of Russian Communism* (trans. R. M. French) (Ann Arbor, 1962), 46.

22 Melvin Cherno, Feuerbach's 'Man is what he eats': A Rectification. *Journal of the History of Ideas*, XXIX (1963), 399–406.

23 F. Venturi, *The Roots of Revolution* (1960), 222 ff.

24 A. Vicunich, 'Mathematics in Russian Culture', *Journal of the History of Ideas*, XXI (1960), 161–79.

25 Max. M. Laserson, *The American Impact on Russia—Diplomatic and Ideological 1784–1917* (New York, 1950), 72–93.

26 R. U. Daniels, 'Intellectuals and the Russian Revolution', *The American Slavic and Eastern European Review*, XX (1961), 270–8; Willi Ley, *Rockets and Space Travel* (1948), 91–92.

27 Robert Henriques, *Marcus Samuel* (1960), 71.

28 *Towards an Understanding of Russia* (1906). See also Daniel Z. Posin, *Mendeleev* (New York, 1948).

29 Leon Trotsky (1925), *Marxism and Science*—a speech delivered on 17 September 1925.

30 I. M. Sechenov, *Reflexes of the Brain*, 35.

31 B. P. Babkin, *Pavlov* (London, 1951).

32 Yuri Semyonov, *Siberia: Conquest and Development* (trans. J. R. Foster) (London, 1963), 309–10.

33 ibid., 328.

34 R. E. C. Long was impressed by his policy: 'While in England learned economists write in *The Times* on the ills and evils of Municipal Socialism . . . in Russia everything, from the bakery to the publishing trade, has been municipalised.'

R. E. C. Long, *Fortnightly Review* (1903), 109–26; S. R. Tomkins, 'Witte as Minister of Finance 1892–1903', *Slavonic and East European Review* (1933), 590–606; T. H. Von Laue, *Sergei Witte and the Industrialisation of Russia* (New York, 1963); Mark Aldanov 'Count Witte', *Russian Review* II (1941), 56–64.

[35] 'Special Schools of Science and the Arts in Russia', *The American Journal of Education*, XXI (1870), 721–34.

[36] Arthur P. Mendel, *Dilemmas of Progress in Tsarist Russia* (Cambridge, Mass., 1961), 19.

[37] Richard Pipes, *Social Democracy and the St. Petersburg Labour Movement 1885–1897* (Cambridge, Mass., 1963), 19–20.

[38] Arthur P. Mendel, *Dilemmas of Progress in Tsarist Russia: Legal Marxism and Legal Populism* (Cambridge, Mass., 1961), 124–5.

[39] Alan Townsend, 'Soviet Science Fiction', *The Listener*, LXX (1963), 465.

[40] K. Galkin, *The Training of Scientists in the Soviet Union* (Moscow, 1959), 25.

[41] *Works*, vol. 19, p. 115, quoted Galkin, op. cit., p. 28.

[42] For a good study of Ostwald see F. G. Donnan in *Chemical Society Memorial Lecture 1933–1942*, vol. lv. (London, 1951), 1–17.

[43] A. A. Bogdanov (1873–1928). In 1913 he published a volume on Tectology or 'Universal Organisational Science'. He was a surgeon during the First World War, and afterwards devoted himself to blood transfusion, dying after an experiment on himself. See also Bertram Wolfe, *Three who Made a Revolution* (1948); Lennard Schapiro, *The Communist Party of the Soviet Union* (1960); S. V. Utechin in Leopold Labedz (ed.), *Revisionism, Essays on the Theory of Marxist Ideas* (1962), 117–18. It is interesting to compare his views with those of Henry Adams who wrote from Paris on 2 August 1910. 'Society is ready for collectivism; it has no fight left in it; and our class is as defunct as the dodo. We are just jellyfish, and flabby all through', and earlier on 20 June 1910: 'I am trying to find out what your friend Ostwald . . . thinks or teaches or intends. I come as a student in a spirit of love and moral chastity.' Adams had previously described himself on 9 September 1909 as 'a poor bit of materialised energetic'. W. C. Ford, op. cit., 546, 543 and 523.

[44] A. Lunacharsky (1875–1933) joined the Social Democrats in 1897, sided with Lenin in 1913, quarrelled over religion, returned to Petrograd as a Bolshevik in 1917, and was commisar for education until 1929, during which time pragmatism flourished in pedagogical circles.

[45] V. I. Lenin, 'Empirio-Criticism and Historical Materialism', in *Works*, vol. XIV (London, 1962), 342.

[46] Lawrence A. Cremin, *The Transformation of the School* (1961), 24–25, 27.

[47] Taylor won the Doubles championship of the U.S. Tennis Association in 1881, and invented for golfers a two-handed putter shaped like the letter 'Y', and was an enthusiast for 'picture windows'. Copley, ii, 189–80; *Classified Guide to the F. W. Taylor Collection*. Stevens Institute of Technology, 1951.

[48] Frank Barkley Copley, *Frederick W. Taylor—Father of Scientific Management* (1923), ii, 24, 30. Of Barth, Copley remarks, in connection with Taylor's paper on metal cutting experiments in 1906, that he 'has not received in this connection the credit to which he is entitled'. Practically all the mathematical formulae in Taylor's paper were worked up by Barth, and many of the standard tools there pictured and described represented Barth's personal ingenuity; if they became known as Taylor tools, they were only so in the sense that Taylor had inspired and directed the general course of the experiments of which they were the outcome.

[49] The New York Society for Ethical Culture was founded by Felix Adler (1851–1933) in 1876, and took up progressive ideas—see R. H. Beck, 'Pro-

gressive Education and American Progressivism: Felix Adler', *Teachers College Record*, LX (1958–9). C. M. Woodward remarks that Adler 'greatly stimulated the general interest in manual training following the work of Della Vos'. *Report of the Commissioners of Education for the Years 1893–94* (Washington, 1896), i, 888.

[50] F. B. Copley, *F. W. Taylor, Father of Scientific Management* (1923), ii, 288 quoting *Pravda*, 2 April 1918.

[51] ibid., i, xxii.

[52] Copley, ii, 258.

[53] W. H. Gantt (ed.), J. P. Pavlov, *Lectures on Conditioned Reflexes* (1928), 1, 341.

[54] S. V. Utechin 'Bolsheviks and their Allies after 1917: The Ideological Pattern', *Soviet Studies*, X (1958), 113–33.

13: THE NEW POLITICAL ARITHMETIC IN BRITAIN

[1] *Nature*, 18 November 1869.

[2] *The Engineer*, 9 April 1869.

[3] C. W. Dilke, *Greater Britain: A Record of Travel in English-Speaking Countries During 1866 and 1867* (London, 1868), 1, 92–93, 113. He continued, 'Not only have the appropriations for educational purposes by each state been large, but those of the Federal Government have been upon the most splendid scale. What has been done in the Eastern and Central States no man can tell, but even west of the Mississippi twenty two million acres have already been granted for such purposes, while fifty-six million more are set aside for similar gifts.'

[4] *Report of the Fifty Fifth Meeting of the British Association for the Advancement of Science of Aberdeen* (1885).

[5] E. D. Eddy, *Colleges for our Land and Time* (1957), 53; James Bryce, *The American Commonwealth* (1897), ii, 893.

[6] *University and Historical Addresses* (1913), 170.

[7] *Report on Agricultural Colleges and Experimental Stations of the U.S.A.*, C.7699 (H.M.S.O., 1895). P. G. Craigie (1843–1930) became assistant secretary of the Board of Agriculture and Fisheries in 1897, and was regarded as the founder of modern agricultural statistics (*Nature*, CXXV (1930), p. 135).

[8] Bernard Semmel, *Imperialism and Social Reform* (1960), 189.

[9] *Culture and Anarchy* (ed. J. Dover Wilson), 22.

[10] ibid., 17; Thorold Rogers (ed.), *Public Addresses* (1879), 62.

[11] *Culture and Anarchy*, 113.

[12] E. W. Vincent and Percival Hinton, *The University of Birmingham: Its History and Significance (1947)*, 28.

[13] ibid., 34.

[14] *The Problem of Agricultural Education in America and England with special reference to a Policy of Developing the work at University College, Reading* (Reading, 1910).

[15] A. Trowbridge, 'The New Ph.D. in Great Britain and France', Association of American Universities, *Proceedings* (1931), 101–3; Stephen Duggan, *Observations on Higher Education in Europe*, Bulletin No. 3. (New York, Institute of International Education, 1920), 380–1; C. K. Allen, *Forty years of Rhodes Scholarships* (O.U.P., 1944).

[16] Quoted by R. H. Heindel, *The American Impact on Great Britain* (Philadelphia, 1940).

[17] *Moseley Industrial Commission to the U.S. Report of the Delegates* (Manchester, 1903); W. P. Groser, another member, who represented the Parliamentary Industry Committee, was asked to write a book on *Education and Industrial Success*

(1904) because he presented so strong a case for reform. *Report of the Moseley Educational Commission to the U.S. of A. Oct.–Dec. 1903* (London, 1904), and A. Edmund Spender, 'Random Notes on the Moseley Education Commission' (reprinted from *Western Morning News*, 1903). It was also published in the *Annual Reports of the Department of the Interior (Commissioner for Education) for 1906* (Washington, 1902), edited by W. T. Harris, pp. 1–37.

[18] National Association of Education Officers, *Education in Relation to Industry: A Report on Technical Schools in Canada and the U.S.A.* (Leeds, 1912).

[19] L. E. Mather (ed.), *Sir William Mather* (1920).

[20] *Nature*, XCVII (25 May 1916), 270–2, see also 23 March 1916, XCVII, 91. The Advisory Council later published a pamphlet of his on the subject. A. P. M. Fleming, *Industrial Research in the U.S.A.* (1915).

[21] Non-metallurgical products had 5: Coal (1938), Coke (1944), Ceramics (1948), Whiting (1948) and Coal Tar (1949); metallurgical processes 7: Cast Iron (1921), Non-Ferrous Metals (1919), Iron and Steel (1944), Gold, Silver, Jewellery (1946), Coil Springs (1946), Welding (1946), Cutlery (1952); electrical engineering 8: Electrical Engineering (1920), Scientific Instruments (1918), I/c engines (1943), Shipbuilding (1944), Marine (1945), Motor (1945), Production Engineering (1946) and Hydromechanics (1947); hosiery, footwear and textile industries 9: Cotton (1919), Linen (1919), Jute (1946), Rayon (1946) Felt (1947), Hosiery (1949), Lace (1949) and Linoleum (1949), Boots and Shoes (1919) and Leather (1920); and food 4: Flour (1927), Baking (1946), Food (1946), Fruit and Vegetable Canning (1952). The remaining 7 deal with various uncategorizable industries like Rubber (1919), Laundry (1920), Paint (1926), Printing and Packing (1930), Paper (1945), Gelatine and Glue (1945) and Furniture (1950). *Nature*, XCVII (1916), 230. R. S. Edwards, *Co-operative Industrial Research* (1950), 32–52.

[22] Henry Longhurst, *Adventure in Oil* (1959), 188–93.

[23] F. Soddy, *Science and Life* (1920), 203.

[24] *Manchester Guardian*, 7 January 1961.

[25] J. H. Dunning, *American Investment in British Manufacturing Industry* (1958), 310.

[26] Cited in *Science*, 8 April 1960.

[27] Michael Sadler, 'Education for Life and Duty', *International Review of Missions*, October, 1921, pp. 454–5.

[28] *Nineteenth Century*, XLIII (1898), 281.

[29] See *Centenary of the Birth of Andrew Carnegie* (1935). The real credit for the proposal goes to W. G. S. Adams who wrote the report for the Carnegie trustees. Nineteen authorities were so helped before 1919.

[30] A. Flexner, *Universities American, English, German* (1930).

[31] W. H. G. Armytage, 'Rockefeller Money and British Universities', *Universities Quarterly*, XI (1957), 254–61.

[32] As Perry Miller wrote: 'America is a perpetual declaration that Western European society can become open-ended if it tries. Men can be mobile and careers open to talents. Violence and vulgarity, improvised jazz, philosophical pragmatism, and decent bathrooms are so many declarations of man's mastery over his resources. And this mastery—here is the American contention—is as possible in Europe and America. It is as possible because America is Europe working out, still in the process of working out—far as yet from attaining—ambitions that were conceived and cradled in Europe.' *The Impact of America on European Culture* (Boston, 1951), 84–85.

[33] H. F. Heath and A. L. Hetherington, *Industrial Research and Development in the United Kingdom* (London, 1946).

[34] C. W. Forman, *Science for Empire: Britain's Development of the Empire Through Scientific Research 1895–1940* (Ph.d University of Wisconsin (1941)).

PART IV

14: AMERIKANSKI TEMPO

[1] N. A. Borodin in *Russian Review*, ii (New York, 1916), 75.

[2] V. I. Vernadsky, 'What Russia Expected from the War', *Russian Review*, iii (1917), 3–14.

[3] Richard Pipes, *Social Democaracy and the St. Petersburg Labour Movement, 1885–1897* (Cambridge, Mass., 1963), 48.

[4] D. Shut, *Lenin* (New York, 1948), 38.

[5] According to Naum Jasny, *Soviet Industrialisation 1928–1952* (Chicago, 1961), 39, Lenin obtained the idea of GOELRO from a Moscow professor of engineering, V. I. Grinevetsky, author of *Post War Perspectives of Russian Engineering* (Kharkov, 1919), and only intended it to be 'a lure to capture the support of the people'.

[6] S. and B. Webb, *Soviet Communism. A New Civilisation* (3rd edition, 1947), 505.

[7] ibid., 507.

[8] M. Cole (ed.), *Beatrice Webb's Diaries 1912–1924* (1952), 190ff., 201.

[9] G. M. Krzhizhanovsky, *The Basis of the Technological Economic Plan of Reconstruction of the U.S.S.R.* (1931).

[10] Allan Nevins and Frank E. Hill, *Ford: the Times, the Man, the Company* (New York, 1954). In the Soviet economic journal, *The Planned Economy*, Stalin had to compete for space with Henry Ford. See 'The Soviet Model of Growth' in Evsey D. Domit, *Essays on the Theory of Economic Growth* (1957), 223–61, and Dana G. Dalrymple 'The American Tractor comes to Soviet Agriculture: The Transfer of a Technology', *Technology and Culture*, V (1964), 191–214.

[11] Walter A. Leuchtenburg, *The Perils of Prosperity 1914–1932* (1958), 186–203, who points out that the generation of electric power in the U.S.A. increased from 6 billion to 117 billion kWh. per year.

[12] For Albert Kahn (1869–1942), see *Architectural Forum*, August 1938 and George Nelson, *Industrial Architecture of Albert Kahn Inc.* (New York, 1939).

[13] Harriet Borland, *Soviet Literary Theory and Practice During the First Five Year Plan, 1928–32* (New York, 1950), 87.

[14] R. W. Davies, 'Some Soviet Economic Controllers—I', *Soviet Studies*, XI (1960), 298.

[15] R. V. Daniels, 'Intellectuals and the Russian Revolution', *American Slavic and East European Review*, XX (1961), 270–8.

[16] Julian Towster, *Political Power in the U.S.S.R. 1917–1947* (Oxford, 1948), 396.

[17] Eric Johnston, *We're all in It* (1948), 81.

[18] J. L. Barton, *The Story of Near East Relief* (1930); Markoosha Fisher, *My Lives in Russia* (New York, 1944).

[19] General William S. Graves, *America's Siberian Adventure* (New York, 1931).

[20] Dept. of State Publication 3480, *Cultural Relations between the United States and the Soviet Union* (Washington, 1949).

[21] Saul G. Bron, *Soviet Economic Development and American Business* (1930), 46 ff.

[22] Bron., op. cit., 66. Personal conversations with Tom Barker, a member for the mission, and W. H. Chamberlain, 'Missionaries of American Techniques in

Russia', *Asia*, v (1932), 422–7, 460–3; W. C. White, 'American Big Business and the Soviet Market', *Asia*, v (1930), 746–53.

23 George Clemow, 'Foreign Technical Assistance', in Gerhard Debbert (ed.), *Soviet Economics* (trans. Malcolm Cambell) (1933).

24 Obituary notice, *New York Times*, 25 June 1937.

25 H. R. Knickerbocker, *The Soviet Five Year Plan and its Effect on World Trade* (1931), 42 ff.

26 W. A. Williams, *American Russian Relations 1781–1947* (New York, 1952), 215.

27 Obituary notice, *New York Times*, 3 February 1938.

28 Newton Fuessle, 'The Brawn of the St. Lawrence. An interview with Hugh Lincoln Cooper', *The Outlook* (17 January 1923), CXXXIII, 226–9.

29 Colonel H. L. Cooper, 'An Engineer's Suggestions on Government', *The World's Work*, XLX (May 1925), 29. The Government Council should be, he wrote, absolutely non-political, appointed from and supported by, the states, and should have a membership of about one hundred, two from each State, and, say, four at large. The appointees should cover all the major walks in U.S. industrial and civil life. This membership should be able to serve for life, if satisfactory service is rendered. The first term should be for five years, and the succeeding terms should be for fifteen years. Reappointment should be contingent upon a two-thirds vote of the council recommending such appointment. See also 'Hugh Cooper touches a Dream', *Nation*, CXXIII (No. 3196) (1926), 311.

30 H. L. Cooper, 'Observations of Present Day Russia', *Annals of the American Academy of Political and Social Science*, XXXVIII (1928), 117–19.

31 M. J. Shore, *Soviet Education—Its Psychology and Philosophy* (New York, 1947), 135.

32 Scott Nearing, *Education in Soviet Russia* (New York, 1926).

33 M. J. Shore, *Soviet Education—Its Psychology and Philosophy* (1947), 149.

34 M. Kalinin, *On Communist Education: Selected Speeches and Articles* (Moscow, 1950).

35 Luigi Volpocelli, *L'Évolution de la Pedagogie Soviétique* (Neuchatel, 1954), 120.

36 J. B. S. Haldane, *The Inequality of Man* (1932), 85.

37 Quoted E. H. Carr, *The Soviet Impact on the Western World* (1946), 29.

38 D. B. Shimkin, *Minerals, A Key to Soviet Power* (Cambridge, Mass., 1953).

39 The output of fertilizers rose from 89,000 tons in 1913 to 135,000 tons in 1928 and 3,238,000 tons in 1949.

40 V. I. Ipatieff, 'Modern Science in Russia', *Russian Review*, ii, 2 (1942), 68–80.

41 Ruth C. Christman, Conway Zirkle and H. A. Mayerhoff, (ed.), *Soviet Science* (Washington, 1952), 62 ff.

42 Paul I. Medow.

43 J. G. Crowther, 'Science in the U.S.S.R.' *Endeavour*, I (1942), 21–25.

44 M. J. Ruggles and A. Kramish, *The Soviet Union and the Atom: the early years* (Rand Corporation Memorandum, 1956), 7–9.

45 J. G. Crowther, *Soviet Science* (1936), 94.

46 A. Modelski, *Atomic Energy in the Communist Block* (Melbourne, 1959), 26.

47 Vavilov, later president of the Academy of Sciences from 1945 to 1951 and chief editor of the *Large Soviet Encyclopaedia*. His name is commemorated by the foundation of the Vavilov Institute of Physical Problems in 1951 under Peter L. Kapitsa.

48 T. A. Taracouzio, *Soviets in the Arctic* (1938), 189.

49 J. G. Crowther, *Science in Soviet Russia* (1930), *Industry and Education in Soviet Russia* (1932), *The New Russia* (1931); Julian Huxley, *A Scientist among*

the Soviets (1932); S. and B. *Soviet Communism—a new Civilisation* (1938);
Alexander Vucinich, *The Soviet Academy of Sciences* (Stanford, 1956).
50 A. A. Baykov, *Twenty Five Years of the Academy of Sciences of the U.S.S.R.*
(New York, 1943).
51 Eric Ashby, *Scientist in Russia* (1947).
52 G. H. Hampsch, 'The Link between Science and Philosophy within Soviet
Ideology', *American Slavic and East European Review*, XX (1961), 118–22.
53 Frederick Gulheim (ed.), *Frank Lloyd Wright: Selected Writings 1894–
1940* (New York, 1941), 226.
54 ibid., 171.
55 ibid., 227.

15: TECHNOCRATS AND THE POLITICS OF POWER

1 J. T. Broderick, *Steinmetz and his Discoverer* (Schenectady, 1924); J. W.
Hammond, *C. P. Steinmetz* (1924); S. A. Lavine, *Steinmetz, Maker of Lightning*
(1955).
2 J. N. Norton, *Loki. The Life of C. P. Steinmetz* (1929), 262–4.
3 Personal conversations with Tom Barker, a member of the mission.
4 Stuart Chase, *Technocracy, an Interpretation* (1933), 7.
5 Thorstein Veblen, *The Engineers and the Price System* (1919), 87. For an
illuminating discussion of the likeness between Chernyshevsky and Veblen see
Max M. Laserson, *The American Impact on Russia—Diplomatic and Ideological
1784–1917* (New York, 1957), 239 and 256. Indeed he remarks that 'Chernyshevsky may be called a forerunner of Veblen'.
6 T. Veblen, *Engineers and the Price System* (1919), 100.
7 ibid., 137.
8 e.g. in the *New York Times*, 21 August 1932; George Soule, 'Technocracy',
The New Republic, LXXXVIII (1932), 178–9; Leon Ardrooni, 'Veblen and
Technocracy', *The Living Age*, CCCXLIV (1933), 39; Stuart Chase, 'Technocracy',
An Interpretation (1933); Allen Raymond, *What is Technocracy* (1933); Howard
Scott, *An Introduction to Technocracy* (1933). For a variant see W. J. Hale,
'Epistemocracy', *Review of Reviews*, LXXXVII (February 1933), 27.
9 Archibald Macleish, 'Technocracy Speaks', *Saturday Review of Literature*,
28 January 1933, IX, 400.
10 *Commonweal*, 20 March 1942, 53; Will Chasen and Victor Riesel, 'Technocrats in Uniform', *The Nation*, CLIV, 4 April 1942, 395–6.
11 Ralph Chaplin, *The Rough and Tumble Story of an American Radical* (Chicago,
1948), 295–6; Robert L. Tyler, 'The I.W.W. and the Brainworkers', *American
Quarterly*, XV (1963), 41–51.
12 Charles Ferguson, *The Revolution Absolute* (New York, 1918), 54.
13 ibid., 64.
14 ibid., 107.
15 ibid., 246.
16 Sidney Kaplan, 'Social Engineers as Saviours! Effects of World War I on
some American Liberals', *Journal of the History of Ideas*, XVII (1956), 347–69.
17 Introduction to C. Lindeman, *Social Discovery* (New York, 1925).
18 M. de Wolfe Howe (ed.), *Holmes-Laski Correspondence*.
19 Francis Jehl, *Menlo Park Reminiscences* (Dearborn, 1937), i, 169. See also:
Boyd, T. A., *Research, the pathfinder of Science and Industry* (1935); Pound, Arthur,
Industrial America, its ways of work and Thought (1936); H. R. Bartlest, 'The
Development of Industrial Research in the United States', *Research—a National
Resource II* (1941); Bechowsky, F. Russell, *Industrial Research* (1942); Killefer,

D. H., *The Genius of Industrial Research* (1948), and W. R. Maclaurin, *Invention and Innovation in the Radio Industry* (1949)..

[20] See C. G. Suits, 'Seventy-five Years of Research in General Electric', *Science*, CXVIII (3069), 23 October 1953, 451–6, and Kendall Birr, *Pioneering in Industrial Research* (Washington, 1957).

[21] The Westinghouse Laboratory, originally established in an old mill at Great Barrington, Massachusetts under W. Stanley, once had A. H. Crompton for a short time on the staff, whilst S. P. Timoshenko taught their engineers, and was sent by them to study research in England and Germany before taking up an academic teaching career once more at Michigan, and later at Stanford. D. H. Young in *The Collected Papers of Stephen Timoshenko* (1953), xvii.

[22] *Scientific Monthly*, XLVIII (1939), 195–202. Their headquarters are on West Street, New York. See Arthur W. Page, *The Bell Telephone System* (New York, 1945), and I. Bernard Cohen, *Science, Servant of Man* (1949), 305.

[23] Kendall Beaton, *Enterprise in Oil. A History of Shell in the United States* (New York, 1957), 682–91.

[24] W. S. Dutton, *Du Pont* (1942).

[25] Beaton, op. cit., 682–91.

[26] See his *Organisation of Industrial Scientific Research* (1950) (with J. A. Leermakers) and his *The Path of Science* (1946) with J. R. Baker.

[27] Lawrence A. Hawkins, *Adventure into the Unknown* (New York, 1950). William Kornhauser Berkeley, *Scientists in Industry* (1962).

[28] Bernard Barber, *Science and the Social Order* (Glencoe, Illinois, 1952), 159–60. E. W. Scott (ed.), *Applied Research in the U.S.* (National Academy of Sciences, National Research Council, 1952).

[29] J. Jewkes, D. Sawers and R. Stillerman, *The Sources of Invention* (London, 1958), p. 127.

[30] Thorstein Veblen, *Higher Learning in America* (1918)—it was first written in 1904, 263.

[31] ibid., 272.

[32] C. E. Kenneth Mees and John A. Leermakers, *The Organisation of Industrial and Scientific Research* (London, 1958), 127.

[33] National Science Foundation, *Basic Research. A National Resource* (Washington, U.S., G.P.O., 15 October 1957), 31–36, see p. 30, table 2.

[34] A national Economic and Social Planning Association was organized in 1934 with its own journal, *The Plan Age*. Amongst its leading members were George Soule, Lewis Lorwin, H. Pearson, D. C. Coyle, A. Ford Henricks and Marion H. Hedges.

[35] *Soviet Russia in the Second Decade: A Joint Survey by the Technical Staff of the First American Trade Union Delegation.*

[36] The adjective *New* gripped public imagination. In addition to Henry A. Wallace's *New Frontiers* (1934), there was Harold Ickes's *The New Democracy* (1934), Walter Lippman's *The New Imperative* (1935). (There was nothing new in the use of the word 'new' by Presidents! Theodore Roosevelt started it with his 'New Nationalism' and Woodrow Wilson continued it with his 'New Freedom', F. D. Roosevelt had his 'New Deal' and President Kennedy had his 'New Frontier'.) But Ickes and Lippman had something new to say as well as proclaim. H. A. Wallace, *New Frontiers* (1934), 274.

[37] Gerard Swope, President of General Electric had such a plan, see J. George Frederick (ed.), *The Swope Plan* (1931).

[38] H. A. Wallace, 'The Social Advantages and Disadvantages of the Engineering Science Approach to Civilisation', *Science* (N.S.), LXXIX (1934), 2, 3, 5.

[39] A. Hunter Dupree, *Science in the Federal Government* (Cambridge, Mass

1957), 350–1. It was to survey the forty-odd Government bureaux then, in one way or another, conducting scientific research. Before the committee came to an end two years later it saved these from being too savagely pruned. When the Second World War began Karl T. Compton became a member of the National Defence Research Committee organized to supplement the work of the army and navy's own research boards in June 1940. This, an executive committee, was composed of Vannevar Bush of the Carnegie Institute of Washington, F. B. Jewett of the Bell Telephone Laboratories, J. B. Conant of Harvard, C. P. Coe of the Patent Office and Roger Adams of Illinois, together with service representatives. In its first year, 10 million dollars in research contacts were given to colleges, universities and industrial libraries. In addition J. B. Conant established an office in London to exchange technical information with Britain. The N.D.R.C. was placed on 28 June 1941, in the Office of Scientific Research and Development, a body established on the day to advise the President, enlist scientific personnel and support research for national Defence. It could enter into agreement with other bodies like the National Academy of Sciences (set up in the Civil War), as the National Research Council (set up in World War I). Conant took over the National Defence Research Committee, whilst Vannevar Bush became the head of the O.S.R.D.

40 Harold Ickes, *The New Democracy* (1934), 120–1.

41 Walter Lippman, *The New Imperative* (1935), 47–48.

42 H. G. Wells, *Experiment in Autobiography* (1934), 681–2.

43 *New York Times*, 24 September 1932; Curtis Nettels, 'Frederick Jackson Turner and the New Deal', *Wisconsin Magazine of History*, XVII (1934), 257–65

44 E. I. Miller, *A Selected List of Books, Theses and Pamphlets on T.V.A.* (Knoxville, 1942). Subsequent studies are by Joseph Ransmeir (Nashville, 1942); Julian Huxley (Cheam, Surrey, 1943); Charles H. Pritchett (Chapel Hill, 1943); R. L. Duffus (New York, 1944). Arthur M. Schlesinger, jun., *The Coming of the New Deal* (1959), 319–26. E. B. Nixon (ed.), *Franklin D. Roosevelt and Conservation 1911–1945* (Hyde Park, 1957).

45 *Time*, LXXXII, No. 19 (8 November 1963), 21.

46 J. A. Schumpeter, *Capitalism, Socialism and Democracy* (New York, 1950), 134.

47 E. V. Hollis, *Philanthropic Foundations and Higher Education* (Columbia, 1938); W. S. Rich and N. R. Deardoff, *American Foundations and their Fields*, 7th edition (New York, 1955); E. C. Lindeman, *Wealth and Culture: A Study of One Hundred Foundations* (New York, 1936); Shelby M. Harrison and F. Emerson Andrews, *American Foundations for Social Welfare* (New York, 1946); R. M. Lester, *Forty Years of Carnegie Giving* (New York, 1941).

48 For a critical assessment of its work, see A. Flexner, *Funds and Foundations: Their Policies Past and Present* (New York, 1952), 113–24.

49 S. and J. T. Flexner, *William Welch and the Heroic Age of American Medicine* (New York, 1941), 285.

50 R. L. Heilbroner, 'The Fabulous Ford Foundation', *Harper's Magazine*. CCIII (1961), 23–32.

51 A. Flexner, *Funds and Foundations: Their Policies Past and Present* (New York, 1952). Sixty foundations gave specifically to scientific research some 13 per cent of their expenditure or 33 millions in 1957, a growth of 7 millions from the total in 1953. Between the two periods a significant alteration took place in the distribution of this help. For whereas in 1953 the relative percentages of the 26 millions between Physical, Life and Social sciences was 10, 48 and 42 per cent in 1957 it shifted to 31, 41 and 28 per cent.

As pioneers in technical assistance overseas, the Carnegie, Rockefeller and Ford Foundations set an example to governments. Carnegie worked in the British

Commonwealth, Rockefeller throughout the world and Ford embarked on a huge programme in south-east Asia in 1950. Other foundations were established for special areas like the American-Scandinavian Foundation (1911), the Rotary Foundation (1917), the Commonwealth Foundation (1920), the Belgian-American Foundation (1920), the Edward Hazen Foundation (1925), the John Simon Guggenheim Foundation (1925), the W. K. Kellog Foundation (1930), the Doris Duke Foundation (1934), the Wenner-Grenn Foundation (founded as the Viking Fund in 1941) and the American-Korean Foundation (1952). These, and others, promote the easy flow of scientific and medical information to and from America and form a substantial element in the present American technical assistance programme. Their help to world scientific institutions and universities has been considerable. The third aspect of the work of these foundations is the object lesson they afforded. For just as their founders gave an example of the value of planning and technical knowledge, so the foundations themselves afforded an example to governments as to the best way to organize the patronage of science by leaving it free.

F. Emerson Andrews, *Scientific Research Expenditures by the Larger Private Foundations* (National Science Foundation, 1956); A. D. Walton, F. Emerson Andrews and M. O. Lewis, *The Foundation Directory* (New York, 1960).

[52] *The Autobiography of Lincoln Steffens* (New York, 1931), 891.

[53] *Letters of Lincoln Steffens*, ii (1938), 1007. See also Dimitri von Mohrenschildt, 'Lincoln Steffens and the Russian Bolshevik Revolution', *Russian Review*, v (1945), 31–41, and 'American Intelligentsia and Russia of the N.E.P.' ibid., vi (1947), 59–76.

[54] *Autobiography*.

[55] Malcolm Cowley, *Exile's Return* (1934), 229.

[56] W. H. Chamberlin, *Confessions of an Industrialist* (New York, 1940), 54.

[57] Robert Moats Miller, *American Protestantism and Social Issues 1919–1939* (Chapel Hill, 1958), 41, 64–65.

[58] C. M. Muchnic, 'A Business Man's View of Russia', *Harpers*, CLIX (1929), 442.

[59] Jacob Crane, 'Whither State Planning' (National Conference on City Planning, Pittsburg, 16 November 1932).

[60] Jacob Crane, 'Large Scale Regional Planning', *American City*, XLIX (1934), 61; 'China and Russia Secure Services of Chicago City Planner', *American City*, XLIV (1931), 126; Joseph Barnes, 'City Planning in New Russia', *Asia*, XXXII (1932), 514.

[61] H. J. Freyn, 'An American Engineer Looks at the Five Year Plan', *New Republic*, LXVI (6 May 1931), 317.

[62] Edmund Wilson, *New Republic*, LXVII (20 May 1931), 38.

[63] M. L. Cooke, 'The Early Days of the Rural Electrification Idea: 1914–1936', *American Political Science Review*, XLII (1948), 431–414; K. E. Trombley, *The Life and Times of a Happy Liberal: A Biography of Morris Llewellyn Cooke* (New York, 1954); Richard Lowitt, *George W. Norris, The Making of a Progressive 1861–1912* (Syracuse Univ. Press, 1963).

[64] Copley, op. cit., ii, 246.

[65] Copley, op. cit., ii, 394–5.

[66] A. M. Schlesinger, jun., *The Politics of Upheaval* (1960), 384.

[67] A. M. Schlesinger, jun. and Morton White, *Paths in American Thought* (1964), 381.

16: SCIENCE AND SOCIAL RECUPERATION IN BRITAIN

[1] J. B. S. Haldane, *Daedalus—or Science and the Future* (1923). In a characteristic forecast, *Man's World* (1926), Charlotte Haldane pictures the elimination of

NOTES

all politicians and philosophers by a great chemical war, leaving scientists and geneticists in control.

2 Bertrand Russell, *Icarus—or the Future of Science* (1924), 5, 63. T. S. Eliot was a pupil of Russell's at Harvard and found him 'very delightful . . . because he had no pomposity and was so approachable'. He later immortalized him as Mr. Appollinax whose 'dry and passionate talk devoured the afternoon'.

3 Alan Wood, *Bertrand Russell. The Passionate Sceptic* (1957), 101, 120, 131.

4 B. Russell, *The Impact of Science on Society* (1952); see also his *Icarus—or the Future of Science* (1924). *The Prospects of Industrial Civilisation* (1923); *Freedom and Organisation* 1814–1914 (1934).

5 *The Scientific Outlook* (1931) discusses the future of societies managed by a scientifically minded bureaucracy.

6 B. and D. Russell, *The Prospects of Industrial Civilisation* (1923), 267.

7 *The Open Conspiracy* (1928), 33–34, 162–3. Wells considered that universities had no place in the new world order except as centres of research and specialized training. Liberal education according to Wells was best given in the last three years at school: 'A time must come,' said William Clissold, 'when Oxford and Cambridge would signify no more in the current intellectual life of the world than the monastery of Mount Athos or the lamaseries of Tibet do now, when their colleges will stand empty and clean for the amateur of architecture and the sightseeing tourist.' *The World of William Clissold* (1936), ii, 659–60.

8 Margaret Cole, *Beatrice Webb* (1945), 158.

9 Alan Bullock, *The Life and Times of Ernest Bevin*, 137 and 508; Neal Wood, *Communism and British Intellectuals* (1959).

10 *The Spectator*, July 1931, reprinted J. D. Bernal, *The Freedom of Necessity* (1943), 336, 339.

11 Ronald W. Clark, *Sir Julian Huxley*, F.R.S. (1960), 44, 90.

12 J. Stalin, *Foundations of Leninism*, 93.

13 L. Urwick, *Management of Tomorrow* (1933), 197 and 199.

14 J. H. Dunning, *American Investment in British Manufacturing Industry* (1958), 36, 47. It is worth remarking that in 1930 W. Olaf Stapledon published a story of the near and far future entitled *Last and First Men*, virtually proclaiming the epiphany of American technology.

15 J. H. Dunning, op. cit., 173.

16 H. C. Metcalf and L. Urwick, *Dynamic Administration. The Collected Papers of Mary Parker Follett* (Bath, 1941), 249.

17 ibid., 213.

18 ibid., 295.

19 L. Urwick, *Management of Tomorrow* (1933).

20 Alan Bullock, *The Life and Times of Ernest Bevin* (1960).

21 Elton Mayo, *Human Problems of an Industrial Civilisation* (New York, 1933); F. J. Roethlisberger and W. J. Dickson, *Management and the Worker* (Boston, 1934); L. J. Henderson, T. N. Whitehead and Elton Mayo, 'The Effects of Social Environment', in *Papers on the Science of Administration* (ed. Luther Gulick and L. Urwick) (Boston, 1937).

22 Mabel Newcomer, *The Big Business Executive* (New York, 1955), 2.

23 Acton Society Trust, *Management Succession* (London, 1956), but G. H. Copeman, *Leaders of British Industry* (1955), gives 56 per cent.

24 R. Bendix, *Work and Authority in Industry* (1956), 214.

25 Quoted by Charlotte Erickson, *British Industrialists. Steel and Hosiery 1850–1950* (Cambridge, 1959), 188. She points out (pp. 42–43) that the percentage of steel manufacturers known to have taken a scientific training at university, technical school, military or naval college rose from 6 in 1865 to 16 in 1935–47, whilst

those known to have served apprenticeships dropped from 21 to 3 per cent.

[26] Though accused by Professor Lancelot Hogben, in *The Retreat form Reason* (1936) and Enid Charles, *The Twilight of Parenthood* (1934), 31, of advocating a moratorium for scientific discovery, Sir Josiah Stamp energetically rebutted it in *The Science of Social Adjustment* (1937), 59.

[27] H. H. Ballin, *The Organisation of Electricity Supply in Great Britain* (1946).

[28] *Planning*, No. 12, 24 October 1933, 10.

[29] Quoted by R. A. Brady, *Business as a System of Power* (New York, 1943), 162. Their heavy emphasis on vocational training and education could be construed as yet another offensive against 'labour'. In 1926 there was founded, on the initiative of Voegler, chairman of the Vereinigte Stahlwerke, an organization known as DINTA (Deutsches Institut fur Technische Arbeitsschulung). Its director, Arnhold, announced his intention in 1927 of 'taking in hand leadership of all from earliest childhood to the oldest man'.

The F.B.I. considered education to be 'the problem which lies at the root of our difficulties', as it had 'particular relevance to the problem of industrial unrest'. Members of the F.B.I. took seriously the need for continuation schools (envisaged by the Fisher Education Act of 1918 but never implemented), and the proposal to raise the school-leaving age to 15. They also held meetings with the various headmasters' groups of the private and public schools with a view to bringing them into closer relationship.

[30] *Science and the Nation* (1947), 160.

[31] *The World of William Clissold*, 2, 563–4; *After Democracy* (1932), 100; W. Warren Wager, *H. G. Wells and the World State* (New Haven, 1961), 185.

[32] Sir Alfred Mond, *Industry and Politics* (1927), 154.

[33] W. H. G. Armytage, *Sir Richard Gregory* (1957), 87–91.

[34] ibid., 141–4.

[35] ibid., 87–91.

[36] Personal information from the late Major Church. A fine study of the role of the B.M.A. in politics can be found in Harry Eckstein, *Pressure Group Politics* (1960), 46. E. M. Little, *The British Medical Association* (1932), 79–80.

[37] *Royal Commission on the Civil Service* (Cmd. 3909, H.M.S.O., 1930–1); The Tomlin Commission.

[38] *Committee on the Post Office* (Cmd. 4149, 1932).

[39] F. A. A. Metzler in W. A. Robson (ed.), *The British Civil Servant* (1937), 183.

[40] M. Philips Price, 'The Parliamentary and Scientific Committee of Great Britain', *Impact of Science on Society*, III (1952), No. 4; S. A. Walkland, 'Science and Parliament: The Origins and Influence of the Parliamentary and Scientific Committee', *Parliamentary Affairs* XVII (1964), 308–20.

[41] *Report of the Machinery of Government Committee* (Cmd. 9230, 1918).

[42] *Economic Advisory Council Committee Report* (H.M.S.O., 1932). A. Zimmern, *Prospects of Democracy* (1929), 351: 'unless the modern world works out a satisfactory relationship between expert knowledge and popular control the days of democracy are numbered'.

[43] J. B. Seymour, *The Whitley Councils Scheme* (1932). Fifty-six were set up by 1920.

[44] S. and B. Webb, *Constitution for a Socialist Commonwealth of Great Britain* (1920).

[45] For a fuller discussion see J. W. Grove, *Government and Industry in Britain* (1962), 36–61.

[46] *Week End Review*, 14 February 1931. This paper was founded by Gerald Barry in March 1930 with the majority of the staff of the *Saturday Review*, who

had all rebelled against supporting Beaverbrook's Empire Free Trade Campaign. For a good history see 300th Broadsheet *Planning*, XVI, No. 300, 11 July 1959.

47 *Planning*, i (1933–4), No. 23, 5–9. D. Marshall, 'War of the Machines: Enemies of the Modern World', *Catholic World*, CXLV (1937), 184–6; I. Maynard, 'Aldous Huxley, Moralist', *Catholic World*, CXLIV (1936), 12–22; Thomas Merton, 'Huxley's Pantheon', *Catholic World*, CLII (1940), 206–9; M. de la Bedoyère, 'Huxley decries "Social Engineering"', *Catholic World*, CLXXXIX (1959), 148–52. He believed Catholicism to be in closer contact with real man than the optimism of the eighteenth century.

48 André Maurois, *Poets and Prophets* (1936), 219. Cf. also p. 215: 'The scientist in him realises that the modern view of human nature is much closer to the traditional Catholic conception than to that of Helvetius, Babeuf or Shelley.' See also Gai Eaton, 'Monk at Large: Aldous Huxley', *The Richest Vein* (1949), 166–82.

49 Julian Huxley, *Scientific Research and Social Policy* (1934).

50 H. Macmillan, *Reconstruction: A Plea for a National Policy* (1933).

51 *PEP*, No. 16-19, December 1933, 12.

52 Christopher Hollis, *Can Parliament Survive?* (1949), 127–8. See also W. S. Churchill, *Romanes Lecture for 1930*; L. S. Amery, *Thoughts on the Constitution*; Harold Macmillan, Speech, 5 March 1949.

53 A. M. Carr-Saunders and P. A. Wilson, *The Professions* (1933), 496.

54 D. N. Dunlop, *British Destiny*. *The Principles of Progress* (1916), 67, 81, 111.

55 *Transactions of the First World Power Conference* (1924), iii, 1286.

56 *Nature*, 6 February 1926.

57 *Hansard*, CXCIV, 29 April 1926, 2208.

58 *What Science Stands For* (1937), 110. These were addresses given to the British Association meeting at Blackpool.

59 ibid.

60 C. P. Snow, *Science and Government* (1960); Roy Harrod, *The Prof* (1959); P. M. S. Blackett, 'Operational Research', *The Advancement of Science* (1948).

61 J. D. Bernal in *Contact*, autumn 1945, reprinted in *The Freedom of Necessity* (1949), 217.

62 *Science and Government* (A. Sc. W., 1946).

63 *Science and the Nation* (Penguin Books, 1947), 175.

64 One can trace the growth of contemporary comment in R. V. Vernon and N. S. Mansergh, *Advisory Bodies* (1940); K. C. Wheare, *Government by Committee* (1955) and the PEP study of 1960. Sir Harry Melville, *The Department of Scientific and Industrial Research* (1962).

65 Sir David Eccles in the House of Commons 29 April 1954 quoted by R. Darcy Best, 'The United Kingdom Atomic Energy Authority', *Public Administration*, XXXIV (1956), 1–16.

66 R. Darcy Best, op. cit., 116.

67 *Committee of Enquiry into the Organization of Civil Service* (Cmd. 2171, H.M.S.O., October 1963).

68 George Orwell, *Collected Essays* (1961), 164.

69 George Orwell, *The Road to Wigan Pier* (1937).

70 For a stimulating exegesis see John Atkins, *George Orwell* (1954), 232.

71 *Nineteen Eighty-Four* (1949), 190–1. cf. Aldous Huxley, in 'A Footnote about 1984', in *World Review*, June 1950, and Martin Kessler, 'Power and the Perfect State', *Political Science Quarterly*, LXXII (1957), 565–77, who argues that both Huxley and Orwell are rebelling against a 'sort of operational determinism'.

72 R. V. Clements, *Managers. A Study of their Careers in Industry* (1958), 148.

73 PEP, op. cit., 95.

74 Tom Burns and G. M. Stalker, *The Management of Innovation* (1961), 175.
75 J. D. Jones ('Manager, Project Development, Ontario Research Foundation') in *The Times*, 5 August 1964, p. 9.
76 Donald McLachlan, in *Daily Telegraph*, 25 January 1960.
77 A. P. Herbert, 'Anything but action', in R. Harris (ed.), *Radical Reaction: Essays in Competition and Affluence* (1961), 298.
78 Hans Daalder, *Cabinet Reform in Britain 1914–1963* (Stanford, 1964), 257.
79 Viscount Hailsham, *Science and Politics* (1963), 72.
80 R. H. S. Crossman, 'Scientists in Whitehall. Thoughts on the Eve', *Encounter*, XXIII (1964), 3–10.
81 Harold Wilson, *The Relevance of British Socialism* (London, 1964).

17: THE TWO LEVIATHANS
1 Laurens van der Post, *Journey into Russia* (1964).
2 E. Strauss, *The Ruling Servants* (1961), 19.
3 James Burnham, *The Managerial Revolution* (1941, reprinted as Penguin in 1962), 186, 201.
4 Daniel Bell, *The End of an Ideology* (New York, 1960), 373–4.
5 W. W. Roston, *The Stages of Economic Growth* (1960), 93.
6 Jawaharhal Nehru was impressed by the reports of the great progress made by the backward regions of Central Asia under the Soviet régime. *Towards Freedom* (1941), 229. See also Eric Fischer, *The Passing of the European Age* (Cambridge, Mass., 1948).
7 Balysh Ovezov, *Turkmenia* (1959), 10, points out that it is the third biggest oil producer in the U.S.S.R. after the Russian Federation and Azerbaizan, and cites Nebit-Dag, Kum-Dag and the Cheleken peninsula.
8 H. S. Dinerstein, 'The Sovietisation of Uzbekistan', 'The First Generation' in *Harvard Slavic Studies*, vol. iv ('s—Gravenhage, 1957), 499–513, points out how before the First World War, Fitrat, the famous Uzbek writer, preached that 'science is that very potent means, the existence of which led the savage Americans to their present high status and power and whose . . . absence brought the Persians to their present lowly state and humiliation', but was anathema to the obscurantist Moslem clergy of Central Asia. Hence the collaboration between Fitrat's followers and the Bolsheviks. See also Arif Alimov, *Uzbekistan* (1959); *Report on the Soviet Union in 1956* (Carnegie International Centre, New York, 1956), 135, and Maurice Hindus, *House without a Roo* (1962), 470–504.
9 Nazarsho Dodkhudoyev, *Tajikistan* (1959). The awards given in 1954 on its 25th anniversary were analysed by J. A. Newth, in 'The Establishment in Tajikstan', *Soviet Studies*, xiv (April and July 1963), 72–81. See also A. Bennigsen, 'The Moslem Intelligentsia in the U.S.S.R.' *Soviet Survey* (April–June 1959), 3–10.
10 Kazy Dikambayev, chairman of the Council of Ministers in *Kirghizia* (1959), p. 12, writes: 'Annual production of electric power in the Republic will surpass 2,000 million kWh or 1,000 kWh per inhabitant. It is proposed to raise production of electric power by the end of the seven year period by 360 per cent by 1963.'
11 *Report on the Soviet Union in 1956*. A Symposium of the Institute for the Study of the U.S.S.R. (New York, 1956), 71.
12 'The trains and planes to Siberia, Asia, and the Far Eastern Soviet Republics are jammed every summer with the graduates of the schools and colleges of European Russia headed eastward to begin their careers. And before the annual summer migration stops, a major part of this year's crop of graduates will have made the

transfer to the vast Soviet industrial and agricultural frontier beyond the Urals.' Howard Norton, *Only in Russia* (1961), 186.

[13] Vannevar Bush, *Science, the Endless Frontier* (1945).

[14] N. de Witt, *Soviet Professional Manpower: Its Education, Training and Supply* (1955).

[15] D. Wolfle in *Science*, CXXVI (1957), 335.

[16] S. Chase, R. Dunn and R. G. Tugwell, *Soviet Russia in the Second Decade* (New York, 1928), 289.

[17] *New York Times*, 1 April 1956.

[18] See *Proceedings of a Conference on the Utilisation of Scientific and Professional Manpower* (New York, 1953); *Policy for Skilled Manpower* (1954). In 1955 it promoted another conference which issued *Improving the Work Skills of the Nation* (1955); 'Russia is overtaking U.S. in Training of Technicians', *New York Times*, 7 November 1954; *Soviet Science*, ed. Ruth C. Christman, Conway Zirkle, H. Mayerhoff (Washington, 1952).

[19] Russian work on nuclear energy began to acquire momentum from 1943, especially in Moscow. For though at Leningrad Khlopin and Kurchatov were active, Kurchatov's own laboratory was separated from the Physico-Technical Institute of Leningrad and the Institute of Chemical Physics was moved from Leningrad to Moscow in 1943 under N. N. Semenov.

[20] G. A. Modelski, *Atomic Power in the Soviet Bloc* (Melbourne, 1959).

[21] N. De Witt, 'Professional and Scientific Personnel in the U.S.S.R.' *Science*, 120 (2 July 1954), 1–4.

[22] L. Trilling, *Research and Development in the U.S.S.R.* (M.I.T., Cambridge, Mass., 1960).

[23] Both the Minister and the deputy-ministers of the 31 ministries existing in 1956 were not 'politicians in the Western Sense', but 'promoted managers, often with an engineering background . . . technical executants, not policy-makers'. Alec Nove, *The Soviet Economy* (1961), 659. They worked under Gosplan, itself progressively weakened, in 1949, by being pared of three vital departments: *Gossnab* (materials allocation), *Gostekhnika* (technical department) and the Central Statistical Office.

In 1956, the shortcomings of the sixth Five-Year Plan led to the whole system being revised. What emerged in 1957 was a territorial system, based on the division of the U.S.S.R. into 103 *sovnarkhozy* nominated by, and responsible to, the republics—some of which like Georgia and Latvia were of themselves a *sovnarkhoz* whilst others like Kazakhstan embraced 9 and the R.S.F.S.R. 68. Each *sovnarkhoz* possesses its own technical economic council and its own functional divisions. Co-ordinating the work of the *sovnarkhozy*, big economic regions were created in 1960. One of these regions was formed by Uzbekistan, Turkimenistan, Kirghizia and Tadzikstan; another by Kazakhstan, a third by the Baltic states, a fourth by the 3 Transcaucasian republics. These, with 3 in the Ukraine and 10 in the R.S.F.R., made up a total of 17.

One of the major reasons for the change was technological. The complex by-products of modern industry, notably in the oil industry, demanded, for their better utilization, more flexible coupling of the command pipes. The old 'ministry' system put too many premiums on self-containment and vested the interest in matters too firmly where more operational attitudes were required (e.g. utilization of by-products). See also Howard R. Swearer, 'Decentralisation in recent Soviet Administrative Practice', *Slavic Review*, XXI (1962), 456–70.

[24] G. W. Elbers and Paul Duncan (ed.), *The Scientific Revolution, Challenge and Promise* (Washington, 1959), 7, 67–68.

[25] Alan T. Waterman, 'The National Science Foundation', *Science*, CXXXI

(1961), 1341–54. The increase is spectacular when compared to its grant for
1956—16 million dollars.

26 Philip H. Abelson, 'The President's Science Advisers', *Minerva*, iii (1965),
149–58.

27 James R. Killian jun., 'Science and Public Policy', *Science*, 129 (1959), 129.

28 *Soviet Commitment to Education. Report of the First U.S. Official Educational
Mission to the U.S.S.R.* (Bulletin 1959, No. 6, Washington, 1959); *Journal of
Engineering Education*, XLIX (1959), 844 and 872.

29 *Science*, 161 (1960), 1407–17. Dael Wolfle, in *Science and Public Policy*
(Lincoln, Nebraska, 1959), pleaded for increased generosity by industry and
private philanthropy, the re-establishment of O.S.R.D. and a Department of
Science and Technology. 'Perspectives on Government and Science', *Annals of the
American Academy of Political and Social Science*, CCCXXVII, ed. N. Wengert
(Philadelphia, 1960).

30 Reported in *Science*, 30 August 1957.

31 C. W. Elbers and Paul Duncan (ed.), *The Scientific Revolution, Challenge and
Promise* (Washington, 1959), 139; R. A. Bauer, Alex Inkeles and Clyde Kluck-
hohn, *How the Soviet System Works* (Cambridge, Mass., 1956), 179.

32 *Foreign Assistance Activities of the Communist Bloc and their Implications for
the United States* (Washington, Special Committee to Study the Foreign Aid Pro-
gramme, 1957), *New York Times*, 4 January 1958; R. L. Allen, 'The Soviet and
East European Foreign Credit Program', *American Slavic and East European
Review*, XVI (1957); *An Act for International Development* (U.S. Department of
State Publication 7205, Washington, 1961).

33 Joseph S. Berliner, *Soviet Economic Aid* (New York, 1958); 'Communist
China and the Soviet Bloc', special number of the *Annals of the American Academy
of Political and Social Science*, September 1963; Walter Kolarz, *Communism and
Colonialism* (1964).

34 Paul S. Bodenman, *American Co-operation with Higher Education Abroad: A
Survey of Current Programs* (Bulletin 1957, No. 8, Washington).

35 Samuel P. Hayes, jun., 'An Appraisal of Point Four', *Proceedings of the
Academy of Political Science*, XXV (New York, 1953), 291–306.

36 *American Universities in Technical Co-operation* (Washington, 1955).

37 *An Act for International Development* (Department of State Publication 7205,
Washington, 1961), 3.

38 Alex Nove, *The Soviet Economy* (1961), 299.

39 Robert E. Marshak, 'Re-examining the Soviet Scientific Challenge', *Bulletin
of the Atomic Scientists*, XIX (1963).

40 Edward T. Chase, 'Politics and Technology', *Yale Review*, LII (1963), 324.

41 ibid., 334.

42 *The Times*, 26 May 1964.

43 Sir Leon Bagrit, *The Age of Automation* (1965), 64.

PART V

18: THE CONVERSION OF THE MANDARINS

1 Henri Bernard, *Matteo Ricci's scientific contribution to China* (trans. E. C.
Werner) (Peiping, 1935), remarks (p. 68), 'Thus, little by little, through the
energetic impulsion of Ricci, a kind of centre of scientific culture, an embryo
university or at least the equivalent of what we call a university extension course,
was organised in the very capital of China.'

[2] H. Bosmans, *Ferdinand Verbiest, Directeur de l'Observatoire de Pekin* (Louvain, 1921).

[3] G. H. G. Wong, 'China's Opposition to Western Science during the late Ming and early Chi'ing', *Isis*, LXIV (1963), 29–49, argues that the Chinese 'were not seriously affected' by Western scientific ideas and techniques at this time. Cheukwoon Taam, *The Development of Chinese Libraries under the Ch'ing Dynasty 1964–1911* (Shanghai, 1935), Tang Ssu-yd (Cambridge, 1954).

[4] *Historia de las cosas mas notables, ritos y costumbres del gran regno de la China* (1585), French trans. 1589.

[5] Jean Baruzi, *Leibnitz et l'organisation religeuse de la Terre* (Paris, 1907). Leibnitz corresponded with Father Joachim Bouvet at Pekin.

[6] Arnold H. Rowbotham, 'Voltaire—Sinophile' *PMLA*, XLVII (1932), 1050–65.

[7] W. Engemann, *Voltaire und China* (1933); Virgile Pinot, *La Chine et la formation de l'esprit philosophique en France* (1932); Basil Guy, *The French Image of China Before and After Voltaire* (Geneva, 1963).

[8] Knight Biggerstaff, 'The T'ung–Wen Kuan', *Chinese Social and Political Science Review XVIII* (1934–5), 307–40.

[9] E. B. Boardman, *Christian Influence on the Ideology of the Taiping Rebellion* (Madison, 1952); F. H. Michael and G. E. Taylor, *The Far East in the Modern World* (London, 1956), 183; S. F. Wright, *Hart and the Chinese Customs* (Belfast, 1950).

[10] Wan-Han Kiang, *The Chinese Student Movement* (New York, 1948), 11.

[11] K. S. Latourette, *A History of the Expansion of Christianity* (1954), VI, 353 ff.; *A History of Christian Missions in China* (1929), 622–40; Kwang Ching Liu, 'Early Christian Colleges in China', *Journal of Asian Studies*, XXI (1960).

[12] Kwang-Ching Liu, 'Early Christian Colleges in China', *Journal of Asian Studies*, XX (1960), 73.

[13] M. C. Wright, *The Last Stand of Chinese Conservatism. The T'ung Chih Restoration 1862–1874* (Stanford, 1957), 212.

[14] Known as 'the Bismarck of Asia' Li Hung-Chang was China's representative with foreign powers from 1870 to 1894.

[15] Victor Purcell, *Problems of Chinese Education* (London, 1936), 56.

[16] G. C. Allen and A. G. Donnithorne, *Western Enterprise in Far Eastern Economic Development* (London, 1954), 94. Biographies of both Tseung Kuo-fan and Tso Tsung-t'ang were published by Gideon Chen in Peiping in 1935 and 1938.

[17] P. Huard et Ming Wong, 'Le développement de la technologie dans la Chine du XIXe Siècle', *Cahiers d'histoire Mondiale*, VII (Neuchâtel, 1962), 68–85. G. C. Allen and A. G. Donnithorne, *Western Enterprise in Far Eastern Economic Development* (1954), 94.

[18] G. B. Endacott, *A Short History of Hong Kong* (Oxford, 1958), 282–3.

[19] Victor Purcell, *Problems of Chinese Education* (1936), 55.

[20] Li Chien-Nung, *The Political History of China 1840–1929* (1956), 145.

[21] Wan-Han Kiang, *The Chinese Student Movement* (1948), 26.

[22] V. Purcell, *The Chinese in South East Asia* (R.I.I.A., Oxford, 1952), 46, described it as 'the most revolutionary happening in the history of Chinese education'. Rhoads Murphey, *Shanghai, Key to Modern China* (Cambridge, Mass., 1957).

[23] ibid., 44.

[24] Quoted W. Baczkowski, *Towards an Understanding of Russia* (Jerusalem 1947), 155.

[25] Wan-Han Kiang, *The Chinese Student Movement* (New York, 1948), 76. See also C. B. McLane, *Soviet Policy and the Chinese Communists 1931–46* (Columbia, 1958); Henry Wei, *China and Soviet Russia* (Princeton, 1956); Conrad Brandt, *Stalin's Failure in China 1924–1927* (Cambridge, Mass., 1958).

[26] X. J. Eudin and Robert C. North, *Soviet Russia and the East 1920–1927, A Documentary Survey* (Stanford, 1957), 85–88; C. M. Wilbur, Julie Lien and Ying How, *Documents on Communism, Nationalism and Soviet Advisors in China, 1918–1927* (New York, 1956); R. C. North and Xenia Eudin, *M. N. Roy's Mission to China: the Communist Kuomintang Split of 1927* (Berkeley, 1962).

[27] Robert C. North, *Moscow and Chinese Communists* (Stanford, 1963), 80, 91, 120.

[28] Wan-Han Kiang, op. cit., 140.

[29] Lionel Curtis, *The Capital Question of China* (London, 1932), 301.

[30] J. Needham, *Chinese Science* (London, 1945), 2, 12. My friend Professor William Empson (who was a professor in China at the time) assures me that the forced uprooting of Arts departments like his own had impressive effects.

[31] J. K. Fairbank, *The United States and China* (Cambridge, Mass., 1948); J. R. Levenson, *Confucian China and its Modern Fate* (Berkeley, 1958).

[32] Theodore H. E. Chen, *Thought Reform of the Chinese Intellectuals* (Hong King, 1960), 5.

[33] 22 March 1903. W. C. Ford, op. cit.

19. SCIENCE AND THE SAMURAI

[1] D. W. Thompson 'Japan and the New Atlantis', *Studies in Philology*, XXX (1933), 59–68. *Scientific Japan, Past and Present, Prepared in Connection with the 3rd Pan-Pacific Science Congress* (Tokyo, 1926).

[2] B. Szczesniak, 'Astronomical and Mathematical Studies in Japan', *Journal of The Royal Asiatic Society* (1944).

[3] Hiraga Gennai made a frictional electrical machine on a Dutch model in 1770.

[4] Kenjiro Kumamoto, 'Intellectual and Aesthetic Currents in Japan 1775–1905: Principles, Schools and Influences', *Journal of World History*, vi (1960); C. R. Boxer, *Jan Compagnie in Japan 1600–1850. An Essay on the Cultural artistic and scientific influence exercised by the Hollanders in Japan* (The Hague, 1950).

[5] G. B. Sansom, *The Western World and Japan* (1950), 273; H. Keenleyside and A. F. Thomas, *History of Japanese Education* (London, 1937); Y. Fujikawa, *Japanese Medicine* (trans. John Ruhrah); M. Paske-Smith, *Western Barbarians in Japan and Formosa in Tokugawa Days 1603–1868* (Kobe, 1930), 218.

[6] S. Sakamaki, 'Japan and the United States 1790–1853', *Transactions of the Asiatic Society of Japan* XVII (1939); Arthur Walworth, *Black Ships of Japan* (1946); F. M. Jones, 'Foreign influence in the Early Press of Japan', *Transactions of the Japan Society London* XXXIII (1934–5); Herbert Norman, *Japan's Emergence as a Modern State* (Institute of Pacific Relations, 1940).

[7] H. Keenleyside and A. F. Thomas, *History of Japanese Education* (1937), 69.

[8] G. C. Allen and A. G. Donnithorne, *Western Enterprise in Far Eastern Economic Development* (1954), 190. For a good critical study of Fukuzawa Yukichi see Carmen Blacker, *The Japanese Enlightenment* (Cambridge, 1964).

[9] John A. Harrison, 'The Capron Mission and the Colonisations of Hokkaido 1868–75', *Agricultural History*, XXV (1951), 132–42, and his *Japan's Northern Frontier* (Gainsville, Fla., 1953). R. S. Schwantes, 'Christianity versus Science: A Conflict of Ideas in Maiji Japan', *Far Eastern Quarterly*, v (1953), 125–7, and *Japanese and Americans: A Century of Cultural Relations* (New York, 1955).

[10] R. S. Schwantes, 'Educational Influence of the United States of America', and

Kimura Ki 'American Cultural Impact on Japan', in *Contemporary Japan*, XXVI (1960), 442–81.

[11] E. O. Reischauer, *The United States and Japan* (Harvard, 1957), 12–13.

[12] Yoshida Kumaji, 'European and American Influences in Japanese Education', in Inazo Nitobe (ed.), *Western Influences in Modern Japan* (Chicago, 1931), 25–55.

[13] *Nature*, 17 May 1877.

[14] Earl Miner, *The Japanese Tradition in British and American Literature* (Princeton, N.J., 1958), 32.

[15] Elizabeth Bisland, *The Life and Letters of Lafcadio Hearn* (1906), i, 365, 392, 397. He was taught to do so by a lieutenant in the U.S. Army in 1884. See also E. Stevenson, *Lafcadio Hearn* (New York, 1961), 146–8. After a friend disciplined him to read Herbert Spencer: 'I suddenly discovered what a waste all my oriental metaphysics had been. . . . In short, from the day when I first finished the "First Principles"—a totally new intellectual life opened to me.'

[16] Bisland, op. cit., ii, 137. He was referring to C. H. Pearson's *National Life and Character: A Forecast* (1893), which said (p. 83): 'We are the blind instruments of fate for multiplying the races that are now our subjects, and will one day be our rivals. We carry the Samurai science and the engineering skill of Europe into the East.'

[17] Bisland, op. cit., ii, 162.

[18] ibid., ii, 275.

[19] Earl Miner, op. cit., 254.

[20] ibid., 134.

[21] Ayao Kuwaki, 'Development of the Study of Science in Japan', in Inazo Nitobe, op. cit., 89–101. *Education in Japan* (1961), 49.

[22] Jan Romein, *The Asian Century* (1962), 331–44.

[23] B. C. Roberts, 'Japan's leap into the Boom Years', *Sunday Times*, 9 May 1965, 31.

20: MAO'S MODEL: THE RED EXPERT FOR EXPORT

[1] Mao Tse-Tung, *China's New Democracy* (New York, 1945), 15, 61. See also H. A. S. Steiner, 'The Curriculum in Chinese Socialist Education: An Official Bibliography of Maoism', *Pacific Affairs*, XXXI (1958), No. 3.

[2] Three of these were in Shanghai (Fuh Tan University (f. 1905), Tatung or Utopia University (f. 1912) and Tahsia or Great China University (f. 1924): two were in Peiping (China College (f. 1912) and the Catholic Univerity (f. 1925)) and one in Canton (the University f. 1927). Shanghai also had three mission universities with more than 1,000 students: St. John's (f. 1879), the University of Shanghai (f. 1906) and the Catholic Aurora University (f. 1903). The reactions of a conventionally educated girl to such a policy at National Peking University have been put on record by Maria Yen in her book *The Umbrella Garden* (1954).

[3] C. T. Hu, 'Higher Education in Mainland China', *Comparative Education Review*, IV (1961), 160.

[4] Hu, op. cit., 164, but the raise was from 87 to 114 according to Chao Chung and Yang I-fan, *Students in Mainland China* (Hong Kong, 1957), pp. 16–17.

[5] Hu, op. cit., 162. Chung Shih, *Higher Education in Communist China* (Kowloon, 1964), gives earlier figures. By 1957 84 new institutions of higher education had been established and 64 were 'readjusted' or abolished. Ten were devoted to 'training cadres, of national minority origins', 14 were universities 'of general studies'. Others included engineering colleges (42), medical schools (28), agricul-

ture and forestry schools (28), fine arts institutions (14) and teachers' colleges (40). The total number of all institutions of higher education crept up from 191 in 1949 (with 130,000 students) to 208 (with 202,107 students) in 1953 and by 1957 was expected to be 230. The most astonishing feature of the reorganization was the rise in the percentage of engineering students. These numbered only 18.9 per cent in 1949, but by 1952 were nearly 40 per cent.

[6] Existing universities there were the Medical College (1906), China College (1912), Chaoyang College (1913) and the Franco Chinese University (1917) (the Catholic University (1925)).

[7] Chang-Tu Hu, *China, its people, its Society, its culture* (New Haven, 1960), 445.

[8] Alfred Zee Chang, 'Scientists in Communist China', *Science*, CXIX (1954), 785.

[9] Chang-Tu Hu, *China, its people, its Society, its culture* (New Haven, 1960).

[10] Choh Ming Li, 'Economic Development', *China Quarterly* (London, 1960), 35–50.

[11] J. D. Bernal, 'Science and Technology in China', *Universities Quarterly*, XI (1956), 64–75, estimates the increase of student numbers at this time as of the order of 25 per cent per annum. See also F. C. Ikle, *The Growth of China's Scientific and Technical Manpower* (Santa Monica, 1957).

[12] Chalmers A. Johnson, *Communist Policies toward the Intellectual Class* (Union Research Institute Kowloon, Hong Kong, 1960), 119.

[13] Chang-Tu Hu, op. cit., 437.

[14] G. A. Modelski, *Atomic Energy in the Communist Bloc* (Melbourne, 1959), 190.

[15] Choh Ming Li, op. cit.

[16] Chao Kuo-Chun, *Agrarian Policy of the Chinese Communist Party* (London, 1960).

[17] Professor Mandelbaum in *American Economic Review*, XLIV (1959), 297 ff.

[18] Vladimir Dedijer, 'Chinese Theory of Revolution', *The Times*, 18 November 1963.

[19] Hu in *Comparative Education Review*, IV (1961), 167.

[20] See also Evan Luard, 'The Chinese Communes', *St. Anthony's Papers*, No. XIV (1963), 59–79 and George Lichtheim, 'Mark and the Asiatic Mode of Production', ibid., 86–112. Sun Yat-Sen, *The International Development of China* (1921), 123.

[21] A. S. Whiting and Sen Sheng Shih ts'ai, *Singkiang: Pawn or Pivot* (Lansing, 1958).

[22] Owen Lattimore, *Nomads and Commissars* (New York, 1962), 214.

[23] F. C. Barghoorn, *The Soviet Cultural Offensive* ((Princeton, 1960), CXXXI.

[24] G. B. Kistiakowsky, 'Science and Foreign Affairs', *Science* 131 (1960), 1019–24.

[25] Sumner H. Schlicter, 'Technological research as related to the growth and stability of the economy', National Science Foundation, *Proceedings of a Conference on Research and Development and its Impact on the Economy* (Washington, D.C., 1958), 107.

[26] A. Bonni, *Studies in Economic Development* (London, 1957).

[27] Guy Wint, *The British in Asia* (1957), 204 ff.

[28] Charles Wolf, jun., *Foreign Aid: Theory and Practice in Southern Asia* (Princeton, 1960); George Lister, *The New Statecraft* (Chicago, 1960).

[29] Barbara Ward, *India and the West* (1961), 148.

[30] T. J. Hughes and D. E. T. Luard, *The Economic Development of Communist China 1949–1958* (1959).

[31] Merle Curti and Kendall Birr, *American Technical Missions Overseas* (Madison, 1954); H. M. Teaf, jun. and P. G. Franck (ed.), *Hands Across Frontiers,*

Case Studies in Technical Co-operation (Ithaca, 1955); R. T. Mack, jun., *Raising the World's Standard of Living* (Citadel Press, 1953); W. R. Sharp, *International Technical Assistance* (Public Administration Service, 1952).

32 *Science*, 12 February 1960.

33 Peter Lessing, *Africa's Red Harvest* (London, 1961), 61–62.

34 ibid.

35 *'Pravda* on Supporting the "Bourgeoisie in New Nations" ', *Current Digest of the Soviet Press*, XII (21 September 1961), 18. Quoted by Robert C. North, *Moscow and Chinese Communists* (Stanford, 1963), 284. Werner Klatt, 'Development Aid for Development's Sake', in Jane Degras and Alec Nove (ed.), *Soviet Planning* (1964), 117, estimates that since 1954, China's contribution to the 5,000 million dollars-worth of economic aid has been just over 10 per cent; that of the Soviet Union, 70 per cent.

36 Tom Stacey, 'Yellow Peril in Africa', *Sunday Times*, 13 September 1964, p. 10, who adds: 'The Chinese preach the attractive gospel of a self-dependent nation economy, based on co-operation among the poor nations of Africa, Asia and Latin America. The Russians are cast as a rich, developed nation able to think only on terms of paternalist gifts.'

21: AN OPERATIONAL WORLD?

1 *Der Untergang des Abendlandes—Gestalt und Wirklichkeit* (Munich, 1918), and *Der Untergang des Abendlandes—Welthistorische Perspektiven* (Munich, 1922). Both were translated by C. F. Atkinson. This reference occurs in i, 41.

2 ibid., i, 293.

3 Geoffrey Atkinson, *Les Relations des Voyages du 17ème siècle et l'evolution des idées* (Paris, 1926); Ph.B. Gove, *The Imaginary Voyage in Prose Fiction 1700–1800* (New York, 1941).

4 Hans Treyer, *Die Politische Insel* (Leipzig, 1936); Marjorie Nicolson, *Voyages to the Moon* (New York, 1948).

5 I. F. Clarke, 'The Reign of George VI, A Fantasy of 1763', *History Today*, xiii (1964), 830–7.

6 The author, later revealed as Louis Sébastien Mercier (1740–1814) played a part in the French Revolutionary Government. His book was later translated into English and published in London, Liverpool and Philadelphia.

7 I. F. Clarke, *The Tale of the Future* (London, 1961).

8 Arthur Koestler, *The Trail of the Dinosaur* (New York, 1956), 144.

9 *The Listener*, LXII (1964), 977.

10 E. T. Chase, 'Politics and Technology', *Yale Review*, LII (1963), 321–39.

11 Jose Ortega y Gasset, *The Revolt of the Masses* (originally published in 1930, translated 1932, 2nd edition 1951, Penguin Books 1961), 64, 86, 106. Ortega did not consider this 'technical drive' a result of American influence on Europe. 'That,' said Ortega y Gasset, 'is simply to trivialise a question which is much more subtle and pregnant with surprises.' 'Europe has not been Americanised,' he insisted, 'it has received no great influence from America. . . . The triumph of the masses and the consequent magnified uprising of the vital level have come about in Europe for internal reasons, after two centuries of education of the multitude towards progress and a parallel economy improvement in society.' 'This,' Ortega concluded, was why 'for the first time the European understands American life which was to him before an enigma and a mystery'. Ibid., 19–20.

12 Compare George Orwell's identification of the 'enslavers' as the 'middling people—scientists, technicians, teachers, journalists, broadcasters, bureaucrats and professional politicians. Their 'hunger for more power and prestige' led them, in

his opinion, to admire the Soviet system 'after', Orwell added significantly, 'it became unmistakably totalitarian'. Orwell's sense of foreboding led him to forecast just such an enslaving technocracy of scientists, trade union organizers and journalists, operating in *1948* by doctoring the past, confusing the present and obliterating the future. Their secret was control of science through a permanent state of war. This war was ostensibly waged for reserves of cheap labour in the equatorial regions and for the northern ice-cap. But it was not waged to the death, only to consume the products of industry. For that reason scientists concentrated on improving mass production and detecting thought. The only group to which intellectual liberty was granted the were proles—because they could not think. 'Second Thoughts on James Burnham', in *Collected Essays* (Mercury Books, 1961), 374.

[13] F. G. Jeunger, *The Failure of Technology* (trans. F. D. Wilhelmson) (Chicago, 1956), 96–97, 127–9.

[14] C. S. Lewis, formerly an English don at Oxford and then a professor at Cambridge, was a Christian apologist of some distinction. Apart from his *Screwtape Letters*, his three fantasies *Out of the Silent Planet* (1938), *Voyage to Venus* (1943) and *That Hideous Strength* (1945) are (in spite of Lewis's denial) powerful allegories. In the last named, the National Institute for Co-ordinated Experiments wish to re-create humans as robots, and is capturing the Press and Government in the process and Lewis says (p. 157): 'It was not the great technocrats of Koenigsberg or Moscow who supplied the casualties in the siege of Stalingrad. The effect of modern war is to eliminate retrogressive types, while sparing the technocracy and increasing its hold on public affairs.'

[15] J. J. Beer and W. D. Lewis, 'Aspects of the Professionalisation of Science', *Daedalus*, xcii (1963), 783.

[16] Burton R. Clark, *Educating the Expert Society* (San Francisco, 1962).

[17] Consider, for instance, the remark of one American scholar in 1950: 'Scientific research in the universities has until now completely escaped all the efficacious compulsions of organised freedom.' K. William Kapp, *The Social Costs of Private Enterprise* (Cambridge, Mass., 1950), 212–13.

[18] R. K. Merton, *Social Theory and Social Structure* (Glencoe, 1963), 567–8.

[19] Professor Dennis Gabor, *Technology, Life and Leisure. The Thompson Lecture to the Society of Instrument Technology*. Delivered at the Royal Institution, October 1963. (*Nature*, CC (1961), 513.)

[20] T. Molnar, 'Intellectuals, Experts and the Classless Society', in G. B. de Huszar (ed.), *The Intellectuals* (1960), 194–5.

[21] R. K. Merton, 'The Machine, the Worker, and the Engineer', originally printed in *Science*, CV (1947), and reprinted in his *Social Theory and Social Structure* (Glencoe, 1963), 565. He comments (p. 566) that 'with the increasing rationalisation of managerial procedures, the relations between operating executives and workmen become increasingly formalised and depersonalised'.

[22] Milton J. Nadworny, *Scientific Management and the Unions 1900–1932* (Cambridge, Mass., 1955), 51, 53. But by 1925, the American Federation of Labour was ready to co-operate with management and one of its representatives told the Taylor Society in December of that year that the attitude of himself and his colleagues towards management studies was undergoing 'revision and re-adjustment'.

[23] Richard Pipes, 'Russian Intellectuals', *Encounter*, XXII (1964), 81.

[24] James R. Schlesinger and Almarin Phillips, 'The Ebb Tide of Capitalism: Schumpeter's Prophecy Re-examined', *Quarterly Journal of Economics*, LXXIII (1959), 450. Max Lerner, 'Big Technology and Neutral Technicians', *Perspectives*, 14 (1956); 'Danger to continuance to democratic self government', *Technocratie et Politique* (Lausanne, 1960); Jacques Billy, *Les Techniciens et le Pouvoir* (Paris,

1960); Jacques Ellul, *La Technique ou l'enjeu du siècle* (Paris, 1954); Jean Barets, *La Fin des Politiques*, and K. Denbigh, *Science, Industry and Social Policy* (1963). The last named considered (p. 97) that much might be gained if technologists would become more political in their outlook.

25 Fabian Tract 235. A revealing metaphor can be found in Max Weber, *Essays in Sociology* (ed. H. H. Gerth and C. Wright Mills, 1948), 214. Speaking of the technical superiority of bureaucracy he comments: 'The fully developed bureaucratic mechanism compares with other organisations exactly as does the machine with the non-mechanical modes of production. Precision, speed, unambiguity, knowledge of the files, continuity, discretion, unity, strict subordination, reduction of friction and of material and personal costs—these are raised to the optimum point in the strictly bureaucratic administration, and especially in its monocratic form.' Just as the medieval Church nourished within itself the heresy of antinomianism, and antinomianism nourished the idea of the perfectibility of man by his own efforts, so modern bureaucracy became the established Church of the Welfare State and nourished operationalism. See also: Gaetano Mosca, *The Ruling Class* (New York, 1939); James H. Mersel, *The Myth of the Ruling Class: Gaetano Mosca and the Elite* (Ann Arbor, 1958); H. D. Lasswell, Daniel Lerner and C. Easton Rothwell, *The Comparative Study of Elites: An Introduction and Bibliography* (Stanford, 1952).

26 Bertrand Russell, *The Impact of Science and Society* (1952), 77–78; also: 'A democratic scientific society, by exacting service and conferring security, forbids or prevents much personal initiative which is possible in a less well-regulated world'; and also (p. 134): 'one unavoidable feature of a scientific society is the subordination of individuals to organisations'.

27 R. E. Finch, 'The Scientist as Priest and Saviour', *Christian Century*, 26 March 1958.

28 Elton Mayo, *Social Problems of an Industrial Civilisation* (1949), 129–30.

29 Karl Mannheim, *Freedom, Power and Democratic Planning* (1951), 287. See also his *Ideology and Utopia* (1936), 10, 'The more it [the intellectual stratum] makes itself the exponent of a thoroughly organised collectivity (e.g. the Church), the more its thinking tends towards "scholasticism". It must give a dogmatically binding force to modes of thought which formerly were valid only for a sect, and thereby sanction the ontology and epistemology implicit in this mode of thought.'

30 A. A. Berle, *The Twentieth Century Capitalist Revolution* (1954), 182-3.

31 Raymond Aron, *The Opium of the Intellectuals* (1957), 267–9. For a study of French Marxists and science see David Caute, *Communism and French Intellectuals* (1964), 300–17.

32 Charles E. Raven, *Teilhard de Chardin, scientist and seer* (London, 1962), 214.

33 Cyril Bibby, 'Science as an Instrument of Culture', *Nature*, CCII (1964), 333.

34 *Observer*, 10 June 1945. See also L. Sprague de Camp, *Science Fiction Handbook* (1953); Walter Hirsch, 'The Image of the Scientist in Science Fiction. A Content Analysis', *American Journal of Sociology*, LXIII (1958), 506–12, and Kingsley Amis, *New Maps of Hell* (1961), who remarks (pp. 60–61) that these science-fiction writers 'treat their work very seriously indeed'.

35 *Tribune*, 3 March 1944.

36 Henry B. Adams, *The Degradation of the Democratic Dogma* (1919, edition of 1958), 277, 303.

37 Worthington Chauncey Ford, *Letters of Henry Adams (1892–1918)* (New York, 1950), 49.

38 ibid., 197, 248.

39 ibid., 518. Perhaps more significant than what Adams said was his way of

saying it. For he adopted a process which was at the heart of all the change which was bewildering him, by circulating his ideas amongst those of his friends who could offer valid criticism. 'Although I have no idea of publishing,' he told his brother in 1908, 'I have all the stronger idea of consulting. My notion of work is that of work among workers, that is, by comparison, correspondence and conversation. Ideas once settled so—as you see in Darwin's life—anyone can explain them to the public.' Ibid., 487. But his soundings had little effect. Sadly he told another, 'I get no answer to my appeals to my own historian horde. I have sounded silently in every direction for years, and the air is as dead as dogs. Only the mathematicians show life.' ibid., 489.

[40] J. R. Newman and Byron S. Miller, *The Control of Atomic Energy* (New York, 1948), 4.

[41] Farewell message of Eisenhower, *New York Times*, 22 January 1961, p. 4E; see *Science*, 10 February 1961, p. 355, for comment.

[42] James R. Schlesinger and Almarin Phillips, 'The Ebb Tide of Capitalism?' *Quarterly Journal of Economics*, LXXIII (1959), 460.

[43] C. Wright Mills, *The Power Elite* (New York, 1956), 216–17.

[44] Raymond L. Garthoff, 'The Military as a Social Force', in C. E. Black (ed.), *The Transformation of Russian Society. Aspects of Social Change since 1861* (Cambridge, 1 May 1960), 323–38. For an interpretation of war as an antidote to social *anomie* see Sebastian de Grazia, *The Political Community* (Chicago, 1963), 159.

[45] Edward Shils, 'Political Development in the New States', *Comparative Studies in Society and History* (1959–60), 265–92, 379–411; Morris Watnick, 'The Appeal of Communism to the Underdeveloped Peoples', in B. F. Hoselits (ed.), *The Progress of Underdeveloped Areas* (Chicago, 1952), 155–72; Gabriel Almond, J. S. Coleman, *The Politics of the Developing Areas* (Princeton, 1960); M. F. Millikan and D. L. M. Blackmer, *The Emerging Nations* (Boston, 1961); Paul E. Sigmund, jun., *The Ideologies of the Nations* (New York, 1963).

[46] Gerald W. Grob, *Workers and Utopia. A Study of Ideologies and Conflict in the American Labor Movement 1865–1900* (North Western, 1961).

[47] H. Daalder, *The Role of the Military in the Emerging Countries* (Gravenhage, 1962).

[48] P. J. Vatikiotis, *The Egyptian Army in Politics: Pattern for New Nations?* (Bloomington, 1961).

[49] Edward Lievenen, *Arms and Politics in Latin America* (New York, 1960), 122 ff.

[50] Lucian W. Pye, 'Armies in the Process of Political Modernisation', *European Journal of Sociology*, 11, 1 (1961), 82–92; D. Lerner and R. D. Robinson, 'Swords and Ploughshares: The Turkish Army as a Modernising Force', *World Politics*, XIII (1960–1), 19–44; D. A. Rustow, 'The Army and the Founding of the Turkish Republic', *World Politics*, XI (1958–9), 520.

[51] H. J. Brenda, 'Non-Western Intelligentsias as Political Elites', *Australian Journal of Politics and History*, VI (1960), 205–18; Edward Shils, 'The Intellectuals in the Political Development of New Stages', *World Politics*, XII (1959–60), 329–68.

[52] Francis Williams, *A Prime Minister Remembers* (1961), 56.

[53] Quoted by Daniel Aaron, *Men of Good Will* (New York, 1951), 271. Charles Hirschfeld, 'Brooks Adams and American Nationalism', *American Historical Review*, LXIX (1964), 371–92, quotes him as saying: 'In proportion as the United States consolidates within, in order to evolve the largest administrative mass, so must they be expected to expand without; and, as they expand, they must simplify and cheapen the administrative machinery, until in this direction, also, the limit of economy by mass has been obtained.'

418

54 James Burnham, *The Machiavellians: Defenders of Freedom* (1943), 172.

55 Robert D. Specht, 'War Games', in Max Davies and Michael Verhulst (ed.), *Operational Research in Practice* (1958), 149.

56 Maurice Frechet, 'Emile Borel, initiator of the theory of psychological games and its applications', *Econometrics*, XXL (1953), 95–96. For comment on Von Neumann, D. G. Champernowne, 'A Note on J. Von Neumann's article', *Review of Economic Studies*, *XIII* (1945–6), 10–18; 'What has happened to the theory of games?' *American Economic Association*, LXV (1953), 398–405. David Blackwell, 'Game Theory', in J. F. McCloskey and F. N. Trevethen (ed.), *Operations Research for Management* (Baltimore, 1954), 238–53. R. B. Braithwaite, *Theory of Games as a Tool for the Moral Philosopher* (Cambridge, 1935).

57 R. Duncan Luce and Howard Raiffa, *Games and Decisions, Introductions and Critical Survey* (London, 1957), ii. This book is itself dedicated to John Von Neumann.

58 Max Davies and Michael Verhulst (ed.), *Operational Research in practice. Report on a N.A.T.O. Conference* (London, 1958), 12. 'The Scientist, as the British Prime Minister said seven years ago (1 April 1958), is always ahead of the politician, and one might add, of the soldier.'

59 Claude E. Shannon, 'A Symbolic Analysis of Relay and Switching Circuits', *Transactions of the American Institute of Electrical Engineers*, LVII (1938), 713–23.

60 Norbert Wiener, *Cybernetics, Or Control and Communication in the Animal and the Machine* (New York, 1961), 12.

61 ibid., 28.

62 J. C. R. Lickleider, 'The System System', in Edward Bennett, James Degan and Joseph Spiegel (ed.), *Human Factors in Technology* (New York, 1963), 628.

63 Edward Bennett, James Degan and Joseph Spiegel, 'Human Factors in a Technological Society', op. cit., 10.

64 Esther Brown, *The Professional Engineer* (New York, 1936); John Mills, *The Engineer in Society* (New York, 1945); Simon Marcson, *The Scientist in American Industry* (Princeton, 1960); Opinion Research Corporation, *The Conflict between the Scientific Mind and the Management Mind* (Princeton, 1959); H. A. Shepherd, 'Engineers as Marginal Men', *Journal of Engineering Education*, XLVII (1957), 536–42; William Kornhauser, *Scientists in Industry, Conflict and Accommodation* (Berkley, 1962), 3; George Paloczi-Hovath, *The Facts Rebel: The Future of Russia and the West* (London, 1964).

65 Clark Kerr, John Dunlop, Frederick Harbison and Charles Myers, *Industrialism and Industrial Man* (1960).

66 P. H. Eijkman, *L'internationalisme scientifique* (The Hague, 1911); F. S. L. Lyons, *Internationalism in Europe 1815–1914* (Leyden, 1963), 235.

67 D. McKie, *Lavoisier* (London, 1952), 259.

68 G. P. Speeckaert, 'Un Siècle d'Expositions Universelles leur influences sur les Congrès Internationaux', *Bulletin O.N.C.* (Brussels, 1951), 270.

69 N. M. Goodman, *International Health Organisations and their Works* (London, 1952).

70 L. Couturat and L. Leau, *Histoire de la langue Universelle* (Pons, 1907); F. C. Donnan (translation of L. Couturat, O. Jespersen, R. Lorenz, W. Ostwald and L. Pfaundler), *International Language and Science* (London, 1910); A. L. Guerard, *A Short History of the International Language Movement* (London, 1921); significantly enough it was developed by a Frenchman, Louis Couturat. Another German, I. M. Schleyer, invented 'Volapük' (world speech) in 1880 and a Polish Russian, Louis Zamenhof, devised 'Esperanto' (the language of 'hope') and an Italian, G. Peano, devised in 1903 'Latine' (a modified Latin). By 1964 Peking was publishing 500 Esperanto novels, poems, textbooks and political pamphlets a

year. Kruschev has allowed 400 Esperanto societies to form (Stalin banned them). *Sunday Times*, 2 March 1964, p. 7.

[71] Baron de Borchgrave, 'L'association Internationale des Academies; Son organisation et ses travaux', *La Vie Internationale* (Brussels, 1913), iv, 41.

[72] G. P. Speeckaert, *Les 1,978 Organisations Internationales fondées depuis le Congrés de Vienne* (Brussels, 1957; Jean Meynaud and B. Schröder, *Les Savants dans la vie internationale* (Lausanne, 1962).

[73] F. S. L. Lyons, *Internationalism in Europe 1815–1914* (Leyden, 1963), 38–47.

[74] F. H. Hinsley, *Power and the Pursuit of Peace* (Cambridge, 1963), 261–2.

[75] Harold Courlander, *Shaping our Times* (1960), 95.

[76] Sir Julian Huxley, who suggested in *Unesco—its Purpose and Philosophy* (Washington, 1947)—a pamphlet which the preparatory commission refused to sponsor—that it should be based on a philosophy of 'world scientific humanism'.

[77] W. H. C. Laves and C. A. Thomson, *UNESCO: Purpose, Progress, Progress, Prospects* (Bloomington, 1957), gives a full account of its work.

[78] Pierre Auger, *Current Trends in Scientific Research* (Unesco, 1961).

[79] S. McKee-Rosen, *The Combined Boards of the Second World War. An Experiment in International Admiuistration* (New York, 1951). They specialized in raw materials, shipping, production, resources and food.

[80] Tom Stacey, 'To Save the Commonwealth', *Sunday Times*, 22 March 1964.

[81] William C. Mallaleiu, 'The Origin of the Marshall Plan', *Political Science Quarterly*, LXXIII (1958), 503; 'The Common Market Revisited: Democratic Control or Technocracy', *The Times*, 25 January 1964, p. 9.

[82] Ortega y Gasset, *The Revolt of the Masses* (1930, edn. of 1961), 139.

[83] Karl Mannheim, *Essays on the Sociology of Culture* (1956), 119–20; ibid., 119–20.

[84] A. N. Whitehead, *Science and the Modern World* (1926), 259.

[85] Paul Abrecht, *The Churches and Rapid Social Change* (1961), 199.

[86] K. R. Popper, *The Poverty of Historicism* (1957), 156–7.

[87] *The Listener*, 9 January 1961. See also T. J. Hughes and D. E. T. Luard, *The Economic Development of Communist China, 1949–1958* (1959), 199. The epiphany of the technocrat is not greeted with joy. What the Russians used to call *Makhayevschching* (from V. K. Makhayevsky, 1866–1926, who argued that the intellectual workers were really capitalizing on higher education and that after eliminating the landed and the finance capitalists, they would establish a great joint stock company known as the State) has virtually come to pass; Ingvald Raknem, *H. G. Wells and his Critics* (1964); Max Nomad, *Rebels and Revolutionaries* (New York, 1932); *Aspects of Revolt* (New York, 1961); Makhayevsky influenced Harold D. Lasswell, *Politics: Who Gets What, When, How* (New York, 1936); Harold D. Lasswell and Abraham Kaplan, *Power and Society* (New Haven, 1950), and Joseph A. Schumpeter, 'Social Classes in an Ethically Homogeneous Environment', *Imperialism and Social Classes* (New York, 1951), 137–47; *Capitalism, Socialism and Democracy* (3rd edition, New York, 1950).

[88] Hans J. Morgenthau, *Scientific Man vs Power Politics* (1949), 118 ff., 187 ff., and especially chapter V, 'The Chimera of the Natural Sciences'.

[89] Harold D. Lasswell, *The Future of Political Science* (New York, 1963), 9.

[90] Marston Bates, *The Prevalence of People* (New York, 1955), 248.

[91] Grenville Clark and Louis B. Sohn, *World Peace Through World Law* (1958).

[92] W. H. Ferry, 'Irresponsibilities in Metrocorporate America', in Andrew Hacker (ed.), *The Corporation Takeover* (1964), iii.

[93] Talcott Parsons, 'Authority, Legitimation and Political Action', in Carl J. Friedrich (ed.), *Nomos 1. Authority* (Cambridge, Mass., 1958), 199.

[94] Fritz Machlup, *The Production and Distribution of Knowledge in the United States* (Princeton, 1962), 374, 399.

[95] Clark Kerr, *The Uses of the University* (Cambridge, Mass., 1964), 88. He develops (p. 93) the concept of the multiversity, or ideopolis: a cluster of academics, scientifically oriented industries and governmental enterprises. 'To match the drawing power of the great metropolis, there now arrives the new Ideopolis. The isolated mountain can no longer dominate the landscape: the constellation is greater than the single star and adds to the brightness of the sky'.

[96] Don K. Price, *Government and Science* (1962).

[97] A. N. Whitehead, *Science and the Modern World* (New York, 1957), c, vi.

[98] Joseph Needham, 'Integrative Levels: A Revalation of The Idea of Progress', *Time: The Refreshing River* (1943), 233.

[99] C. H. Waddington in *The Prospect Before Us. Some Thoughts on the Future* (1948), 66.

[100] ibid., 73.

[101] Derek de Solla Price, 'The Scientific Foundations of Science Policy'. *Nature* CCVI (1965), 234.

Index of Persons

Index of Subjects

academies of science, 19–21, 28–40, 44, 154, 292, 367
Academia Sinica, 316, 317, 318
Académie française des Sciences, 19, 26, 30, 31–32, 61, 67–68, 124
ackee, 45
Act for International Development, 299
Adelaide Gallery, 97
Advisory Committees, 22, 254, 294
Advisory to U.S. President, 294
aeronautics, 125, 183, 229
Afghanistan, 290
Africa, 42, 45, 47, 121, 299, 300, 338–9
Agency for International Development, 300
agriculture, 104, 163, 177, 208, 229–30, 291–2
agricultural Research Council, 215, 272, 284
agricultural Sciences, 291–2
agrostology, 117
aid to backward areas, 124, 297–302
Alaska, purchase of, 157
Albania, 291
alkali, 5, 119
Allgemeine Elektrizitäts-Gesellschaft, 86
Alliance Scientifique Universelli, 351
Alma-Ata, 227, 288, 291
America, 5, 7, 12, 47, 131, 144, 281
America as prison, 370 n.24
America—as tree supplier, 42–43
America:
— British influence on, 131–3
— French influence on, 133–9
— German influence on, 139–42
— Russian influence on, 139
— influence of frontier on, 142–4
American Academy of Arts and Sciences, 134
American Academy of Natural Sciences, 134

American Association for the Advancement of Science, 140, 249
American Botanical Society, 134
American Chemical Society, 175, 176
American Cyanamid, 245
American Graduate Schools, 173–5
American Journal of Science and the Arts, 133
American influence:
— on Britain, 115, 165–6, 202, 209, 213–14, 216, 264–6, 274
— on Germany, 378 n.12
—on Japan, 322–6
— on Russia, 219–26, 235–7
— Institute of Mech. Engineers, 248
— Land Grant Colleges, 163–5, 178, 210
— Mathematical Society, 176
— missions to Asia, 337–8
— National University, 135
— Philosophical Society, 132, 134
— Physics Society, 176–7
— Research Contracts, 209
— Research Laboratories in England, 209
— Society for Engineering Education, 296
— Standards Association, 239
— State Universities, 136–7, 171–5
— technology in Russia, 187
— Telegraph and Telephone Co., 260, 301
Amigos Del Pais, 32–33
analogy of garden, 135
Anglo-American technical exchange, 403 n.39
Animal Farm, 281
Annalen der chemie, 82
Annapolis, 138
anthropometry, 122
Arctic Research, 232–234
Argentina, 336
Argonne, 289

communes, 334
communications engineering, 243, 351, 384 n.2
communism, 74, 111, 170, 182, 187, 190, 192, 240, 256–7, 258, 298, 302, 314–15, 341, 344, 345, 350
computers, 98, 350, 371 n.48
conditioned reflex, 192–3
Confederation of British Industry, 288
Congress Committee on Science and Astronautics, 294
conservation of natural resources, 167
Conservatoire des Arts et Métiers, 67
consultants, 98
Co-operative Research Associations, 208–9
Cornell University, 160, 193, 203, 216
Coro Anatomico, 21
correspondence, 24–25
cotton, 14
Cours de philosophie positive, 73
Criticisms of U.S. education, 297
cultural offensives, 297, 338–9
cybernetics, 350
Czechoslovakia, 291

delegations, 187, 207, 290, 337–8
Democracy—criticisms of, 241
Denmark, 37, 49
Department of Education and Science, 281
Department of Scientific and Industrial Research, 120
Deputations to U.S.A., 206
Deutsche Naturforscherversammlung, 78–79
Development Commission, 218
Devonshire Commission, 125
doctorates, 86, 296
Donets Basin, 154
Dorpat, University of, 150, 152, 160, 191
Dow Chemical Co., 245
Dresden, Collegium-medicio chirgicum, 78, 85
Dutch explorers, 4
Dutch influence on Japan, 320–1
dyes, vegetable, 6
— synthetic, 87
dynamo, 179

East German physicists, 290–1
East India Company, 4, 48, 53, 56, 57

Ecole Central des Arts et Manufactures, 66
— de Genie, 67
— des Mines, 37, 139
— Normale, 64
— Polytechnique, 64–66, 68, 72, 137–8, 149, 198, 375 n.11
— des Ponts et Chausees, 64, 67, 375 n.11
— Veterinaire, 375 n.11
early Russian Students in England, 387 n.11
Edinburgh University, 211
Edison dynamo, 206
— Illumination Company, 221
education, as established Church, 210
— and industrial unrest, 406 n.29
— proportion of GNP on, 293
Education of Henry Adams, the, 179
educational planning, 342
efficiency, 120f., 350
Egypt, 290, 347
electric eels, 369 n.12
electrical energy, measurement of, 83
electricity, 21
electronics, 86, 282
electro-magnetic waves, 85
élite, 30, 66, 69, 121, 182, 241, 262, 336, 345, 346
encyclopaedism, 31, 32, 67, 69–70, 141, 197, 240, 290, 320, 367, 371 n.48
energetics, 197
energy, 90, 92, 126, 197, 220–1, 225, 239, 240, 276, 352; see steam power and electricity
engineering electrical, 115, 116, 119, 125, 156–7, 159, 176, 177, 179–80, 196, 207, 215–16, 220ff., 225ff., 276, 326, 332, 338, 348, 350, 387
engineers, 22, 72, 76, 96, 98, 121, 141, 147, 150, 175, 192, 193, 202, 239, 249, 253, 273, 276, 296, 334, 344, 399 n.5
Engineers and the Price System, 239
Englishmen in China, 311
— in Imperial Russia, 387 n.12
Erlangen, U. of, 35, 36, 378 n. 18
eugenics, 120
European Federation, 65
European Union, 195
evolution, 108–10, 167, 325, 361 n.11, 371, n.42

438

447